D1223823

College Trigonometry

FRED RICHMAN
CAROL WALKER
ELBERT WALKER
New Mexico State University

COLLEGE TRIGONOMETRY

SCOTT, FORESMAN AND COMPANY

Library of Congress Catalog Number 69-15228

Regional Offices of Scott, Foresman and Company are located in Atlanta, Dallas, Glenview, Palo Alto, Oakland, N.J. and London, England.

Preface

This book was written with the idea of providing an uncluttered and mathematically sound introduction to the basic ideas of trigonometry, emphasizing the important concepts, without attempting to initiate the student into the mysteries of higher algebra and set theory. To this end, we combine the classical, intuitive approach with the important facets of the modern point of view.

Trigonometry is viewed as the study of the trigonometric functions. The general notion of a function is developed with stress placed upon understanding rather than set theoretical niceties. Real numbers are placed in their natural setting—as the results of measurements. These two topics are treated in some detail at a concrete level, to lay the foundation not only for the rest of the text but also for the calculus. Complex numbers are introduced as a natural extension of the real number system, without the complication of an artificial construction by way of ordered pairs.

The trigonometric functions are introduced via the trigonometric point. This is the "modern way," and seems to have some mathematical if not pedagogical advantages over the classical one. In line with this approach, the addition formulas are motivated and developed by examining rotations of the plane. Angles are not ignored, however, and right triangle trigonometry plays its just role.

In the spirit of the contemporary functional approach, logarithms are developed from consideration of the inverse of the exponential function, and the inverse trigonometric functions from consideration of the inverses of portions of the trigonometric functions.

For the benefit of the student, many examples are provided, and answers are given for odd-numbered problems.

Las Cruces, New Mexico

Fred Richman
Carol Walker
Elbert Walker

Contents

1 The Real Numbers

1–1 Introduction

Historically trigonometry is the study of triangles, particularly right triangles, and the relations between the lengths of their sides and the sizes of their angles. It was developed mainly for use in surveying and astronomy, to help measure the earth and the sky. In the study of right triangles certain numbers came to be associated with angles. These numbers did not directly measure the size of the angles but rather the relationships between the sides of any right triangle having those angles. Thus the notion of a trigonometric function was born.

The child has outgrown the parent in this case, since the trigonometric functions have come to have far-reaching applications—in engineering, physics, and higher mathematics—that completely overshadow their use in the study of triangles. Even the very notion of trigonometric functions no longer depends on their right triangle genealogy, since they may be thought of purely in terms of numbers and not in terms of angles. Thus trigonometry has come to mean the study of the trigonometric functions, and this is the point of view that we shall take: the fundamental objects of study in this book are the trigonometric functions, not triangles. However, the important connections between these functions and triangles are not to be ignored, and they will be brought out in Chapters 4 and 8.

Since our concern is with trigonometric functions, and since these are functions of real numbers, we need to know what real numbers are and what functions are. This chapter presents a quick review of some of the basic properties of real numbers.

1–2 Measuring

The numbers we use to measure things are called *real* numbers. In order to measure lengths we first decide upon a *unit length* which we represent by the number 1. All lengths are measured in terms of the unit length. This unit length might be an inch, a foot, a mile, a light year, or whatever. Suppose, for example, we have chosen an inch-long segment as our unit length. Here is our unit length.

(1)

Now suppose we are faced with another length:

(2)

How do we measure it? We construct a "ruler" by marking off a line at intervals of one inch.

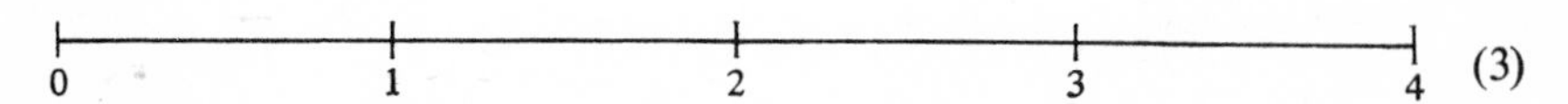

(3)

To measure a length we line up one end with the point marked 0 on our ruler and see where the other end lands. Thus to measure the segment in (2) we simply place our ruler next to it and verify immediately that it is three inches long. The numbers 0, 1, 2, 3, . . . labeling these marks are called *integers*.

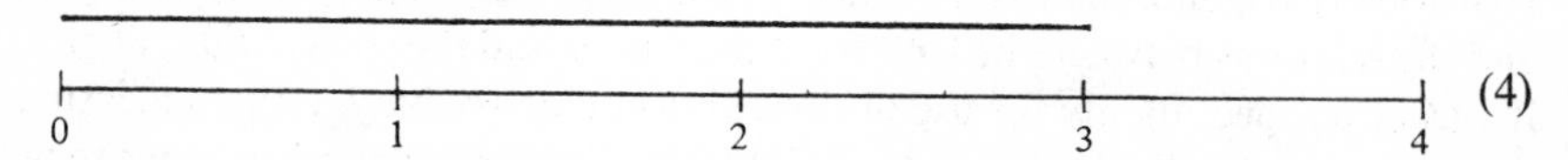

(4)

What happens if the length we are trying to measure falls somewhere between two of the marks on our ruler? For example,

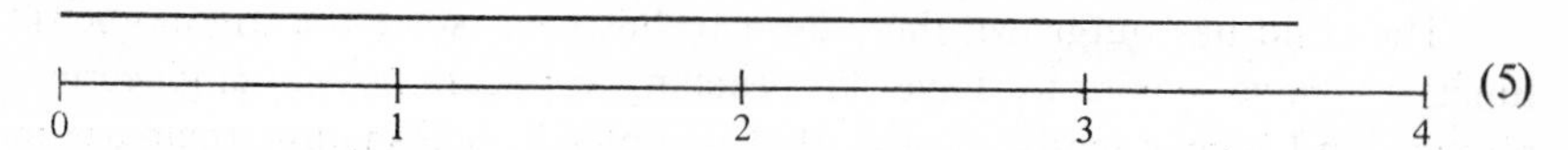

(5)

The length is somewhere between three and four inches. If we wish to be more precise, we shall have to put more marks on our ruler. One way is to divide the interval from 3 to 4 into equal sections like

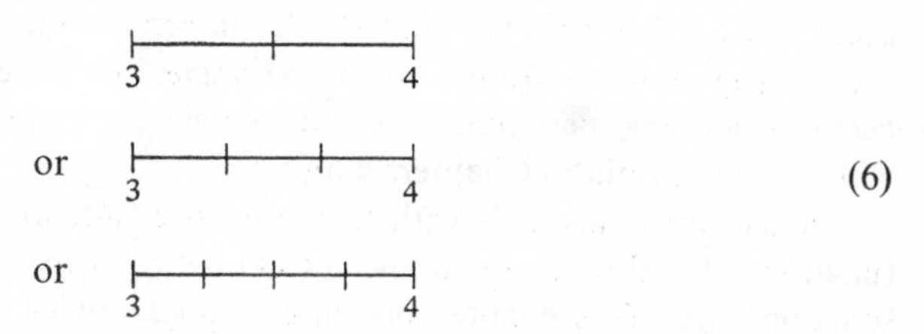

(6)

In the first case we label the new point "$3\frac{1}{2}$," since we divided the segment into two equal sections. The points in the second case would be labeled $3\frac{1}{3}$ and $3\frac{2}{3}$, since the segment was divided into three equal sections. Similarly, the points in the last case would be labeled $3\frac{1}{4}$, $3\frac{2}{4}$, and $3\frac{3}{4}$. Notice that the point labeled $3\frac{2}{4}$ is the same one labeled $3\frac{1}{2}$. These two labels, $3\frac{2}{4}$ and $3\frac{1}{2}$, are different ways of referring to the same length. We may continue in this way to mark our ruler at all of the points which can be labeled by fractions. A few are pictured below.

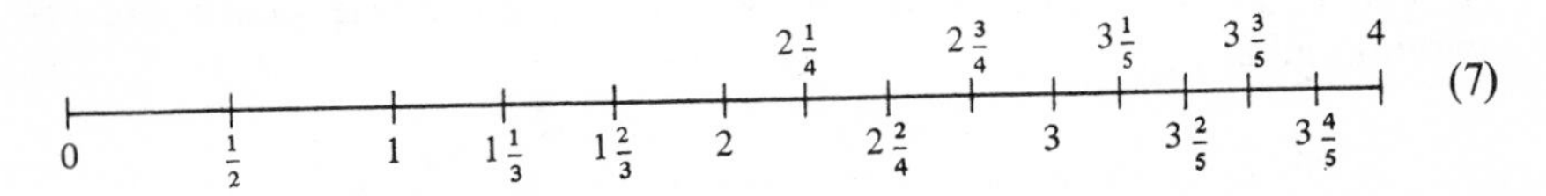

(7)

The numbers used to label these marks—the integers and the fractions—are called *rational* numbers. The distinguishing feature of a rational number is that it can be written as a quotient a/b with a and b integers. For example,

$$6\frac{1}{8} = \frac{49}{8}, \quad 3\frac{1}{2} = \frac{7}{2}, \quad \text{and} \quad 4 = \frac{4}{1}.$$

With the rational numbers we can measure many more lengths than we could with integers alone. Can we measure *all* lengths? This question provoked a stormy controversy among the ancient mathematicians. Pythagoras was reputed to have shown that if a right triangle had sides which were one inch long, then the square of the length of the hypotenuse was equal to 2, the sum of the squares of the lengths of the two sides.

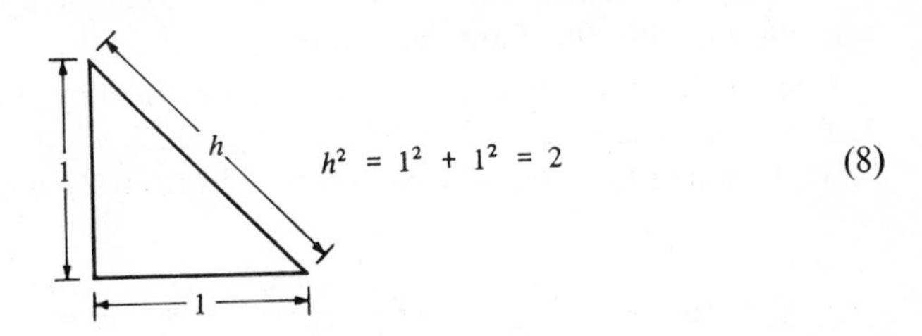

(8)

If we could measure the hypotenuse of this triangle with our ruler which is marked only with rational numbers, then we could write h as a/b, where a and b were integers. This would give us integers a and b, such that $(a/b)^2 = 2$. However, the ancients were able to show that this is impossible. Hence this real number, which we write $\sqrt{2}$ and call "the square root of 2," is not yet marked on our ruler. If we are to measure everything, we shall have to put it on the ruler, along with a host of other numbers which are missing. These missing numbers are called *irrational* numbers. The numbers $\sqrt{2}$ and π are examples of such numbers. Their distinguishing feature is that they *cannot* be written as a quotient a/b with a and b integers.

1–3 *Decimal Representation*

Decimal representation, or expansion, is a unifying technique for labeling real numbers. All of the real numbers, both rational and irrational, have a decimal representation. To see how it works, let us consider the number $\sqrt{2}$. Since the square of $\sqrt{2}$ lies between the square of 1 and the square of 2 ($1^2 = 1$, $(\sqrt{2})^2 = 2$ and $2^2 = 4$), we know that $\sqrt{2}$ must lie somewhere between 1 and 2.

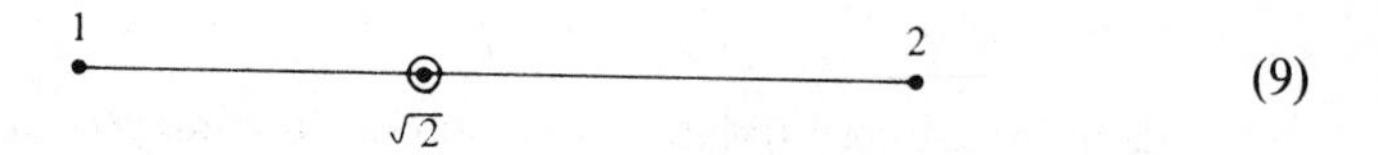

(9)

To get a better idea of where $\sqrt{2}$ is, we divide the interval from 1 to 2 into ten equal segments (hence the terminology "decimal," from the Latin word for ten).

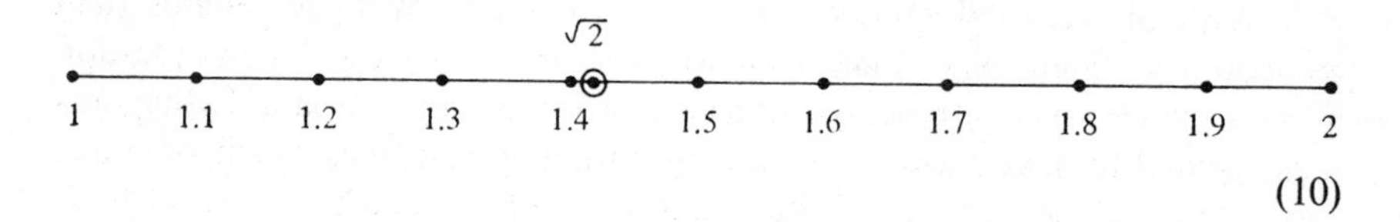

(10)

We label the division points 1.1, 1.2, 1.3, etc., and observe that, in the fraction notation, these are the points $1\frac{1}{10}$, $1\frac{2}{10}$, $1\frac{3}{10}$, and so on. We see that $\sqrt{2}$ lies between 1.4 and 1.5. This is easily verified by checking that $(1.4)^2 = 1.96$ which is less than 2, while $(1.5)^2 = 2.25$ which is greater than 2. Now, breaking the interval from 1.4 to 1.5 into ten equal parts,

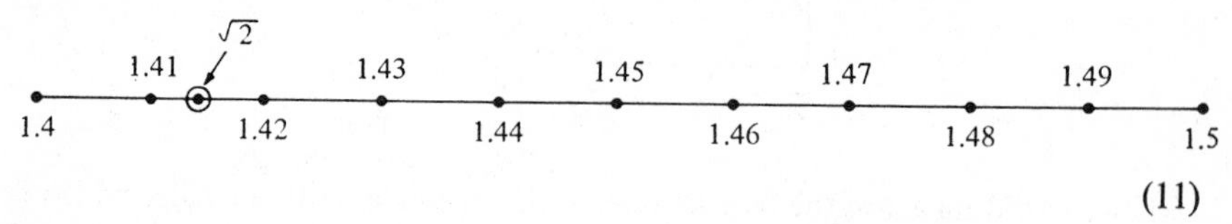

(11)

we find that $\sqrt{2}$ lies between 1.41 and 1.42, the points labeled $1\frac{41}{100}$ and $1\frac{42}{100}$ by the fractions. Once more we divide into ten equal pieces

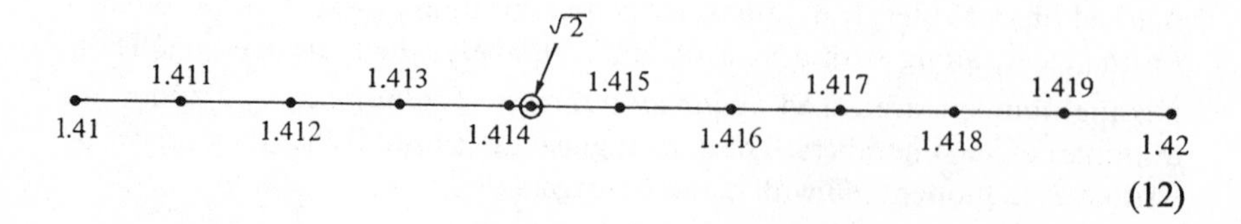

(12)

and find that $\sqrt{2}$ lies between 1.414 and 1.415. Continuing in this fashion we may construct an infinite decimal expansion 1.414213.... This expansion means that $\sqrt{2}$ is at least as big as any of the numbers

$$1, 1.4, 1.41, 1.414, 1.4142, 1.41421, 1.414213, \ldots$$

but no bigger than any of the numbers

$$2, 1.5, 1.42, 1.415, 1.4143, 1.41422, 1.414214, \ldots.$$

Similarly, to say that the decimal expansion of π is 3.14159265358979... simply means that π lies between 3 and 4, between 3.1 and 3.2, between 3.14 and 3.15, between 3.141 and 3.142, between 3.1415 and 3.1416, and so on.

If you know the first few digits in the decimal representation of a number, you know approximately what that number is. For example, if the decimal representation of a number x starts out 3.1652, then x can be no less than 3.1652 and no greater than 3.1653. Indeed, the way the fourth digit 2 was determined was by dividing the interval from 3.165 to 3.166 into ten equal pieces and observing that x lay between the points labeled 3.1652 and 3.1653. Approximations will be discussed in more detail in Section 1–5.

To every point on our ruler we have made correspond a possibly infinite decimal representation. On the other hand, suppose we are given an infinite decimal, for example 0.12345678910111213141516171819202122232425 2.... (Mathematicians are fond of using three dots to mean "etc." when the reader should know what follows, e.g., 1, 2, 3, 4, 5, ... or 2, 4, 8, 16, 32, 64, 128, ..., or in the example above which is obtained from the numbers 1, 2, 3, 4, 5, 6, 7, 8, 9, 10, 11, 12, 13, 14, 15, 16, ... by removing commas and spaces.) Is there some point on our ruler which is labeled by this infinite decimal? That is, is there a point which is at once between 0.1 and 0.2, between 0.12 and 0.13, between 0.123 and 0.124, between 0.1234 and 0.1235 and so on? There is no pressing geometric reason for such a point to exist, as there was for 1.414213.... Yet somehow we feel (or perhaps you don't) that there is some point which separates the points 0.1, 0.12, 0.123, 0.1234, 0.12345, ... from the points 0.2, 0.13, 0.124, 0.1235, 0.12346, ...

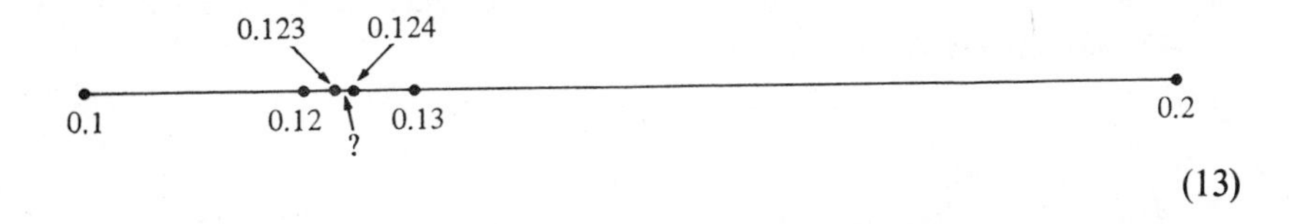

(13)

This point would be labeled by the infinite decimal 0.1234567891011.... We shall adopt the view that indeed such a point exists and that there is a point on our ruler corresponding to any decimal expansion. To do so does not offend common sense at least and is a matter of great convenience.

One last thing needs to be cleared up before we identify the real numbers with the decimal representations of lengths. What is the point represented by 1.9999999... ? This point is between 1 and 2, between 1.9 and 2, between 1.99 and 2, between 1.999 and 2, and so forth. The *only* point it could possibly be is the point labeled 2. Thus we have two different decimal representations of the point 2. Similarly, 1.569999999... *must* label the same point as 1.57. With this in mind we can identify real numbers (or, looking ahead, non-negative real numbers) with possibly infinite decimals and say that two real numbers are equal, if the decimals are the same or if they are related to each other as are, for example, 1.4329999999... and 1.433.

Problems 1–3

1. If the decimal expansion of a real number begins with 2.3156, what can you say about the number?

2. If the decimal expansion of a real number begins with 3.1427, what can you say about the number?

3. The first five digits in a decimal representation of x are 0.76548; the first four digits in a decimal representation of y are 0.7655. What can you say about y as compared to x? Why?

4. The first five digits in a decimal representation of x are 0.35916; the first four digits in a decimal representation of y are 0.3591. What can you say about y as compared to x? Why?

5. The first four digits in a decimal representation of x are 0.2719; the first four digits in a decimal representation of y are 0.2720. What can you say about y as compared to x? Why?

6. The first three digits in a decimal expansion of x are 0.357; the first three digits in a decimal expansion of y are 0.356. What can you say about y as compared to x? Why?

7. Show that the first four digits in a decimal representation of $\sqrt{7}$ are 2.645.

8. Show that the first seven digits in a decimal representation of $\sqrt{2}$ are 1.414213. Why do some tables give $\sqrt{2}$ as 1.414214?

1–4 Negative Numbers, Absolute Value, and Order

Walk 5 miles north and 6 miles south; where are you? You earn \$110 and spend \$125; how much money have you accumulated? The temperature was 5° and dropped 7°; what is the temperature now? Questions like these led to the development of the notions of "directed distances" and "signed numbers." The real numbers that we have looked at so far did not appear quite adequate for measuring along a line; not only do you want to know *how far away* a point is but *in what direction*. We talk about 1 mile *south*, \$15 *in the red*, or 2° *below zero*.

An efficient procedure for indicating direction along with distance is to choose one direction to be *positive* (e.g., north, gain as opposed to loss, above zero) and measure distances or amounts in that direction as we did before. The other direction we call the *negative* direction. We measure distances that way with numbers that are somehow distinguished: by writing them with red ink, for example, or, as is most commonly done, by prefixing them with a dash (minus sign) as -3, -7.2, $-1/2$, $-\pi$. In this context numbers represent two things, a distance and a direction, the direction being indicated by the presence or absence of a minus sign.

We can extend our ruler to enable us to measure in both directions. This extended ruler is often referred to as the *number line*. It looks like this:

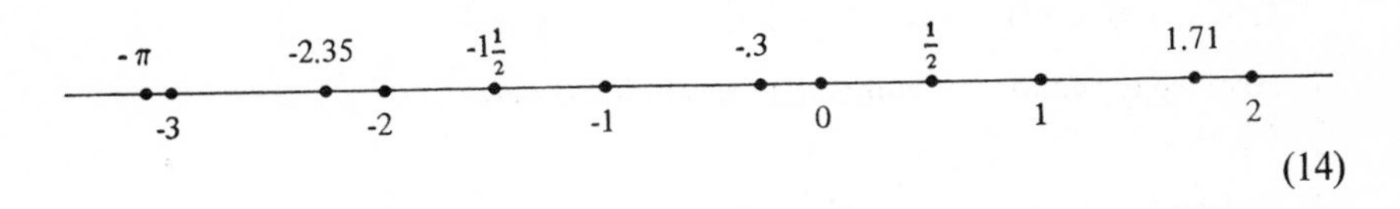

(14)

The points on the number line correspond to the real numbers, positive, negative, and zero. The negatives of integers are also called integers; the negatives of rational numbers are rational numbers, and the negatives of irrational numbers are irrational.

The *absolute value* of a real number is the distance it represents, regardless of direction. If a is a real number, we denote its absolute value by $|a|$. Thus $|2| = 2$, $|-3| = 3$, $|-2/3| = 2/3$, and so on. If we think of the real numbers as being points on a line, then $|a|$ is simply the distance from a to 0. More generally, a simple geometric interpretation is available for $|a - b|$: it is the distance between a and b. A few examples illustrate this: $|3 - 5| = 2 =$ distance between 3 and 5; $|3 + 5| = |3 - (-5)| = 8 =$ distance between 3 and -5; $|-3 - 5| = 8 =$ distance between -3 and 5.

An important property of the real numbers is that they are *ordered*; i.e., we know what it means for a number to be bigger than another. If a is bigger than b, we write $a > b$ or $b < a$ (the smaller part of the symbol "$>$" points to the smaller number). So $5 > 3$, $2 < \pi$, and so on. What about -1 and -1000? If I am \$1 in debt I have more money than if I am \$1000 in debt. Hence we write $-1 > -1000$. The rule is: $a > b$ if a lies to the right of b on the number line. Hence a number a is positive if $a > 0$ and negative if $a < 0$.

The notion of "positiveness" is the key to the notion of order. We have $6 > 2$ because $6 = 2 + 4$ and 4 is positive. If you add a positive number to 2, you get something bigger than 2; conversely, if $a > 2$, then $a - 2$ is positive and $a = 2 + (a - 2)$. In general we can say that

$$a > b \text{ if and only if } a - b \text{ is positive.} \tag{15}$$

For example, $5 > 1$ because $5 - 1 = 4$ is positive; $-3 > -4$ because $-3 - (-4) = -3 + 4 = 1$ is positive.

If we write $a < b$, we mean that a is less than b; in particular we deny that a and b are equal. Thus it is not true that $5 < 5$. If we wish to include the possibility that a and b are equal, we write $a \leq b$ which is read, "a is less than or equal to b." The symbol $\leq$ is a combination of $<$ and $=$, which serves to remind us what it means. Similarly, "$a \geq b$" means "$a > b$ or $a = b$."

Problems 1–4

1. Arrange the following numbers in ascending order.
   $1, -3, \pi, \sqrt{2}, 3/5, -1.4, 2.7, -5/3$.
2. Arrange the following numbers in ascending order.
   $1.6, 0, -2, \pi/2, -9/5, 5/3, -\sqrt{2}$.
3. List all numbers whose absolute value is 17.
4. List all numbers whose absolute value is
   a) $1/2$, b) 0, c) -9.
5. Is the statement, "If $a > b$, then $a + x > b$" true or false? Why?
6. Discuss the following statements.
   a) If $a > |b|$, then $a > b$.
   b) If $|a| > |b|$, then $a > b$.
   c) If $a > b$, then $a + x > b + x$.
7. Show that $-3 > -5$, using the criterion that $a > b$ exactly when $a - b$ is positive.
8. Verify or deny the following statements using the criterion that $a > b$ exactly when $a - b$ is positive.
   a) $3 > -2$, b) $2 > -3$, c) $2 > |-3|$,
   d) $-5 > -7$, e) $-8 > 4$, f) $3 > -5$.

1–5 *Rounding and Significant Digits*

In practice we do not deal with numbers like 3.14159265358979. . . . Suppose we have a wheel whose diameter is 5 feet and wish to know its circumference. Now we know that the circumference is 5π. However, in all probability we really don't know whether the diameter of the wheel is 5 feet or, say, 5.0000001 feet (and we might not care even if we did). In this situation it would be pointless to use all digits in the expansion of π, even if this were possible, to compute the circumference. Depending on how much precision we demanded, and could use, we would approximate π by 3.14 or 3.1416 or 3.14159, and so on. This process is known as *rounding* or *rounding off*.

To round off π *to two decimal places* is to find a number with *two* digits after the decimal point, which is as close as possible to π. Since we know that π lies between 3.14 and 3.15 (why?), we need only determine which of these numbers is closer to π. But we also know that π lies between 3.141 and 3.142, both of which are closer to 3.14 than to 3.15. Hence π is closer to 3.14 than to 3.15 and thus 3.14 is as close as we can come to π using numbers with two digits after the decimal point. We say that π *is* 3.14 *to two decimal places.*

Similarly, we say that π is 3.1416 *to four decimal places*, since 3.1416 is as close as we can come to π using numbers with *four* digits after the decimal point. Here we know that π is between 3.1415 and 3.1416. To decide which of these numbers is closer to π we look at one more place in the decimal expansion. This tells us that π lies between 3.14159 and 3.14160, and thus 3.1416 is a better approximation than 3.1415.

Notice what we do in these two examples. In the first, to round π to *two* decimal places we look at the first *three* places in the expansion of π,

$$3.141.$$

Since the third digit after the decimal point is 1, we see that π is 3.14 to two decimal places. Similarly, all of the numbers

$$3.140, 3.141, 3.142, 3.143, 3.144$$

are 3.14 to two decimal places and so is any number whose decimal expansion starts out in any of these ways. (Why?)

On the other hand, the numbers

$$3.146, 3.147, 3.148, 3.149$$

are clearly closer to 3.15 than to 3.14, as is any number whose decimal expansion begins in one of these fashions. The key as to whether to round *down* to 3.14 or to round *up* to 3.15 lies in the *third* digit. If this is less than 5 we round *down*; if it is greater than 5 we round *up*. When we rounded π to *two* decimal places, we rounded *down* to 3.14 because the *third* digit is less than 5. When we rounded to four decimal places, we rounded up to 3.1416 because the *fifth* digit is greater than 5.

What if the crucial digit is 5? This occurs, for example, if we wish to round π to *three* places. Here we must choose between 3.141 and 3.142. If we go to four places, we have 3.1415 which is equally close to 3.141 and 3.142. When this happens we must consider the rest of the expansion. If *all* the remaining digits were 0, for example 3.1415000000000..., then the number is precisely half way between 3.141 and 3.142. In this situation there is no reason to choose the one approximation over the other. One rule of thumb, which has the advantage of overestimating as often as underestimating, is to round to the number which ends in an even digit, in this case to 3.142. However, if *any* of the remaining digits in the expansion are different from 0, as is the case for π, then you should round *up*. For example, 3.141500000100..., since it is greater than 3.1415, is closer to 3.142 than to 3.141 (although not very much so).

We summarize these ideas with a fresh example. Suppose we wish to round to *two* decimal places. If the first *three* places in the expansion are

7.160, 7.161, 7.162, 7.163, or 7.164,

we round to 7.16. If the first three places are

7.166, 7.167, 7.168, or 7.169,

we round to 7.17. If the first three places are 7.165, we round to 7.17 if there are *any* nonzero digits in the remainder of the expansion. If, on the other hand, the number is *precisely* 7.165 then we (may) apply our rule of thumb and round to 7.16 since this ends in an even digit.

A similar procedure applies to rounding off a number in any place. Consider the number 567.8962. Rounded off to three decimal places, or in the third decimal place, or in the thousandths place, 567.8962 is 567.896. Rounded off to two decimal places, or in the hundredths place, 567.8962 is 567.90; rounded to one decimal place, or in the tenths place, it is 567.9. We may also round 567.8962 in the *units* place, that is, to the nearest integer. Here we would get 568 since that is the closest integer to 567.8962. Similarly, we may round 567.8962 to the tens place, that is, to the nearest integer which is a multiple of ten; if we do this we get 570. In the same spirit we say that 567.8962 is 600 to the nearest hundred, 1000 to the nearest thousand, and 0 to the nearest ten thousand; these statements mean that 567.8962 is nearer to 600 than to 500 or 700, nearer to 1000 than to 0 or 2000, and nearer to 0 than to 10,000.

Computation with approximate numbers, that is, numbers which are approximations, often yields results which appear more precise than they actually are. Let us return to our 5-foot diameter wheel. Suppose we measured the diameter as carefully as we could and found it was, in fact, 5.03 feet to within a hundredth of a foot; that is, we know that 5.03 is closer to the true diameter of the wheel than is either 5.02 or 5.04—and that is the full extent of our knowledge. In computing the circumference we might use 3.1416 as an approximation to π. Then we would estimate the circumference to be $(3.1416) \cdot (5.03) = 15.742248$. Notice that we could only measure the diameter up to one hundredth of a foot while our estimate of the circumference seems to be accurate up to a millionth of a foot! The problem is that the last few digits in our solution have no significance. Indeed, for all we know, the diameter might be anywhere from 5.025 to 5.035. If it were the former, we would compute the circumference to be $(3.1416) \cdot (5.025) = 15.72654$; whereas if it were the latter, we would get $(3.1416) \cdot (5.035) = 15.757956$. Comparing these numbers

$$15.72654,$$
$$15.742248,$$
$$15.757956,$$

we see that only the digits 15.74 have any real meaning and that the last digit, 4, is questionable; the remaining digits tell us nothing.

In discussing the accuracy of these approximations, or *approximate numbers*, the notion of *significant digits* is useful. Roughly speaking, a significant digit in an approximate number is a digit following the leading zeros (if any) which gives real information concerning the true value of the number. The digits, other than the initial string of zeros, which are known to be correct, are significant. In most cases the digit following these correct digits is also significant. For example, if 12.364 is an approximation to some number and we know it might be off by 0.5 either way but no more, then all we know about the true value is that it lies between 11.864 and 12.864; and thus only the first two digits are significant. Similarly, if 0.001356 is an approximation which may be off by 0.000005 but no more, then the true value may lie anywhere between 0.001351 and 0.001361, and only the digits 1, 3, and 5, the first three nonzero digits, are significant. In general, when writing an approximate number, it is assumed that all digits after the leading zeros are significant. The results of actual measurements and the results of rounding exactly known numbers, such as those given in the tables in the back of this book, are the closest numbers to the true values that may be expressed with that many digits.

Our computation with numbers of which one had three significant digits and the other had more, produced a product having three significant digits. In fact a general rule of thumb is that a product has the same number of significant digits as the factor with the fewest significant digits. A similar rule applies to quotients.

Suppose $x = 21.3$ and $y = 9.876$ are results of measurements. Then

$$21.25 \leq x \leq 21.35,$$
$$9.8755 \leq y \leq 9.8765,$$

so that

$$31.1255 \leq x + y \leq 31.2265.$$

Thus $x + y$ certainly cannot be given to more than one decimal place. Adding 21.3 and 9.876, the original approximate numbers, we get 31.176. Rounding to one decimal place gives 31.2, and there may be an error in the last digit. The rule of thumb generally followed in adding or subtracting approximate numbers is that the result is correct to the same place as the least precise number (that is, the one with the fewest places after the decimal point). For example, the sum of the approximate numbers 21324 and 98.76 is 21423.

The sum is given to the nearest integer, since the least precise number is 21324. Similarly the difference of the approximate numbers 410.67 and 0.3942 is 410.28.

In all calculations with approximate numbers the result should be properly rounded off to avoid a misleading impression of accuracy. In making lengthy calculations it is advisable to carry along one or two extra digits, rounding off fully only at the end in order to minimize errors resulting from a succession of roundings-off.

Problems 1–5

In problems 1 to 14 round the indicated numbers to three decimal places; to the nearest integer; to the nearest ten; to three significant digits; to two significant digits.

1. 1.7654. **2.** 3.8461.

3. 0.0004876. **4.** 0.007436.

5. 1/3. **6.** 1/6.

7. 12/11. **8.** 22/7.

9. 5.5. **10.** 16.3.

11. 316.59. **12.** 237.84.

13. 24.7367. **14.** π.

15. Find $\sqrt{3}$ to three decimal places; to three significant digits; to the nearest tenth.

16. Find $\sqrt{56}$ to three decimal places; to three significant digits; to the nearest tenth.

17. Compute $(3.7) \cdot (7.2)$ and properly round off the result.

18. Perform the indicated computations and properly round off the result.

a) $(2.5) \cdot (1.5)$, b) $6 \cdot 6$,
c) $(6) \cdot (6.0)$, d) $(6.0) \cdot (6.0)$,
e) $(6.00) \cdot (6.00)$, f) $(5.5) \cdot (6.6) \cdot (7.8)$,
g) $(322) \cdot (3.21)$, h) $1.1111 \div 1.11$,
i) $2.365 \div .003401$, j) $8.88 + 9.999$,
k) $101 - 1.1$, l) $101.0 - 1.1$,
m) $1.010 + .0909$, n) $.38114 + .2145 - .300$,
o) $56.7 + .0685462114364811976$, p) $(69.69) \cdot (96.96) - (69.96)^2$,
q) $(78.39) \cdot (1.000035678910111213) - 78.392$.

2 Functions and Graphs

2–1 The Concept of a Function

When Galileo experimented by dropping objects from high places he discovered that the *time* it took an object to reach the ground depended only on the *height* from which it was dropped (and not, for example, on its weight). He found that any object would fall 16 feet in about 1 second, 64 feet in 2 seconds, 256 feet in 4 seconds, and so on. The height h from which an object was dropped determined the time t it would take to hit the ground. In fact, it turned out that t could be computed by the (relatively) simple formula $t = \frac{1}{4}\sqrt{h}$.

Every state in the U.S. has a capital. The capital of New York is Albany; the capital of Illinois is Springfield; the capital of California is Sacramento. If we know the state we can determine the city that is its capital. There is no "formula" by which we can compute the city from the state, but we do know how to find out what city goes with each state.

The radius of a circle determines what the area of that circle is. Here again we have a formula with which we can compute the area if we know the radius: if r is the radius of the circle, then the area is given by πr^2.

These three situations all have one thing in common. In each we have a way of starting with one thing and ending up with another. In the first we start with a number (of feet) and end up with a number (of seconds). In the second we start out with a state and end up with a city. In the third we start out with a number (the radius) and end up with a number (the area). We may think of these changes as being carried out by a machine: we put something in the machine, and it gives us back something. The first machine accepts positive numbers and gives back positive numbers. If you put in a 4, you get back a 1/8; if you put in a 64, you get back a 2. If you put "Pennsylvania" in the second machine, it will hand you back "Harrisburg"; if you put in "New Jersey," you will receive "Trenton."

Whenever we have a definite way of determining from each object in some set an object in another set, either by computing, looking up, or whatever, we say we have a *function*. A function consists of two sets and a rule. The first set is called the *domain* of the function; the second set is called the *range* of the function. The function assigns an object in its range to each object in its domain, according to some specified rule. Thinking of it mechanically, the domain consists of those things you can feed into the machine; the things that come out are in the range; the machine specifies the rule.

We have examined three functions. Let us denote Galileo's function by the letter f. (The letter f will be used to denote many different functions. The letters g, h, F, G, and so on will also be used for this purpose.) We indicate the fact that an object takes 2 seconds to fall 64 feet by writing $f(64) = 2$. This is read "f of 64 equals 2." Similarly, we have $f(16) = 1$, $f(256) = 4$ and $f(9) = 3/4$. In general, for any number h we have $f(h) = \frac{1}{4}\sqrt{h}$. The domain of f is the set of positive numbers. The range of f is also the set of positive numbers.

If we denote by F the function which assigns to each state its capital city, we have F(Alabama) = Montgomery, F(Alaska) = Juneau, F(Arizona) = Phoenix, and so on. The domain of F is the set of the fifty states; the range of F is a set of cities.

If g is a function with domain A and range B, then g assigns to each element x of A an element $g(x)$ (read "g of x") of B. The element $g(x)$ is called the *value* of g at x. We do not require that every element of B be used. It is sometimes of interest to know just what values a function does attain. The set of values of g will be called the *image* of g. The range of g is some specified set containing the image. The specification of the range of a function is somewhat arbitrary as it can be any set containing the image of the function, and the choice is usually a matter of convenience. If the image is easy to determine, it is usually chosen as the range also. (In fact, many textbooks use the word "range" to mean the set of values of the function.) However, it is sometimes more convenient to make some other choice.

The following examples illustrate how the values of some functions can be found.

Example 1. If $f(r) = \pi r^2$, find $f(6)$.

Solution. When $r = 6$, $\pi r^2 = \pi \cdot 6^2$, or 36π. Thus $f(6) = 36\pi$.

Example 2. If $g(t) = 16t^2$, find $g(7)$.

Solution. When $t = 7$, $16t^2 = 16 \cdot 7^2$, or 784. Thus $g(7) = 784$.

Example 3. If $F(x) = 2x^2 - 5$, find $F(3\pi)$.

Solution. When $x = 3\pi$, $2x^2 - 5 = 2(3\pi)^2 - 5$. Thus $F(3\pi) = 18\pi^2 - 5$.

Example 4. If $C(x) =$ capital of x, find C(New Mexico).

Solution. C(New Mexico) = Santa Fe.

Example 5. If $G(x) = x^3 + 4x - 18$, find $G(a + by)$.

Solution.
$$G(a + by) = (a + by)^3 + 4(a + by) - 18$$
$$= a^3 + 3a^2by + 3ab^2y^2 + b^3y^3 + 4a + 4by - 18.$$

For most of the functions you will encounter in the near future, the domain will be a set of numbers. In cases when a function is given by a formula, the domain and range will often not be mentioned specifically. In such cases the domain is considered to be the set of all real numbers for which the formula is defined. With this convention the formula determines the domain, image, and rule of correspondence of the function. For this reason we often make no distinction between the function and the formula which determines it.

Example 6. What is the domain of

$$f(x) = \sqrt{\frac{1}{x}}\,?$$

What is the image of f?

Solution. If $x > 0$, then $1/x > 0$ and has a square root. (By convention, $\sqrt{}$ denotes the positive square root.) If $x = 0$, $1/x$ is not defined, and if $x < 0$, $1/x < 0$ and has no square root in the set of real numbers. Thus the domain of f is the set of positive real numbers. The image of f is again the set of positive real numbers. (If x is a positive real number, $x = \sqrt{x^2} = f(1/x^2)$ and thus x is in the image of f.)

Example 7. Let $g(x) = (x + 1)/x$. On what set of real numbers is g defined, and what is the image of g on this domain?

Solution. If $x = 0$ the expression $(x + 1)/x$ is not defined and if $x \neq 0$ the expression is defined, so the set on which g is defined is the set of nonzero real numbers. If y is any real number except 1, $g(1/(y - 1)) = y$, so y is in the image of g. (Solve $y = (x + 1)/x$ for x to obtain the equation $x = 1/(y - 1)$.) Clearly $(x + 1)/x = 1$ is impossible (why?). Thus the image of g is the set of all real numbers except 1.

Problems 2–1

Evaluate the functions in 1—10 at the indicated points.

1. $f(x) = 2x^2 - x$.
a) $x = 5$, b) $x = -7$, c) $x = a + b$.

2. $f(x) = \dfrac{2 + \sqrt{x^2 - 1}}{5x}$.

a) $x = 1$, b) $x = 2$, c) $x = 5$.

3. $f(x) = \dfrac{x + 1}{x - 1}$.

a) $x = 0$, b) $x = \pi$, c) $x = 19$.

4. $g(y) = \dfrac{3y^2 + 2}{2y - 7}$.

a) $y = -2$, b) $y = \sqrt{3}$, c) $y = \dfrac{\pi}{4}$.

5. $g(x) = \dfrac{4\pi x^3}{3}$.

a) $x = \pi$, b) $x = 3$, c) $x = -\dfrac{2}{3}$.

6. $F(t) = t^3 + 2t^2 - \dfrac{2}{3}t + 1$.

a) $t = 0$, b) $t = -1$, c) $t = 5$.

7. $G(x) = (3x + 1)(4x - 3)$.

a) $x = 2$, b) $x = -\dfrac{1}{3}$, c) $x = \dfrac{3}{4}$.

8. $f(x) = 2x^2 + 3x - 1$.

a) $x = y^2$, b) $x = \dfrac{1}{a}$, c) $x = a + 2c$.

9. $f(x) = \dfrac{\sqrt{x^2 - 9} + 3}{(x - 2)(x + 3)}$.

a) $x = 3$, b) $x = 5$, c) $x = 9$.

10. $G(x) = \dfrac{(x + 2)(x - 2)}{4x^2(x - 2)}$.

a) $x = -2$, b) $x = \pi^2$, c) $x = \sqrt{3}$.

Describe the domain and image of each of the functions in 11—16.

11. $f(x) = 2x^2 - x$.

12. $f(t) = \dfrac{2 + \sqrt{t^2 - 1}}{5t}$.

13. $f(y) = \dfrac{y + 1}{y - 1}$.

14. $f(x) = \dfrac{\sqrt{x^2 - 9} + 4}{(x - 2)(x + 3)}$.

15. $f(t) = \dfrac{(t + 4)(t - 5)}{8t^2(t - 5)}$.

16. $f(t) = \dfrac{(t + 3)(t - 1)}{2t(t - 1)}$.

Let $f(x) = 2x - 5$. Evaluate the following.

17. a) $3f(2)$, b) $f(4a)$, c) $-f(0)$.

18. a) $f(\sqrt{y})$, b) $f(3x)$, c) $f(|z|)$.

19. a) $\sqrt{f(x^2)}$, b) $|f(-4t)|$, c) $f(t)+f(|t|)$.

20. a) $f(t+1)-f(t)$, b) $f(r^2)$, c) $\sqrt{2f(y)-4}$.

2–2 *Formulas and Tables*

Many functions are most conveniently described by a formula. A formula, by means of symbols (letters, numbers, etc.), gives a rule for finding the value of the function at any point of its domain. It is frequently useful to redescribe a function by a formula. You may have already encountered this idea in the "word problems" of elementary algebra.

Example 1. Let G be the function which assigns to each positive integer the sum of the two preceding integers. Express G in terms of a formula.

Solution. $G(n)=(n-1)+(n-2)=2n-3$.

Example 2. Let F be the function that assigns to each nonnegative real number x one-half the area of a square having x as perimeter. Describe F by a formula.

Solution. If x is the perimeter of a square, the area of that square is $(x/4)(x/4)=x^2/16$. Thus $F(x)=(1/2)(x^2/16)=x^2/32$.

Example 3. Let f be the function given by

$$f(x)=\frac{x^2+2}{3x-1},$$

and let $F(x)=f(2x+3)$. Describe F by a formula.

Solution. To find the formula for F we replace "x" by "$2x+3$" wherever it appears in the formula for f, and simplify.

$$\begin{aligned} F(x) &= \frac{(2x+3)^2+2}{3(2x+3)-1} \\ &= \frac{(4x^2+12x+9)+2}{(6x+9)-1} \\ &= \frac{4x^2+12x+11}{6x+8}. \end{aligned}$$

Some functions cannot be expressed conveniently by a single formula. An example of this is the absolute value function. The absolute value of a real number x is x if $x \geq 0$ and $-x$ if $x<0$. Thus the absolute value of 3 is 3, whereas the absolute value of -5 is 5 (since $-(-5)=5$). Denoting the function which assigns to each real number its absolute value by F, we may describe

F by the scheme:

$$F(x) = \begin{cases} x & \text{if } x \geq 0, \\ -x & \text{if } x < 0. \end{cases}$$

Here we have used *two* formulas in our description of F, namely $F(x) = x$ and $F(x) = -x$. On part of its domain, the nonnegative numbers, F is described by the formula $F(x) = x$. On the rest of its domain, the negative numbers, F is described by the formula $F(x) = -x$.

If a widely used function is not conveniently describable by a single formula, it is common to invent a symbol to describe it. The absolute value of x is denoted by $|x|$. As mentioned above, a function is often referred to by the formula describing it. Also, we speak of "the function x^2" rather than using a cumbersome expression like "the function F such that $F(x) = x^2$." Similarly, we speak of the absolute value function $|x|$.

A more elaborate example of a function which is not expressed by a single formula is provided by:

$$F(x) = \begin{cases} x^2 + 1 & \text{if } x < 0, \\ 1 - x & \text{if } 0 \leq x \leq 1, \\ 0 & \text{if } x > 1. \end{cases}$$

The domain of F is the set of real numbers, and its image is the set of nonnegative real numbers.

You have seen examples of functions described by one, two, and three formulas. In order to describe the *greatest integer* function in this way one must use an infinite number of formulas. Let $[x]$ denote the greatest integer less than or equal to x. Thus $[1] = 1$, $[\pi] = 3$, $[\sqrt{2}] = 1$, and $[-\pi] = -4$. The function $[x]$ has the real numbers as its domain and the integers as its image.

To describe it by formulas we would need a scheme like:

$$[x] = \begin{cases} \quad \vdots \\ -2 & \text{if } -2 \leq x < -1 \\ -1 & \text{if } -1 \leq x < 0 \\ 0 & \text{if } \quad 0 \leq x < 1 \\ 1 & \text{if } \quad 1 \leq x < 2 \\ 2 & \text{if } \quad 2 \leq x < 3 \\ \quad \vdots \end{cases}$$

More compactly, we could write:

$$[x] = n, \quad \text{if } n \leq x < n + 1 \text{ and } n \text{ is an integer.}$$

The function which assigns to each state its capital cannot reasonably be described by formulas at all. The normal way of describing this function is by a *table*, the first few entries being:

Alabama	Montgomery
Alaska	Juneau
Arizona	Phoenix
.	.
.	.
.	.

The table completely describes the function. What *is* a table? This is not an idle question. Consider the following table:

Pennsylvania	Harrisburg
Ohio	Columbus
Nevada	Carson City
Delaware	Dover
.	.
.	.
.	.

If each state appears in the left column across from its capital in the right column, then this table describes the same function as the first table we looked at. If we wish to find the capital of a state, either table will do. That the first is preferable in practice because the states are arranged in alphabetical order is beside the point. Both tables contain the same information.

The information provided by these tables is the *pairing* of states and cities. The same information would be available were we to make out 50 slips of paper like

Illinois	Springfield

and put them in a hat. What the table provides is a set of pairs (x, y), where x is a state and y is the capital of x. These pairs are *ordered*; that is we can tell which is the first entry and which the second. Otherwise we might conclude that Illinois was the capital of Springfield.

Every function F may be described by a table in this general sense. The table consists of all ordered pairs of the form $(x, F(x))$, where x is in the domain of F. The domain of F is the set of all first entries, and the image of F is the set of all second entries. To find out the value of the function at t we look through the table until we find t as the first entry in a pair. The second entry will be $F(t)$. This is precisely how one uses tables in practice. In general it is inconvenient or impossible to make a complete table, but a partial list can be very useful when studying a particular function.

Example 4. Make a partial table for the function $f(x) = \pi x^2$, evaluating f for $x = 0, 1, 2, 3, 4, 5$.

Solution.

x	0	1	2	3	4	.5
$f(x)$	0	π	4π	9π	16π	25π

Example 5. Make a partial table for the function $g(x) = 4x^3 + 6x - 2$, evaluating $g(x)$ for $x = 0, 1, 2, 3, 4, 5$.

Solution.

x	0	1	2	3	4	5
$g(x)$	-2	8	42	124	278	528

Problems 2–2

Express the functions in 1—5 in terms of formulas.

1. f assigns to each real number x the sum of its square and its cube.

2. g assigns to each positive real number x the number of seconds it takes a freely falling object to fall x feet.

3. G assigns to each positive integer n the sum of the first n positive integers. (Hint: $1 + 2 + \cdots + (n-1) + n = (1+n) + [2 + (n-1)] + \cdots$.)

4. H assigns to each positive integer n the average of the first n integers.

5. F assigns to each positive real number x the area of a circle having x as circumference.

Make a partial table for each of the functions in 6—10, evaluating at the indicated points.

6. $f(x) = 3x^2 + 7x - 6$; $x = -5, -3, 0, 3, 5$.

7. $G(x) = \dfrac{x+2}{2x-4}$; $x = 0, 1, 1\frac{1}{2}, 1\frac{3}{4}, 2\frac{1}{4}, 2\frac{1}{2}, 3$.

8. $g(x) = \dfrac{x+3}{x-4}$; $x = a, a+1, a+2$.

9. $h(x) = x^3$; $x = -5, -3, 0, 3, 5$.

10. $F(x) = 16x^2$; $x = -5, -3, 0, 3, 5$.

Describe the domain and image for each of the functions in 11—14.

11. a) $f(x) = |x|$, b) $F(x) = |x| - x$.

12. a) $g(y) = \dfrac{|y|}{y}$, b) $G(y) = \sqrt{|y - 1|}$.

13. $h(t) = 3[t] - t$.

14. $H(t) = \dfrac{t}{[t] - t}$.

Express the functions F in 15—18 in terms of formulas.

15. $F(x) = f(3x)$, where $f(x) = x^2$.

16. $F(x) = g(x^2)$, where $g(x) = 2x - 1$.

17. $F(x) = f(3x - 2)$, where $f(x) = \dfrac{2x^2 - 3}{3x + 1}$.

18. $F(x) = g(4x + 5)$, where $g(x) = \dfrac{\sqrt{2x^2 + 3}}{5x - 1}$.

2–3 *The Cartesian Plane*

In Chapter 1, we discussed the fact that the real numbers can be represented by the real number line. A unit distance and the position of 0 are chosen,

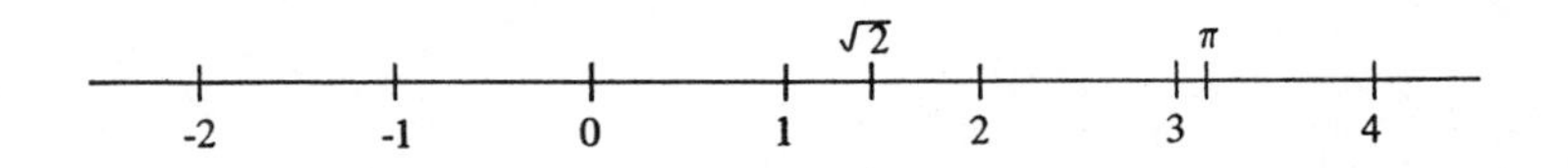

Fig. 2-1

and this determines the position of every number on the line. For example, π is the circumference of a circle of diameter 1. If the circumference is "cut" and pulled out straight to the right with one end at 0, the other end will be at π (Fig. 2-1). The right triangle with sides adjacent to the right angle both having length 1 has hypotenuse of length $\sqrt{2}$. If the left end of this hypotenuse is at 0, the right end will be at $\sqrt{2}$.

Similarly, the set of all ordered pairs of real numbers can be represented by the *Cartesian plane* (named for René Descartes (1596—1650)). A pair of perpendicular real number lines is constructed. These lines are called *axes.* The horizontal line is commonly called the *x axis* and the vertical line the *y axis*. The two axes divide the plane into four parts, called the first, second, third, and fourth *quadrants*, respectively (Fig. 2-2).

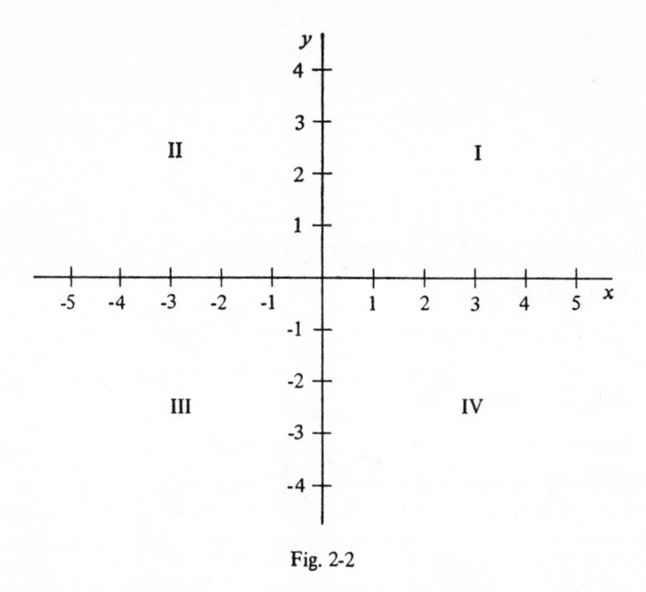

Fig. 2-2

The point at which the two lines cross is called the *origin* and is the 0 of each of the lines. An ordered pair (a, b) of real numbers is represented by the point which lies a units from the origin in the horizontal direction and b units in the vertical direction. The points $(3, 2)$, $(2, -3)$, and $(-2, 1)$ are represented in Fig. 2-3. The numbers 3 and 2 are the *Cartesian coordinates* (or rectangular coordinates) of the point $(3, 2)$, with 3 being the x coordinate and 2 being the y coordinate.

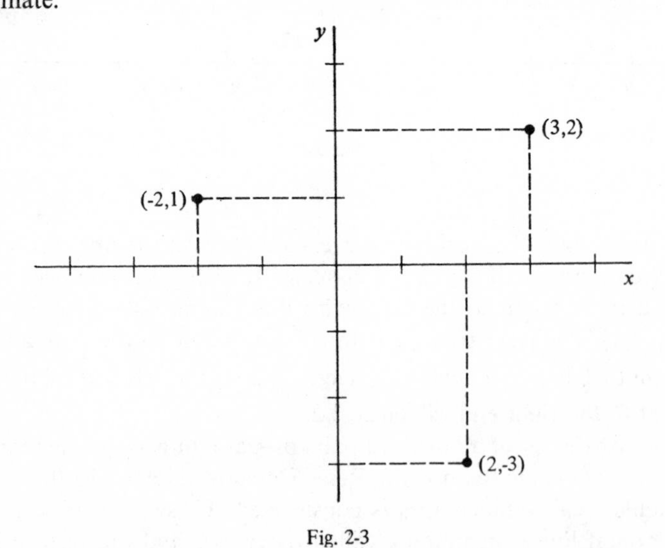

Fig. 2-3

Each number is represented by a point on the real number line, and each point on the line corresponds to a real number. Each ordered pair of numbers then corresponds to a point in the plane. And given a point in the plane, dropping a perpendicular to each of the axes gives an ordered pair of numbers corresponding to that point.

The *distance* between two points on the line is given by the absolute value of the difference between the points. For example, the distance from 2 to 3 is $|2 - 3| = 1$, and the distance from -2 to 1 is $|1 - (-2)| = 3$.

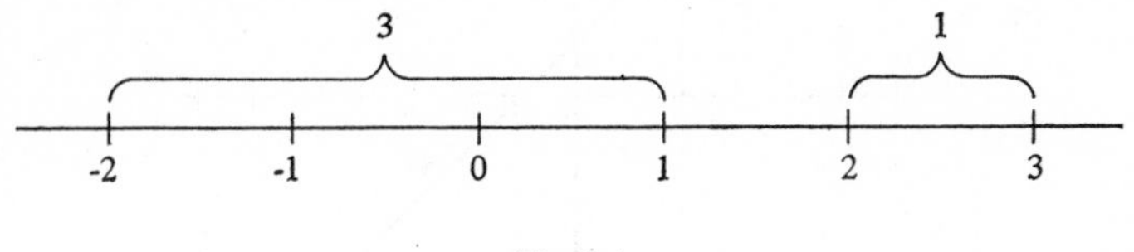

Fig. 2-4

The distance between two points in the plane is simply the length of the line segment connecting them. It can be found as follows. Draw the right triangle formed by drawing lines parallel to the axes, as in Fig. 2-5. The lengths

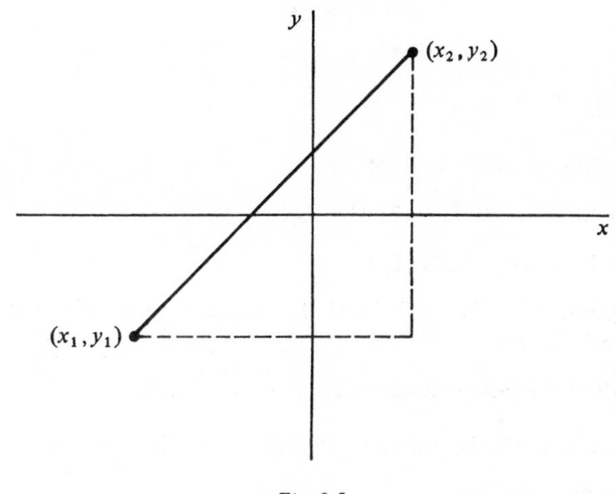

Fig. 2-5

of the horizontal and vertical lines can be easily computed. They are $|x_2 - x_1|$ and $|y_2 - y_1|$, the absolute values of the differences between the x and y coordinates, respectively. By the well-known Pythagorean theorem, the length of the hypotenuse is the square root of the sum of the squares of the other two sides. Thus the distance from (x_1, y_1) to (x_2, y_2) is

$$s = \sqrt{(x_2 - x_1)^2 + (y_2 - y_1)^2}.$$

This is the *distance formula* for the plane.

Example. Find the distance between the points $(-2, 3)$ and $(6, -5)$.

Solution.

$$\sqrt{[(-2)-6]^2+[3-(-5)]^2}=\sqrt{(-8)^2+8^2}=\sqrt{2\cdot 64}=8\sqrt{2}.$$

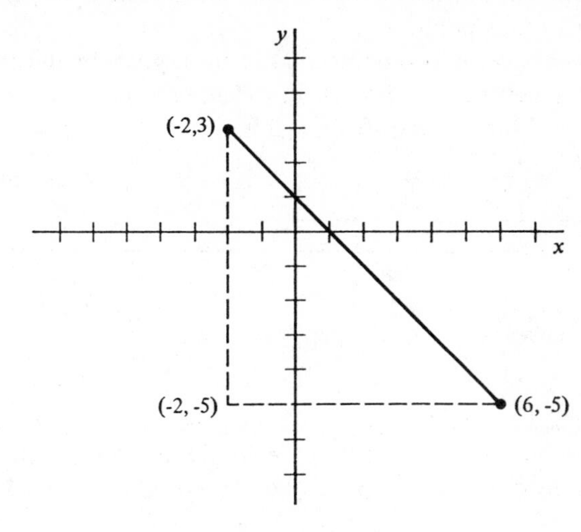

Fig. 2-6

Problems 2–3

1. Plot the points $(0, 0)$, $(-1, 3)$, $(4, 4)$.
2. Plot the points $(2, 3/2)$, $(1, -3)$, $(1, -3/2)$.
3. Plot the points $(0, 4)$, $(2, 0)$, $(2, 4)$.
4. Plot the points $(3, -2)$, $(-2, 3)$, $(1, 1)$, and join each pair of points with a straight line segment.
5. Indicate all of the points having 3 as an x coordinate.

Shade the areas in which the points (x, y) satisfy the following inequalities.

6. $0 \leq x < 4$ and $1 < y < 2$.
7. $-2 < x \leq 3$ and $|y| \leq 1$.

Find the distance between the following pairs of points.

8. $(0, 5)$ and $(6, 3)$.
9. $(-2, 6)$ and $(5, \sqrt{2})$.
10. $(\sqrt{7}, 8)$ and $(5, \pi)$.
11. $(-3, -7)$ and $(8, -2)$.
12. $(a+b, a)$ and $(2b, 2a+b)$.

Shade the areas in which the points (x, y) satisfy the following requirements.

13. The distance from (x, y) to the origin $(0, 0)$ is less than or equal to 1.

14. The distance from (x, y) to the x axis is less than or equal to 1.

15. The distance from (x, y) to the x axis is less than or equal to 1, and also the distance from (x, y) to the y axis is less than or equal to 1.

2–4 *Graphs of Functions*

Let f be a function whose domain and range are sets of real numbers. The set of points in the plane that corresponds to the set of ordered pairs $(x, f(x))$ such that x is in the domain of f is the *graph* of the function f. The graph of a function is a geometric representation of its table.

Example 1. Let f be the function given by the table

x	0	1	2	3	4	5
$f(x)$	0	2	0	1	2	1

The graph of f is the set of points depicted in Fig. 2-7.

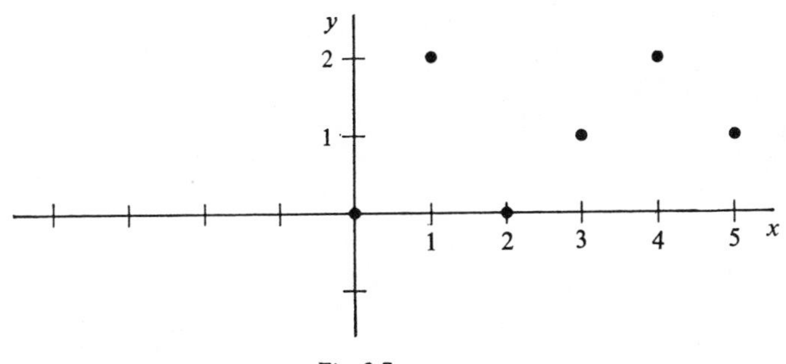

Fig. 2-7

In general, tables which give a partial list of points in the graph, together with knowledge of the general behavior of certain families of functions, enable us to sketch portions of the graphs of many functions.

Example 2. Let $f(x) = x$. The table

x	-2	-1	0	1	2	3
$f(x)$	-2	-1	0	1	2	3

gives the points in Fig. 2-8 on the graph of f, which we connect with a smooth curve.

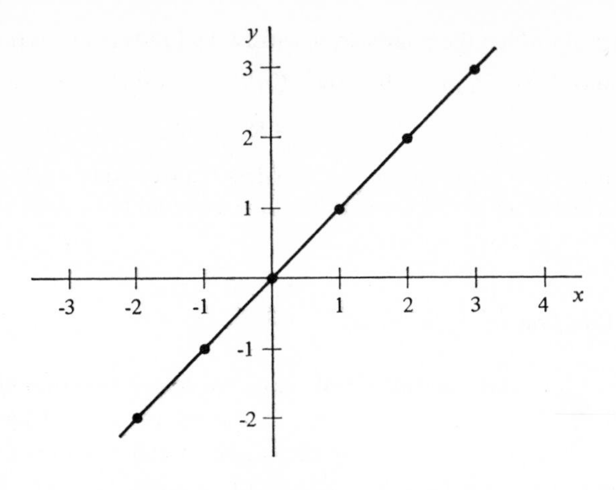

Fig. 2-8

This is a first approximation to the graph of f. The more we know about f, the closer we can approximate its graph. The curve in this case appears to be a straight line. It can be shown that any function of the form $f(x) = ax + b$ has a straight line as its graph. Thus our first approximation here is an accurate one.

Example 3. Let $f(x) = x^2$, and look at the general behavior of f. For all x, $x^2 \geq 0$; hence the graph will lie entirely on or above the x axis. If $0 < x < 1$, then $0 < x^2 < x$; and if $x > 1$, then $x^2 > x$. Thus for $x \geq 0$ the graph of f will lie in the shaded areas in Fig. 2-9.

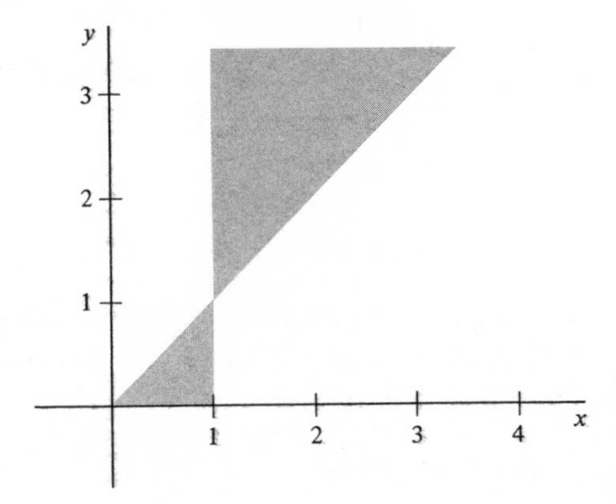

Fig. 2-9

Notice also that $f(-x) = f(x)$ (since $(-x)^2 = x^2$); thus the graph is symmetric about the y axis; i.e., if (x, y) is in the graph, then $(-x, y)$ is also in the graph. Thus if we sketch the right half of the graph, the left half will be a mirror image. Using the table

x	0	$\frac{1}{4}$	$\frac{1}{2}$	$\frac{3}{4}$	1	$\frac{3}{2}$	2	3
x^2	0	$\frac{1}{16}$	$\frac{1}{4}$	$\frac{9}{16}$	1	$\frac{9}{4}$	4	9

and connecting these points with a smooth curve, we obtain Fig. 2-10, which approximates the graph of the function $f(x) = x^2$.

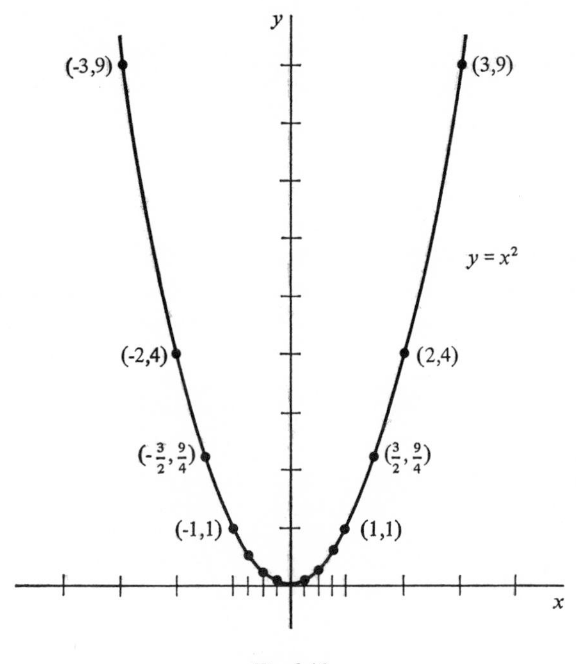

Fig. 2-10

Example 4. Let $f(x) = [x]$ (the greatest integer less than or equal to x). A little thought will convince you the graph of f looks like Fig. 2-11.

Such a function is called a *step function* for obvious reasons.

Example 5. Let f be the following function.

$$f(x) = \begin{cases} 1 & \text{if } x < 0, \\ x^2 & \text{if } 0 \leq x \leq 2, \\ x + 2 & \text{if } 2 < x. \end{cases}$$

The graph of this function is depicted in Fig. 2-12.

Example 6. Let $f(x) = 1/x$. The domain of this function does not include the point 0. If $x > 0$, then $1/x > 0$; and if $x < 0$, then $1/x < 0$. Thus the graph lies entirely in the first and third quadrants.

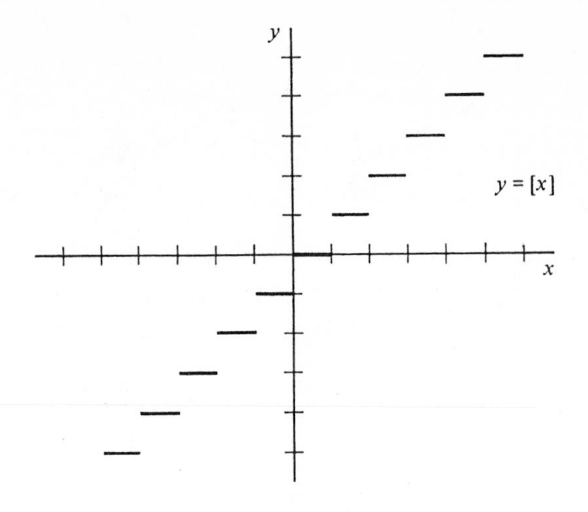

Fig. 2-11

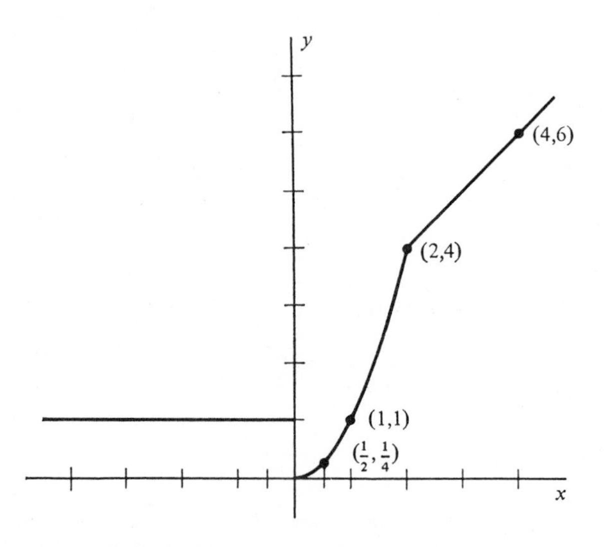

Fig. 2-12

If $0 < x < 1$, then $1/x > 1$; if $1 < x$, then $1/x < 1$. Thus the graph lies within the shaded areas of Fig. 2-13.

This estimate guides us to making a useful table. We see we should compute several points between 0 and 1, for example.

x	1	$\frac{3}{4}$	$\frac{1}{2}$	$\frac{1}{4}$	$\frac{1}{16}$	$\frac{3}{2}$	2	3	4
$\frac{1}{x}$	1	$\frac{4}{3}$	2	4	16	$\frac{2}{3}$	$\frac{1}{2}$	$\frac{1}{3}$	$\frac{1}{4}$

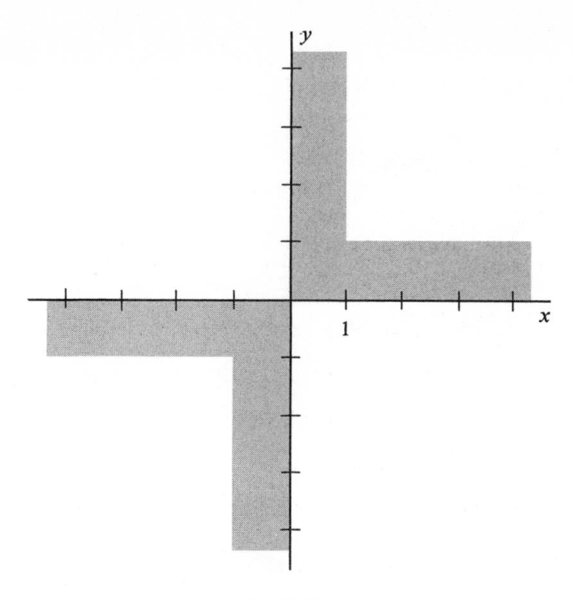

Fig. 2-13

If we imagine a minus sign in front of every number in the table, this provides us with a table to help plot the negative values of x also. Connecting the points given in the table with a smooth curve gives the sketch of the graph of $1/x$ depicted in Fig. 2-14.

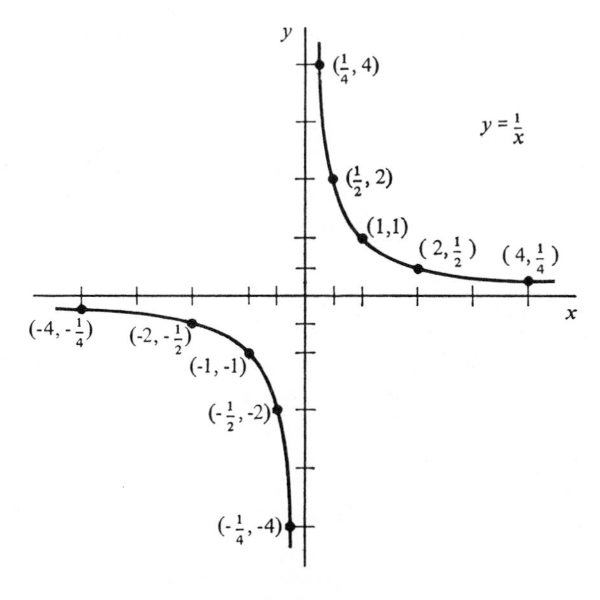

Fig. 2-14

Problems 2–4

Graph the functions in problems 1—7.

1.

x	-3	-2	-1	0	1	2	3
$f(x)$	0	1	3	0	3	1	0

2. a) $f(x) = x + 1$, b) $g(x) = 3x$, c) $h(x) = -x$.

3. a) $f(x) = x^2 + 1$, b) $g(x) = x^2 - 4$, c) $h(x) = 2x^2$.

4. a) $f(x) = 3$, b) $g(x) = 3x$, c) $h(x) = 3x + 3$.

5. a) $f(x) = |x|$, b) $g(x) = 2|x|$, c) $h(x) = |x| + 2$.

6. $f(x) = \begin{cases} 0, \text{ if } x < 0 \text{ or } x \geq 2 \\ x, \text{ if } 0 \leq x < 1 \\ 2 - x, \text{ if } 1 \leq x < 2. \end{cases}$

7. a) $g(x) = \dfrac{x}{2}$, b) $h(x) = [x]x$, c) $f(x) = [x] - x$.

8. Complete the following table. Use this table to sketch the graph of $f(x) = \sqrt{x}$ for $0 \leq x \leq 4$.

x	0	$\frac{1}{4}$	$\frac{4}{9}$	1	$\frac{16}{9}$	$\frac{9}{4}$	$\frac{25}{9}$	4
$\sqrt{x}$								

9. Use your graph from problem 8 to make an estimate of the following numbers:
a) $\sqrt{2}$, b) $\sqrt{\pi}$, c) $2^{1/4}$, d) $\sqrt{1/2}$, e) $\sqrt{3.5}$.

2–5 Graphs of Equations

The graph of a function f consists of all the points (x, y) with x in the domain of f and $y = f(x)$. We can also graph equations not of this special form $y = f(x)$. Given an equation in two variables x and y, a point (a, b) is in the graph of the equation if and only if the equation is true after replacing x by a and y by b.

Example 1. Graph $y = \pm\sqrt{x + 1}$. (This does not describe a function of x, for given any $x > -1$ there are *two* numbers y corresponding to it.) As with functions we make some general observations and then a table before sketching the graph. First it is clear that $x \geq -1$ is necessary. Also if (x, y) is in the graph, then so is $(x, -y)$; i.e., the graph is symmetric about the x axis. If $0<x+1<1$, then $0<x+1<\sqrt{x+1}<1$; and if $1<x+1$, then $1<\sqrt{x+1}<x+1$. Thus the graph lies in the shaded areas of Fig. 2-15. This indicates that we should plot several points between -1 and 0, at least.

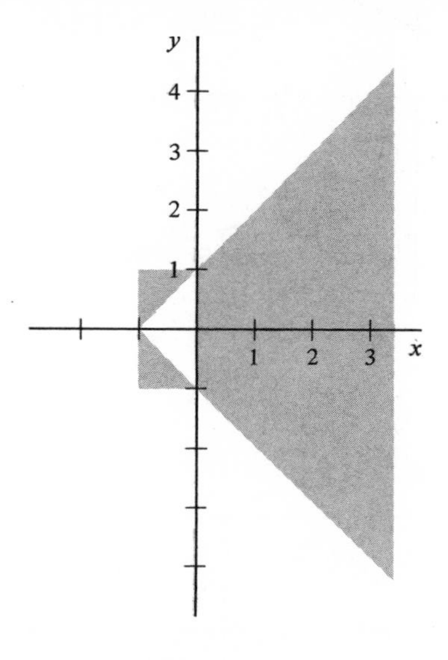

Fig. 2-15

As a result of the observations we have made, we choose the following points on the graph to plot,

x	-1	$-\frac{3}{4}$	$-\frac{1}{2}$	$-\frac{1}{4}$	0	1	2	3	8
$\sqrt{x+1}$	0	$\frac{1}{2}$	$\frac{1}{\sqrt{2}}$	$\frac{\sqrt{3}}{2}$	1	$\sqrt{2}$	$\sqrt{3}$	2	3

Observe that if $-1\leq x_1<x_2$, then $\sqrt{x_1+1}<\sqrt{x_2+1}$; thus the graph is increasing in the upper half of the plane. We obtain the graph in Fig. 2-16.

There is a distinct difference between this graph and the graph of a function. Namely, a vertical line can intersect this graph in more than one point. This phenomenon cannot occur in the graph of a function, where to each x in the domain there corresponds exactly *one* point y in the range.

Example 2. Graph $x^2+y^2=1$. First notice that $x^2\leq x^2+y^2=1$ and $y^2\leq x^2+y^2=1$ for all (x, y) in the graph. Thus the graph lies within the unit square (Fig. 2-17).

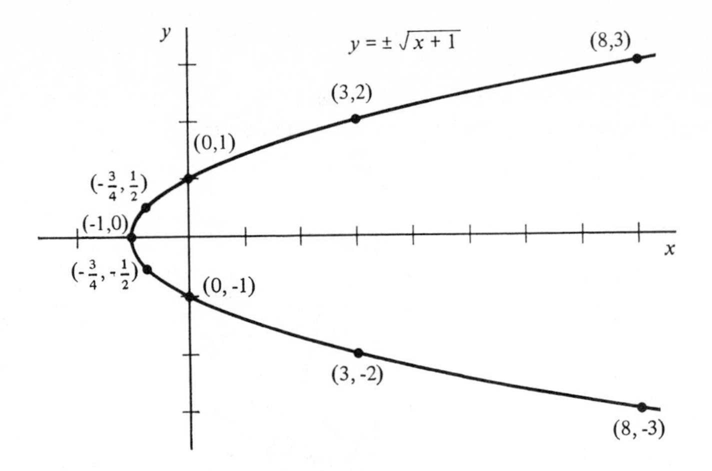

Fig. 2-16

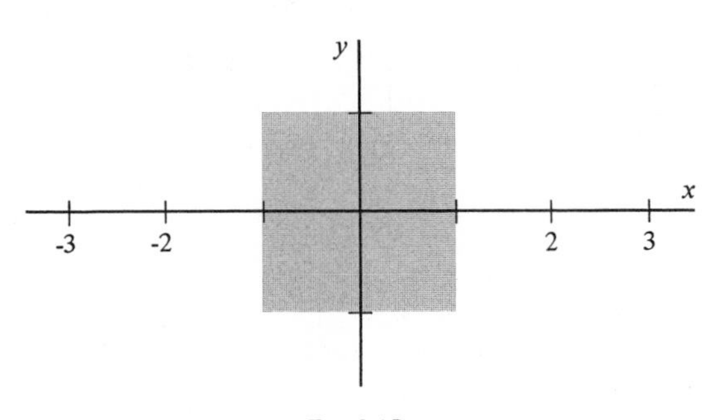

Fig. 2-17

That is, we need only consider $-1 \leq x \leq 1$ in making a table.

x	0	± 1	$\pm\frac{1}{2}$	$\pm\frac{1}{4}$	$\pm\frac{3}{4}$
y	± 1	0	$\frac{\pm\sqrt{3}}{2}$	$\frac{\pm\sqrt{15}}{4}$	$\frac{\pm\sqrt{7}}{4}$

These points yield the graph of Fig. 2-18.

At this point one might be tempted to guess that the graph of the equation $x^2 + y^2 = 1$ is a circle of radius one with center at the origin. Indeed, we can easily prove that this is the case.

Recall what a circle is. It is the set of points in a plane which are at a fixed distance from a certain point. Suppose (x, y) is at the distance 1 from the origin (0, 0). The distance formula for the plane asserts that this distance is $\sqrt{(x-0)^2 + (y-0)^2}$, or $\sqrt{x^2 + y^2}$. Thus $\sqrt{x^2 + y^2} = 1$ which implies, that $x^2 + y^2 = 1$. Thus the graph of the equation $x^2 + y^2 = 1$ includes all

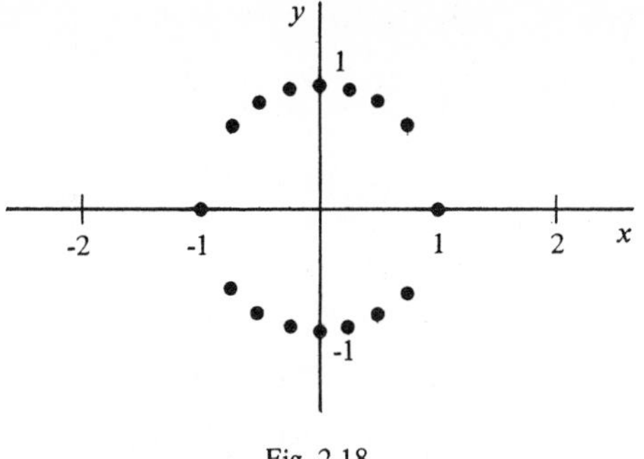

Fig. 2-18

points on the circle of radius one and center at the origin. On the other hand, if (x, y) is a point for which $x^2 + y^2 = 1$, then $\sqrt{(x-0)^2 + (y-0)^2} = \sqrt{x^2 + y^2} = \sqrt{1} = 1$ so (x, y) lies on the circle.
Thus the graph of $x^2 + y^2 = 1$ is a circle of radius one and center $(0, 0)$ (Fig. 2-19).

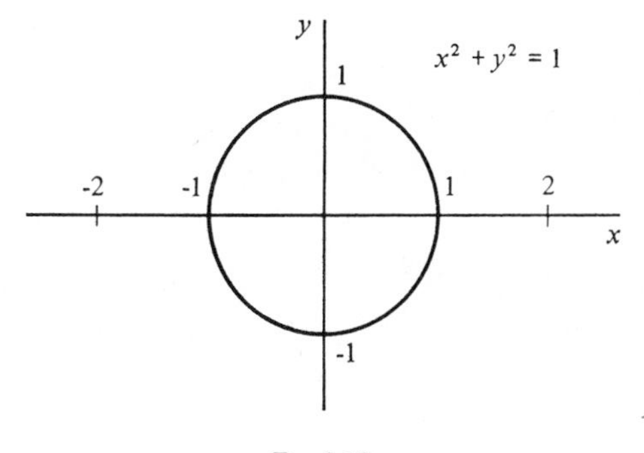

Fig. 2-19

The argument in Example 2 is easily generalized. What is the equation whose graph is the circle with center at the point (a, b) and radius $r > 0$? This is the set of points (x, y) with distance to (a, b) equal to r. We can write this condition, by the distance formula, as $\sqrt{(x-a)^2 + (y-b)^2} = r$. This is equivalent to the equation $(x-a)^2 + (y-b)^2 = r^2$, since $r > 0$.

Example 3. Graph $x^2 + y^2 + 3x - 5y = 7/2$. This happens also to be the equation of a circle. We demonstrate this by "completing the squares." In order to make a square from $x^2 + 3x$ we add $9/4$: $x^2 + 3x + 9/4 = (x + 3/2)^2$. To $y^2 - 5y$ we add $25/4$: $y^2 - 5y + 25/4 = (y - 5/2)^2$. We must add the same amount to the right side to preserve the equality, and we get

$$\left(x + \frac{3}{2}\right)^2 + \left(y - \frac{5}{2}\right)^2 = \frac{7}{2} + \frac{9}{4} + \frac{25}{4} = 12.$$

This has the form $(x-a)^2+(y-b)^2=r^2$ with $a=-3/2$, $b=5/2$, $r=2\sqrt{3}$. Thus the graph of $x^2+y^2+3x-5y=7/2$ is the circle of radius $2\sqrt{3}$ with center at the point $(-3/2, 5/2)$ (Fig. 2-20).

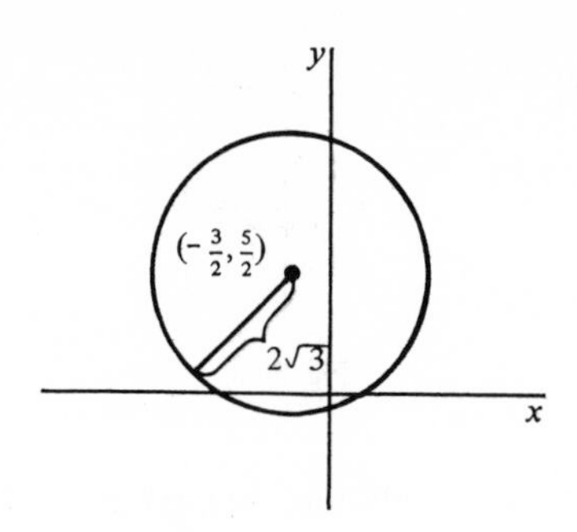

Fig. 2-20

Problems 2–5

Graph the following equations.

1. $y^2=x^2$.

2. $y^2=(x+2)^2$.

3. $(y+1)^2=(x+1)^2$.

4. $(x-3)^2+y^2=4$.

5. $(x-2)^2+(y+2)^2=16$.

6. $x^2+2x+y^2=1$.

7. $x^2+2x+y^2+6y=5$.

8. $x^2+2y^2=3$.

9. $y=|x|+x$.

10. $y=\pm\sqrt{9-x^2}$.

11. $y+|x-5|+3=0$.

12. $y=|\pi-x|$.

13. $xy=1$.

14. $2y+3x=4$.

15. $y^2+3x=9$.

16. $x^2+3y=9$.

17. $y=x-[x]$.

18. $[x]=[y]$.

19. $|x|=|y|$.

20. $x^2+xy=0$.

3 Trigonometric Functions

3–1 The Trigonometric Point

The word "trigonometry" means "triangle measurement," and classically the subject was just that. It was devoted to solving problems about triangles. Certain functions were fundamental in solving these problems, but these functions have turned out to be important in many situations, even in situations which do not involve triangles and angles. As a result, trigonometry has come to mean more than the study of triangles. These days one thinks of it as the study of the "trigonometric functions." In this chapter we will introduce these functions and derive some of their basic properties. The explicit connections of these functions with triangles and angles will be brought out in the next chapter, and further use of them in the study of triangles will appear later.

The trigonometric functions are conveniently defined via another function. Let C be the circle of radius 1 with center at the origin (Fig. 3-1). C is the graph of the equation $x^2 + y^2 = 1$. It consists of all points (x, y) in the plane such that $x^2 + y^2 = 1$. We will define a function P whose domain is the real numbers and whose range is C. Let t be a real number. If $t \geq 0$, starting at the point $(1, 0)$ on C, measure t units in the counterclockwise direction along C. If $t < 0$, measure $|t|$ units from $(1, 0)$ in the clockwise direction. Each case brings us to a point on C, called the *trigonometric point* associated with t. We will denote this point by $P(t)$. Your intuition may be helped by thinking of $P(t)$ as being obtained in the following way. Let $t > 0$. Take a piece of string of length t and attach one end at $(1, 0)$. Wrap the string around C in the counterclockwise direction. The other end winds up at $P(t)$.

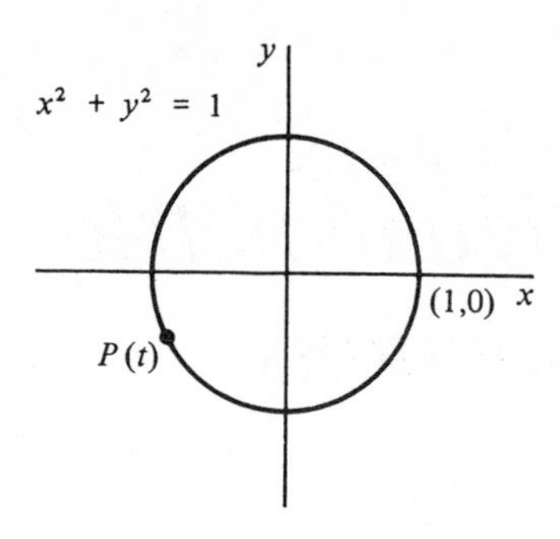

Fig. 3-1

If t is big, the string will go around C lots of times, but in any case, the other end coincides with $P(t)$. If $t < 0$, take a piece of string of length $|t|$ and wrap it around C in the clockwise direction. The other end winds up at $P(t)$.

Now P is a function whose domain is the set R of real numbers and whose range is C. That is, P assigns to each real number t a point $P(t)$ on C. But points on C are pairs of real numbers (x, y) such that $x^2 + y^2 = 1$. Given t, what are x and y?

The circumference of C is 2π. That is, it is 2π units once around C. Looking at Fig. 3-2 then, we see that it is $\frac{1}{4}(2\pi) = \pi/2$ units counterclockwise

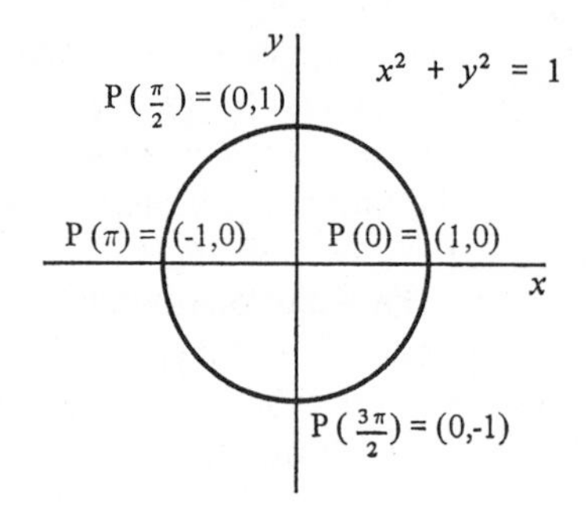

Fig. 3-2

along C from $(1, 0)$ to $(0, 1)$, $\frac{1}{2}(2\pi) = \pi$ units along C from $(1, 0)$ to $(-1, 0)$, and $\frac{3}{4}(2\pi) = 3\pi/2$ units along C from $(1, 0)$ to $(0, -1)$. Thus we have

$$\begin{aligned} P(0) &= (1, 0), \\ P\left(\frac{\pi}{2}\right) &= (0, 1), \\ P(\pi) &= (-1, 0), \\ P\left(\frac{3\pi}{2}\right) &= (0, -1). \end{aligned} \qquad (1)$$

We can find $P(\pi/4)$ using the symmetry of the circle. It is clear that $P(\pi/4)$ is equidistant from the x and y axes (Fig. 3-3). That is, the x and y coordinates of $P(\pi/4)$ are equal, say $P(\pi/4) = (a, a)$. But points (x, y) on the circle satisfy $x^2 + y^2 = 1$. Thus $a^2 + a^2 = 1$, so $a = \sqrt{2}/2$. Hence $P(\pi/4) = (\sqrt{2}/2, \sqrt{2}/2)$.

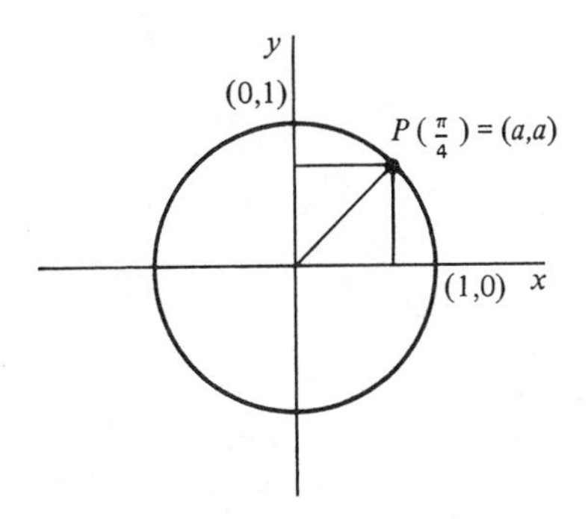

Fig. 3-3

To compute $P(3\pi/4)$ is now easy. Its y coordinate is the same as that of $P(\pi/4)$; its x coordinate is the negative of that of $P(\pi/4)$. Thus $P(3\pi/4) = (-\sqrt{2}/2, \sqrt{2}/2)$. Similarly, we get $P(5\pi/4) = (-\sqrt{2}/2, -\sqrt{2}/2)$ and $P(7\pi/4) = (\sqrt{2}/2, -\sqrt{2}/2)$. These points are shown in Fig. 3-4.

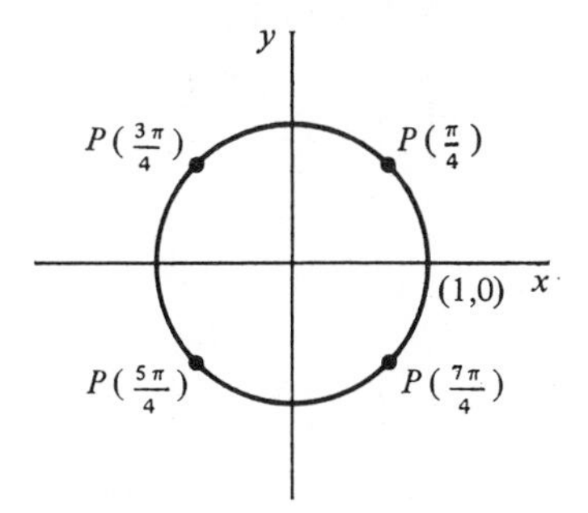

Fig. 3-4

We can also determine $P(t)$ for other values of t by appealing to the geometry of the situation. We will determine $P(\pi/3)$ as an example. Look at Fig. 3-5. The length along the circle from $(1, 0)$ to $P(\pi/3)$ is twice the length along the circle from $P(\pi/3)$ to $P(\pi/2)$, the former being $\pi/3$ and the latter being $\pi/2 - \pi/3 = \pi/6$. The lengths along the circle from $P(\pi/2)$ to $P(2\pi/3)$ and to $P(\pi/3)$ are the same, both being $\pi/6$. Thus if $P(\pi/3) = (x, y)$, then $P(2\pi/3) = (-x, y)$, and the two chords in the figure have the same length. The length of one is $2x$; the length of the other is $\sqrt{(x-1)^2 + y^2}$. Thus $4x^2 = (x-1)^2 + y^2$.

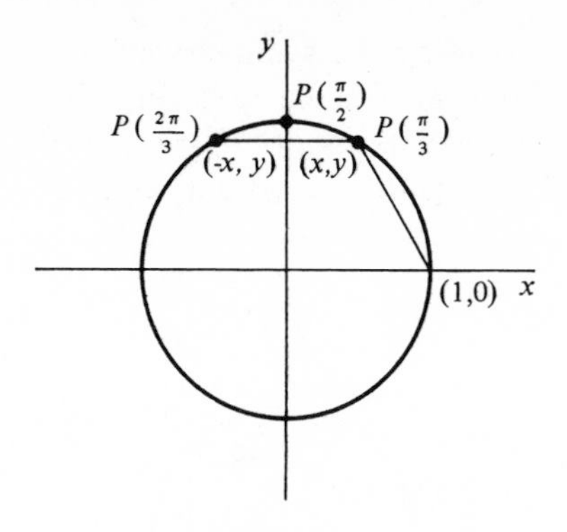

Fig. 3-5

Since $x^2 + y^2 = 1$, we get $4x^2 = (x - 1)^2 + 1 - x^2$. Solving this equation for x yields $x = 1/2$ or -1. But the x coordinate of $P(\pi/3)$ is positive. It follows that $x = 1/2$. Since $x^2 + y^2 = 1$ and y is positive, $y = \sqrt{3}/2$. Thus $P(\pi/3) = (1/2, \sqrt{3}/2)$, and $P(2\pi/3) = (-1/2, \sqrt{3}/2)$.

Consider $P(\pi/6)$. Looking at Fig. 3-6, we see that the distance from $P(\pi/6)$ to the x axis is the same as the distance from $P(\pi/3)$ to the y axis. Similarly, the distance from $P(\pi/6)$ to the y axis is the same as that from $P(\pi/3)$ to the x axis. But this says that $P(\pi/6) = (\sqrt{3}/2, 1/2)$.

To summarize our results on the values of $P(t)$ we list the computed first quadrant values:

$$\begin{aligned} P(0) &= (1, 0) \\ P\left(\frac{\pi}{6}\right) &= \left(\frac{\sqrt{3}}{2}, \frac{1}{2}\right) \\ P\left(\frac{\pi}{4}\right) &= \left(\frac{\sqrt{2}}{2}, \frac{\sqrt{2}}{2}\right) \\ P\left(\frac{\pi}{3}\right) &= \left(\frac{1}{2}, \frac{\sqrt{3}}{2}\right) \\ P\left(\frac{\pi}{2}\right) &= (0, 1). \end{aligned} \tag{2}$$

There are some general facts about the function P that are helpful. Let us compare $P(t)$ and $P(t + 2\pi)$. Suppose $t \geq 0$. To find $P(t)$, measure t units counterclockwise around C, starting at $(1, 0)$ (Fig. 3-7). Going an additional 2π units past $P(t)$ brings us to $P(t + 2\pi)$, but it also just takes us around C once and back to $P(t)$. Thus $P(t) = P(t + 2\pi)$, if $t \geq 0$. Similarly, you can convince yourself that $P(t + 2\pi) = P(t)$, when $t < 0$, so that $P(t) = P(t + 2\pi)$ for all t.

Note that $P(t - 2\pi) = P((t - 2\pi) + 2\pi) = P(t)$, the first equality holding by what we just did in the last paragraph. In fact, for any integer n, it follows

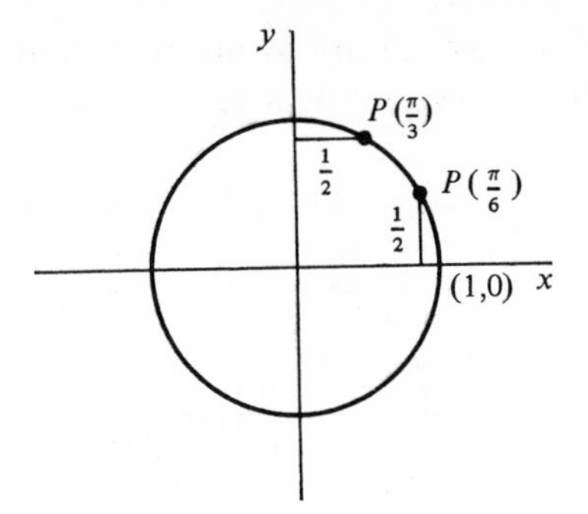

Fig. 3-6

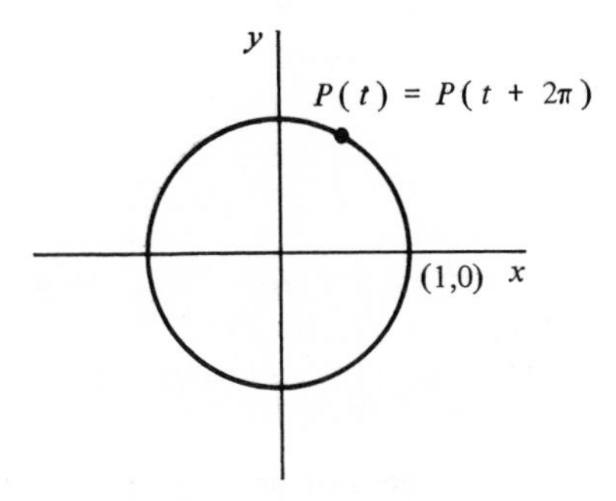

Fig. 3-7

readily that $P(t) = P(t + 2\pi n)$. This is expressed by saying that P is a *periodic* function and $2\pi n$ is a *period* of P. The smallest of these periods, 2π, will be referred to as *the* period of P.

From the symmetry of the circle, as depicted in Fig. 3-8, it is seen that if $P(t) = (x, y)$, then $P(t + \pi) = (-x, -y)$. Note that $t + \pi = (t - \pi) + 2\pi$ so that $P(t - \pi) = P(t + \pi) = (-x, -y)$.

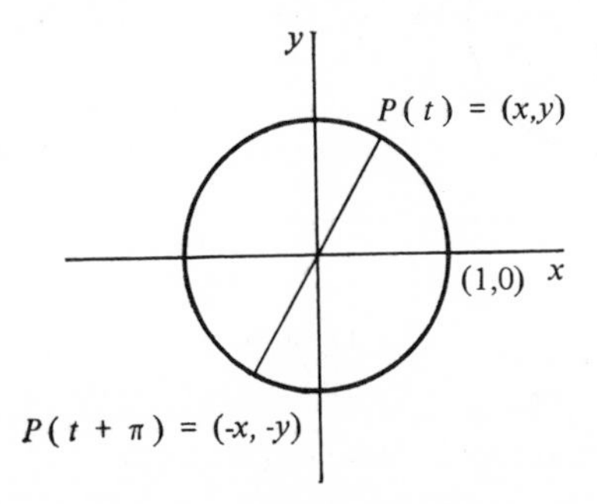

Fig. 3-8

The points $P(t)$ and $P(-t)$ are symmetric about the x axis; that is, $P(-t) = (x, -y)$. This symmetry is depicted in Fig. 3-9.

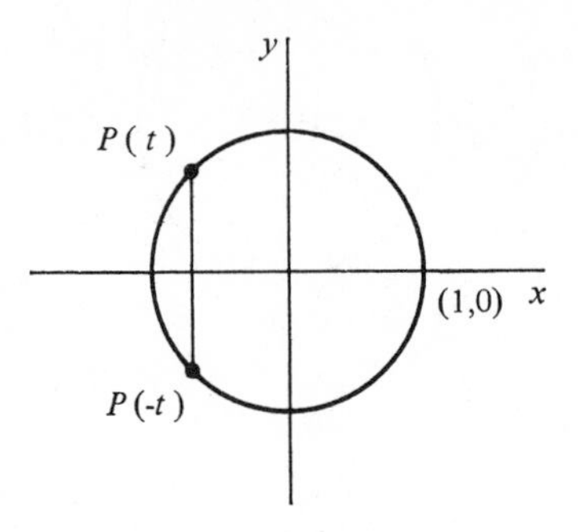

Fig. 3-9

We sum all this up in

Theorem 1. (a) $P(t) = P(t + 2\pi n)$ *for all integers* n.
(b) *If* $P(t) = (x, y)$, *then* $P(t \pm \pi) = (-x, -y)$.
(c) *If* $P(t) = (x, y)$, *then* $P(-t) = (x, -y)$.

These facts reduce the problem of finding the coordinates of $P(t)$ to the case where $0 \leq t < \pi$. The examples below illustrate this.

Example 1. Find the coordinates of $P(69\pi)$.

Solution. By Theorem 1(a), $P(69\pi) = P(\pi)$, so $P(69\pi) = (-1, 0)$.

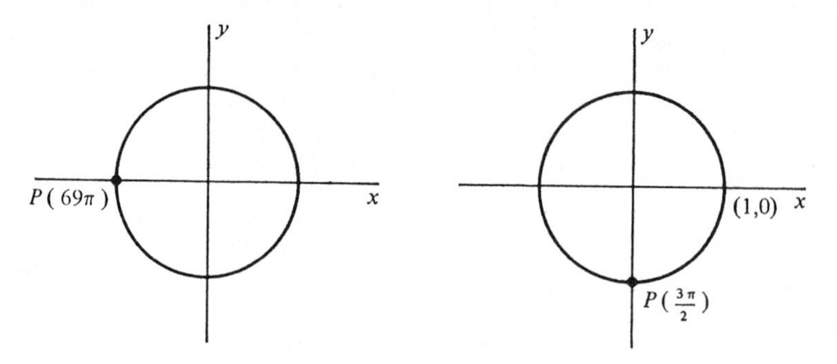

Fig. 3-10

Example 2. Find the coordinates of $P(-13\pi/2)$.

Solution. $P(-13\pi/2) = P(3\pi/2 - 16\pi/2) = P(3\pi/2 - 8\pi) = P(3\pi/2)$, by Theorem 1(a). But $P(3\pi/2) = (0, -1)$.

Example 3. Find the coordinates of $P(-4\pi/3)$.

Solution. Let $P(-4\pi/3) = (x, y)$. Then $(x, -y) = P(4\pi/3)$ by Theorem 1(c), and by Theorem 1(b), $P(4\pi/3 - \pi) = P(\pi/3) = (-x, y)$. But $P(\pi/3)$ we computed earlier and found to be $(1/2, \sqrt{3}/2)$. Thus $P(-4\pi/3) = (-1/2, \sqrt{3}/2)$.

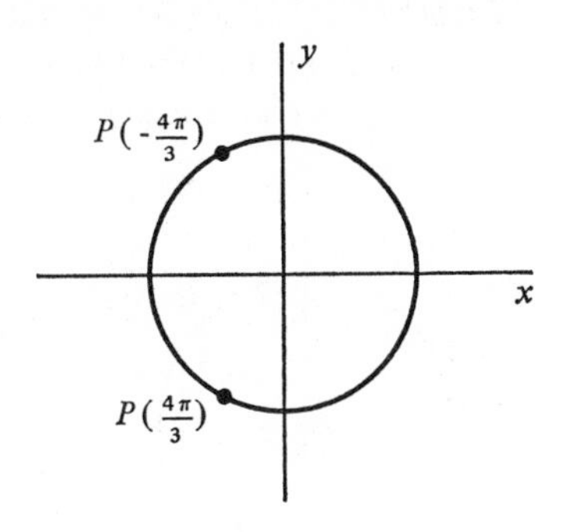

Fig. 3-11

Problems 3–1

Find the coordinates of each of the following trigonometric points.

1. $P(54\pi)$.

2. $P(-54\pi)$.

3. $P(55\pi)$.

4. $P(-55\pi)$.

5. $P\left(-\dfrac{7\pi}{2}\right)$.

6. $P\left(\dfrac{13\pi}{2}\right)$.

7. $P\left(-\dfrac{13\pi}{4}\right)$.

8. $P\left(\dfrac{27\pi}{4}\right)$.

9. $P\left(\dfrac{5\pi}{6}\right)$.

10. $P\left(-\dfrac{85\pi}{6}\right)$.

11. $P\left(\dfrac{\pi}{8}\right)$.

12. $P\left(\dfrac{\pi}{12}\right)$.

Determine in which quadrant each of the following points lies.

13. $P(2)$.

14. $P(4)$.

15. $P(6)$.

16. $P(7/2)$.

17. $P(22/7)$.

18. $P(-108)$.

3–2 The Trigonometric Functions

The function P assigns to each real number t a pair of real numbers, the coordinates (x, y) of the point $P(t)$ (Fig. 3-12). Thus associated with the function P is the function whose value at t is x, and also the function whose value at t is y. In fact, P was introduced merely as a convenience in defining these latter two

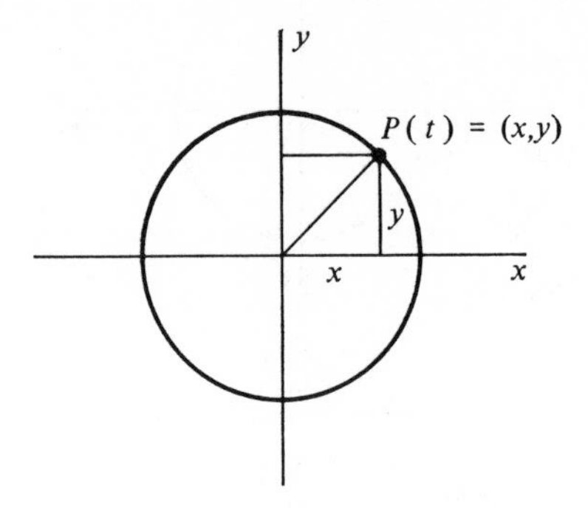

Fig. 3-12

functions (and others), which are our real interest. (The symbols used for these functions—cos, sin, tan, cot, sec, csc—are abbreviations for the words cosine, sine, tangent, cotangent, secant, and cosecant, respectively.)

Definition. $(\cos t, \sin t) = P(t)$.

The equation in this definition defines two functions, cos and sin. The value of the function cos at the real number t is the x coordinate of $P(t)$. The value of sin at t is the y coordinate of $P(t)$. The domain of each is the real

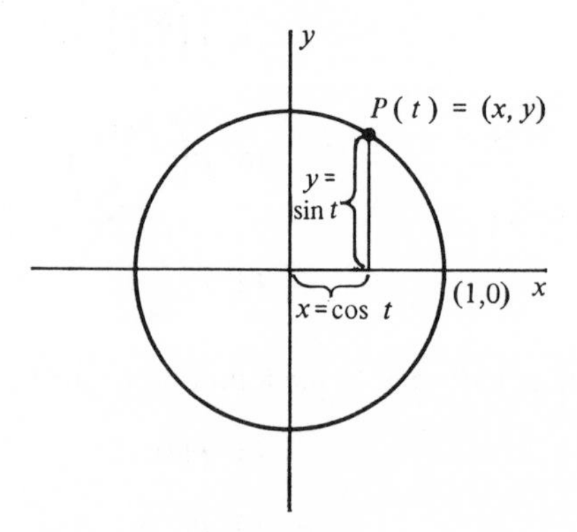

Fig. 3-13

numbers, and the range of each consists of those real numbers between -1 and 1.

In terms of cos and sin, the other "trigonometric functions" are defined as follows.

$$\begin{aligned} \tan t &= \frac{\sin t}{\cos t}, \quad \text{if } \cos t \neq 0, \\ \cot t &= \frac{\cos t}{\sin t}, \quad \text{if } \sin t \neq 0, \\ \sec t &= \frac{1}{\cos t}, \quad \text{if } \cos t \neq 0, \\ \csc t &= \frac{1}{\sin t}, \quad \text{if } \sin t \neq 0. \end{aligned} \tag{3}$$

Equivalently, if $P(t) = (x, y)$ we have

$$\begin{aligned} \cos t &= x, \\ \sin t &= y, \\ \tan t &= \frac{y}{x}, \quad \text{if } x \neq 0, \\ \cot t &= \frac{x}{y}, \quad \text{if } y \neq 0, \\ \sec t &= \frac{1}{x}, \quad \text{if } x \neq 0, \quad \text{and} \\ \csc t &= \frac{1}{y}, \quad \text{if } y \neq 0. \end{aligned} \tag{4}$$

Note that the domain of tan is not all the real numbers, but consists only of those real numbers t such that $\cos t \neq 0$. Similar remarks hold for cot, sec, and csc. For example, $\sec \pi/2$ is not defined, since $\cos \pi/2 = 0$.

We know some values of the function P in special cases. Thus in those cases we know the values of the six trigonometric functions. You should check the entries in Table 3-1 (page 44).

We can write down various relations between the trigonometric functions directly from their definitions and from properties of the function P given in Theorem 1. Since the other trigonometric functions are defined in terms of sin and cos, we will concentrate on properties of these two. Properties of the others will follow from their definitions in terms of sin and cos, and from the properties of sin and cos. Theorem 1 asserted the following:

(a) $P(t) = P(t + 2\pi n)$ for all integers n.
(b) If $P(t) = (x, y)$, then $P(t \pm \pi) = (-x, -y)$.
(c) If $P(t) = (x, y)$, then $P(-t) = (x, -y)$.

t	$P(t)$	$\sin t$	$\cos t$	$\tan t$	$\cot t$	$\sec t$	$\csc t$
0	$(1, 0)$	0	1	0	undefined	1	undefined
$\frac{\pi}{2}$	$(0, 1)$	1	0	undefined	0	undefined	1
π	$(-1, 0)$	0	-1	0	undefined	-1	undefined
$\frac{\pi}{4}$	$\left(\frac{\sqrt{2}}{2}, \frac{\sqrt{2}}{2}\right)$	$\frac{\sqrt{2}}{2}$	$\frac{\sqrt{2}}{2}$	1	1	$\sqrt{2}$	$\sqrt{2}$
$\frac{3\pi}{4}$	$\left(\frac{-\sqrt{2}}{2}, \frac{\sqrt{2}}{2}\right)$	$\frac{\sqrt{2}}{2}$	$\frac{-\sqrt{2}}{2}$	-1	-1	$-\sqrt{2}$	$\sqrt{2}$
$\frac{\pi}{6}$	$\left(\frac{\sqrt{3}}{2}, \frac{1}{2}\right)$	$\frac{1}{2}$	$\frac{\sqrt{3}}{2}$	$\frac{\sqrt{3}}{3}$	$\sqrt{3}$	$\frac{2\sqrt{3}}{3}$	2
$\frac{\pi}{3}$	$\left(\frac{1}{2}, \frac{\sqrt{3}}{2}\right)$	$\frac{\sqrt{3}}{2}$	$\frac{1}{2}$	$\sqrt{3}$	$\frac{\sqrt{3}}{3}$	2	$\frac{2\sqrt{3}}{3}$
$\frac{2\pi}{3}$	$\left(\frac{-1}{2}, \frac{\sqrt{3}}{2}\right)$	$\frac{\sqrt{3}}{2}$	$\frac{-1}{2}$	$-\sqrt{3}$	$\frac{-\sqrt{3}}{3}$	-2	$\frac{2\sqrt{3}}{3}$

Table 3-1

From (a) we get

$$\begin{aligned} \sin t &= \sin (t + 2\pi n) \quad \text{for all integers } n, \text{ and} \\ \cos t &= \cos (t + 2\pi n) \quad \text{for all integers } n. \end{aligned} \tag{5}$$

In fact, this is true for all six of the trigonometric functions. That is, they are all periodic, and 2π is a period of each one.

From (b) we get

$$\begin{aligned} \sin (t \pm \pi) &= -\sin t, \quad \text{and} \\ \cos (t \pm \pi) &= -\cos t. \end{aligned} \tag{6}$$

This is not true of all the others. For example,

$$\tan (t + \pi) = \frac{\sin (t + \pi)}{\cos (t + \pi)} = \frac{-\sin t}{-\cos t} = \tan t, \tag{7}$$

whenever $\tan t$ is defined.

From (c) we get

$$\begin{aligned} \sin (-t) &= -\sin t, \quad \text{and} \\ \cos (-t) &= \cos t. \end{aligned} \tag{8}$$

Finally, since $P(t) = (\cos t, \sin t)$, and since $(\cos t, \sin t)$ is a point on the unit circle (Fig. 3-14), we get $(\sin t)^2 + (\cos t)^2 = 1$. This is the most important equation relating the trigonometric functions. (For positive integers n, $(\sin t)^n$ is usually written $\sin^n t$, etc., and this last equation becomes $\sin^2 t + \cos^2 t = 1$.)

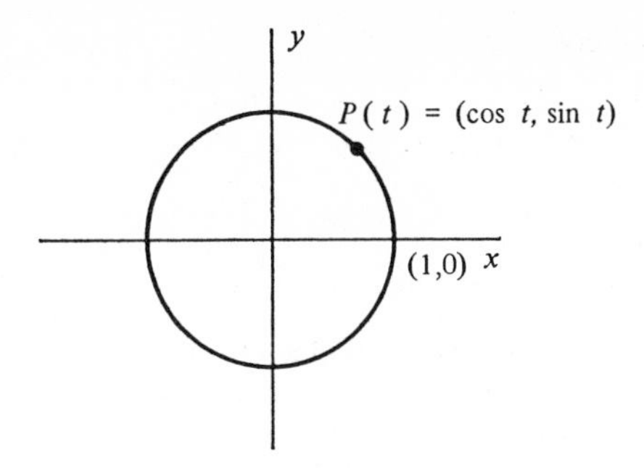

Fig. 3-14

These fundamental properties of sin and cos are compiled in the following theorem.

Theorem 2. (a) $\sin t = \sin(t + 2\pi n)$ *for all integers n.*
(b) $\cos t = \cos(t + 2\pi n)$ *for all integers n.*
(c) $\sin(t \pm \pi) = -\sin t.$
(d) $\cos(t \pm \pi) = -\cos t.$
(e) $\sin(-t) = -\sin t.$
(f) $\cos(-t) = \cos t.$
(g) $\sin^2 t + \cos^2 t = 1.$

Deeper relations between the trigonometric functions will be developed in Chapter 5. The statements (a)—(g) above can be used to give us facts about the other trigonometric functions.

Example 1. Show that $\cot(t + \pi) = \cot t$.

Solution. (Whenever we write $\cot t$ we are implicitly assuming that $\cot t$ is defined.) $\cot(t+\pi) = \dfrac{\cos(t+\pi)}{\sin(t+\pi)} = \dfrac{-\cos t}{-\sin t} = \cot t.$

Example 2. Show that $\dfrac{\sec t \csc t}{\tan t + \cot t} = 1$ whenever defined.

Solution. Write everything in terms of sin and cos. Then $\dfrac{\sec t \csc t}{\tan t + \cot t}$ becomes

$$\frac{\left(\dfrac{1}{\cos t}\right)\left(\dfrac{1}{\sin t}\right)}{\dfrac{\sin t}{\cos t} + \dfrac{\cos t}{\sin t}} = \frac{\dfrac{1}{\cos t \sin t}}{\dfrac{\sin^2 t + \cos^2 t}{\cos t \sin t}} = \frac{1}{\sin^2 t + \cos^2 t} = 1.$$

Example 3. Find $\sin(19\pi/3)$.

Solution. $\sin 19\pi/3 = \sin(\pi/3 + 6\pi) = \sin \pi/3 = \sqrt{3}/2$, using (a).

Example 4. Find $\cos(-21\pi/4)$.

Solution. $\cos(-21\pi/4) = \cos(21\pi/4) = \cos(5\pi/4 + 4\pi) = \cos 5\pi/4$
$= \cos(\pi/4 + \pi) = -\cos \pi/4 = -\sqrt{2}/2,$
using (b) and (d).

Example 5. Determine the values of t for which $\sin t = -\sqrt{3}/2$.

Solution. From Table 3-1, we see that $\sin(\pi/3) = \sqrt{3}/2$ and $\sin(2\pi/3) = \sqrt{3}/2$. Thus, using the fact in Theorem 2 that $\sin(-t) = -\sin t$, we have two of the desired values, namely $t = -\pi/3$ and $t = -2\pi/3$. Using part (a) of Theorem 2, which states that $\sin t = \sin(t + 2\pi n)$ for all integers n, we have infinitely many of the desired values: $t = -\pi/3 + 2\pi n$ and $t = -2\pi/3 + 2\pi n$ for all integers n. From Fig. 3-15, it is evident that these are the only values of t for which $\sin t = -\sqrt{3}/2$.

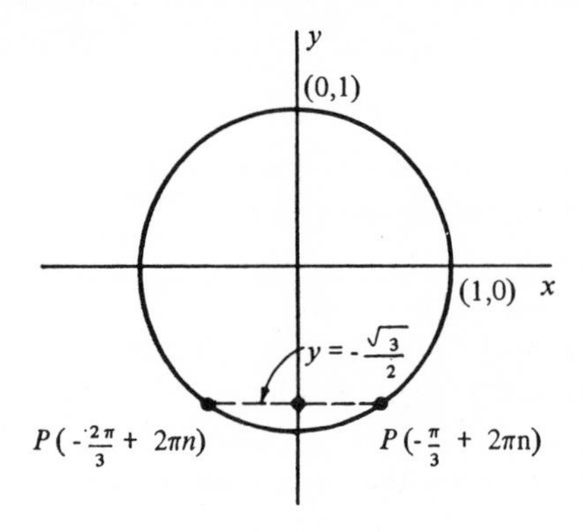

Fig. 3-15

Problems 3–2

Determine $\sin t$, $\cos t$, $\tan t$, $\cot t$, $\sec t$, and $\csc t$ for the following t, when defined.

1. 7π.

2. $-\dfrac{9\pi}{4}$.

3. $\dfrac{11\pi}{6}$.

4. $-\dfrac{\pi}{4}$.

5. -4π.

6. 3π.

Determine all the values of t for which the following are true.

7. $\sin t = 0$.

8. $\sin t = \dfrac{1}{2}$.

9. $\sin t = \dfrac{\sqrt{2}}{2}$.

10. $\sin t = \dfrac{\sqrt{3}}{2}$.

11. $\sin t = 1$.

12. $\sin t = -\frac{\sqrt{2}}{2}$.

13. $\sin t = -1$.

14. $\cos t = 0$.

15. $\cos t = \frac{1}{2}$.

16. $\cos t = \frac{\sqrt{2}}{2}$.

17. $\cos t = \frac{\sqrt{3}}{2}$.

18. $\cos t = 1$.

19. $\cos t = -\frac{\sqrt{2}}{2}$.

20. $\cos t = -1$.

Determine the numbers t for which:

21. $\tan t$ is undefined.

22. $\cot t$ is undefined.

23. $\sec t$ is undefined.

24. $\csc t$ is undefined.

Verify that the following hold for all t for which the expressions are defined. (Hint: write everything in terms of sin and cos.)

25. $1 + \tan^2 t = \sec^2 t$.

26. $\tan t + \cot t = \csc t \sec t$.

27. $\dfrac{\cos t + \sin^2 t \sec t}{\sec t} = 1$.

28. $1 + \cot^2 t = \csc^2 t$.

29. $\tan(\pi - t) = -\tan t$.

30. $\csc(\pi - t) = \csc t$.

31. $\dfrac{\cos t - \sin t}{\cos t} = 1 - \tan t$.

32. $\dfrac{1 + \tan^2 t}{\csc^2 t} = \tan^2 t$.

33. $\sec t - \cos t = \tan t \sin t$.

34. $(\sec^2 t - 1)(\csc^2 t - 1) = 1$.

35. $\dfrac{1}{\sec t - \tan t} = \sec t + \tan t$.

36. $\dfrac{1 - \cos t}{\sin t} = \dfrac{\sin t}{1 + \cos t}$.

3–3 *Graphs of the Trigonometric Functions*

In this section we will graph the trigonometric functions and other appropriate functions in the Cartesian coordinate system. Since $P(t) = P(t + 2\pi)$, it follows that $T(t) = T(t + 2\pi)$ if T is any one of the six trigonometric functions. Thus to graph one of the trigonometric functions we need only plot it for an interval of 2π. The rest of its graph will just be duplications of the graph for that interval. Since the axes of the Cartesian coordinate system are generally labeled x and y, we will henceforth use the letter x where we have previously used t (Fig. 3-16). That is, we write $\sin x$, $\cos x$, etc., instead of $\sin t$, $\cos t$, etc. First we graph the function sin. The graph of sin consists of all those

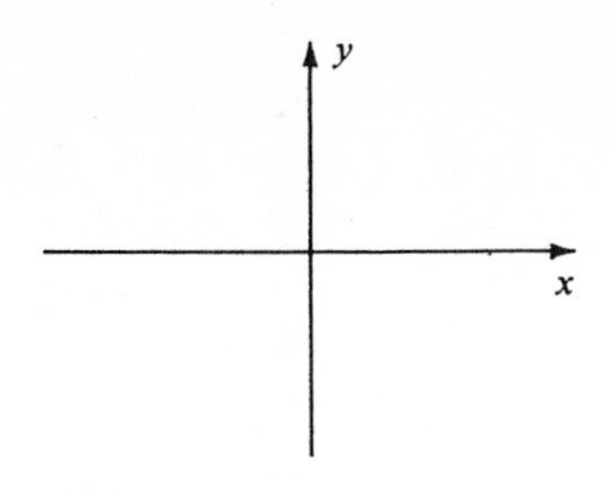

Fig. 3-16

points (x, $\sin x$) in the plane. We know some of these points already. From the previous sections we have the following table.

x	0	$\frac{\pi}{6}$	$\frac{\pi}{4}$	$\frac{\pi}{3}$	$\frac{\pi}{2}$	$\frac{2\pi}{3}$	$\frac{3\pi}{4}$	$\frac{5\pi}{6}$	π
$\sin x$	0	$\frac{1}{2}$	$\frac{\sqrt{2}}{2}$	$\frac{\sqrt{3}}{2}$	1	$\frac{\sqrt{3}}{2}$	$\frac{\sqrt{2}}{2}$	$\frac{1}{2}$	0

Table 3-2

This yields the points in Fig. 3-17 on the graph of sin.

Joining these points with a "smooth" curve gives a picture something like Fig. 3-18.

We know that $\sin(x + \pi) = -\sin x$. Thus having the graph of sin for $0 \le x \le \pi$ tells us what the graph is for $\pi \le x \le 2\pi$. Namely, it is the set of points $(x + \pi, -y)$ such that (x, y) is on the graph of sin for $0 \le x \le \pi$.

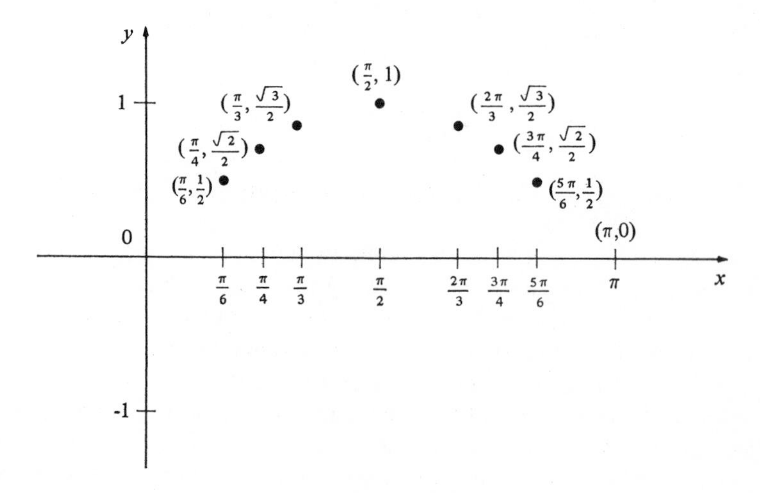

Fig. 3-17

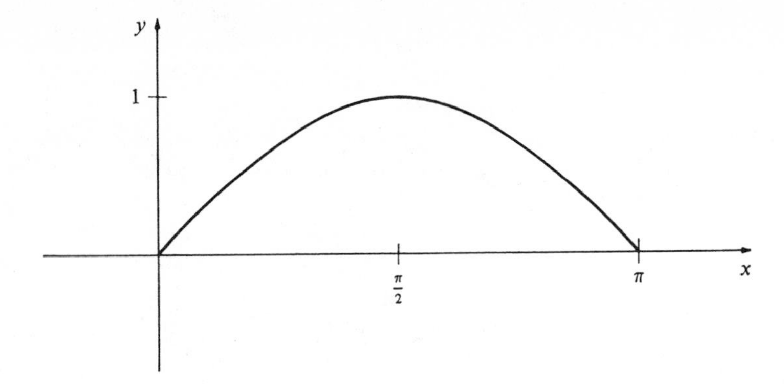

Fig. 3-18

Hence the graph of sin for $0 \leq x \leq 2\pi$ looks like Fig. 3-19. This tells us what the whole graph of sin is, since $\sin x = \sin(x + 2\pi n)$. A portion of the graph of $y = \sin x$ is depicted in Fig. 3-20. Following the same procedure, we can graph the function cos (Fig. 3-21).

The graph of cos looks like the graph of sin shifted $\pi/2$ units to the left. This reflects the identity $\sin(x + \pi/2) = \cos x$ which will be proved in Chapter 5.

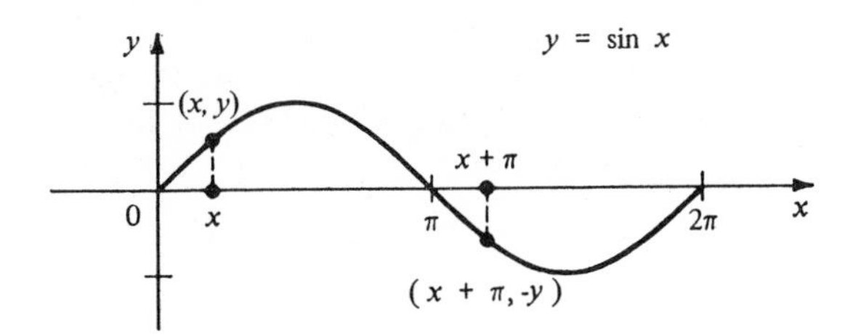

Fig. 3-19

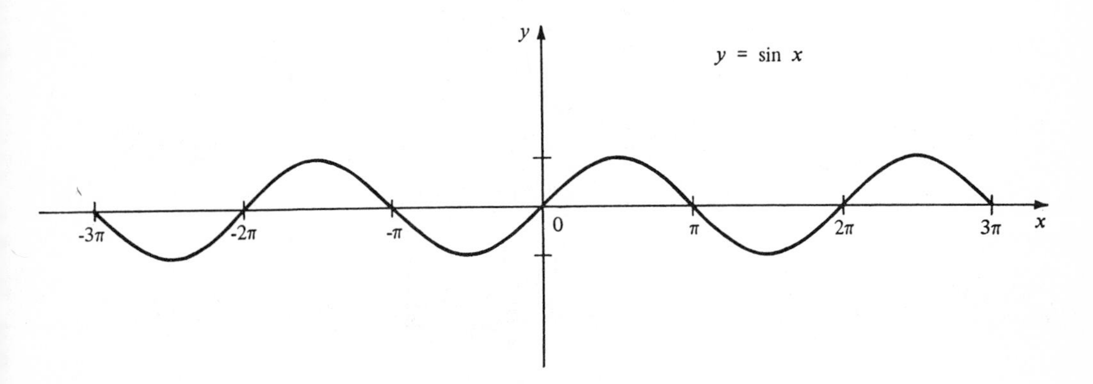

Fig. 3-20

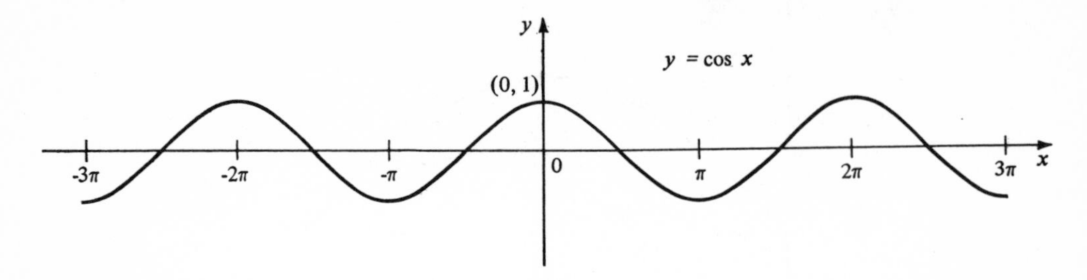

Fig. 3-21

Since $\sec x = 1/\cos x$ for $\cos x \neq 0$, the graph of sec may be drawn from that of cos. Note that when $\cos x = 1$, $\sec x = 1$; when $\cos x = -1$, $\sec x = -1$; when $\cos x$ is small and positive, $\sec x$ is large and positive; when $\cos x$ is small and negative, $\sec x$ is large and negative. With this in mind we may plot $\sec x$ from the graph of $\cos x$ (Fig. 3-22). Similarly, one may draw the graph of csc from that of sin.

We have seen earlier that $\tan(x + \pi) = \sin(x + \pi)/\cos(x + \pi) = (-\sin x)/(-\cos x) = \tan x$ (when defined) so that tan is periodic and π is a period. Thus the graph of tan repeats every π units. Also $\tan(-x) = \sin(-x)/\cos(-x) = -\sin x/\cos x = -\tan x$; to graph tan, it is enough to know its graph for $0 \leq x \leq \pi/2$. Some values for x in this range are in Table 3-3.

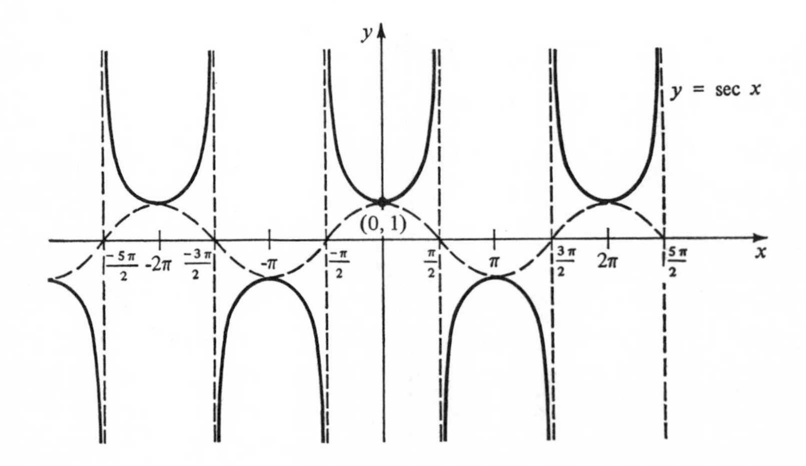

Fig. 3-22

x	0	$\frac{\pi}{6}$	$\frac{\pi}{4}$	$\frac{\pi}{3}$	$\frac{\pi}{2}$
tan x	0	$\frac{\sqrt{3}}{3}$	1	$\sqrt{3}$	undefined

Table 3-3

Thus the graph of tan looks like Fig. 3-23.

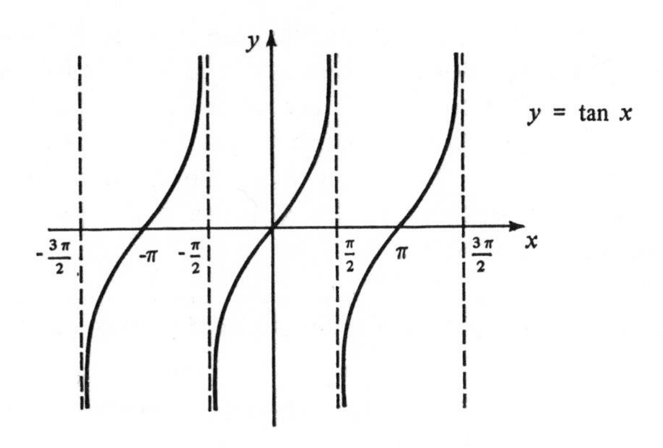

Fig. 3-23

Problems 3–3

1. Graph csc.

2. Graph cot.

3. Graph the equations $y = \sin x$ and $y = x$ on the same axes. How are the sizes of $\sin x$ and x related, at least for $x > 0$?

Referring to the appropriate graphs, find those x satisfying the following.

4. $\tan x < 0$.

5. $\sin x > 0$.

6. $\cot x \geq 0$.

7. $\csc x \geq 1$.

8. $\cos x \leq 1$.

9. $\csc x \leq -1$.

3–4 Aids in Graphing

In graphing the trigonometric functions we took advantage of some special properties that they possessed. For example, since $\sin (x + 2\pi) = \sin x$ for all x, we know the graph of sin once we know it in any interval of length 2π. In graphing tan we used the fact that $\tan (-x) = -\tan x$. Knowing that a function possesses properties such as these greatly facilitates graphing it.

Recognizing and using such properties in graphing is the topic of this section. It was shown in Section 3–1 that the function P was periodic. We repeat the definition here.

Definition. Let f be a function whose domain is contained in the real numbers. If there is a real number p such that $f(x+p)=f(x)$ for all x in the domain of f, then f is *periodic*, and p is a *period* of f. If there is a smallest positive p such that $f(x+p)=f(x)$ for all x in the domain of f, then p is *the period* of f.

All six of the trigonometric functions are periodic. If T is any one of them, then $T(x+2\pi)=T(x)$ for x in the domain of T. This follows from the fact that $P(x+2\pi)=P(x)$ for all x. Each of the trigonometric functions has a smallest period. Looking at the graph of sin, it is clear that the period of sin is 2π. However, $\tan(x+\pi)=\tan x$ for all x in the domain of tan; and from the graph of tan, it is easily seen that its period is π. Similarly, cos has period 2π, and cot has period π.

Example 1. Show that the function f defined by $f(x)=\sin^2 x$ is periodic with period π.

Solution. $\sin^2(x+\pi)=(\sin(x+\pi))(\sin(x+\pi))=(-\sin x)(-\sin x)=\sin^2 x$. But π is the smallest positive number for which $\sin^2(x+\pi)=\sin^2 x$, since $\sin^2 0=0$ and the smallest positive number p for which $\sin^2 p=0$ is π. Thus the function $\sin^2 x$ is periodic with period π (Fig. 3-24).

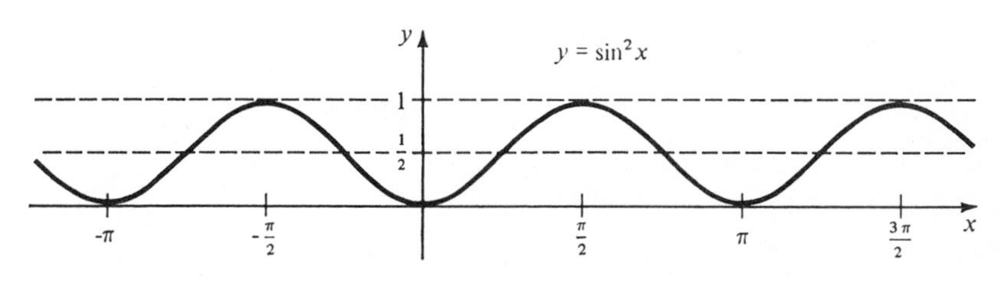

Fig. 3-24

Example 2. Show that the function f defined by $f(x)=\tan\pi x$ is periodic with period 1.

Solution. $\tan\pi(x+1)=\tan(\pi x+\pi)=\tan\pi x$, so the function is periodic. Also, if p is a positive number such that $\tan\pi(0+p)=\tan\pi 0$, then $\tan\pi p=0$. Since tan has period π, p must be at least 1. Hence the period of $\tan\pi x$ is 1 (Fig. 3-25).

Example 2 illustrates a property of periodic functions which is extremely useful.

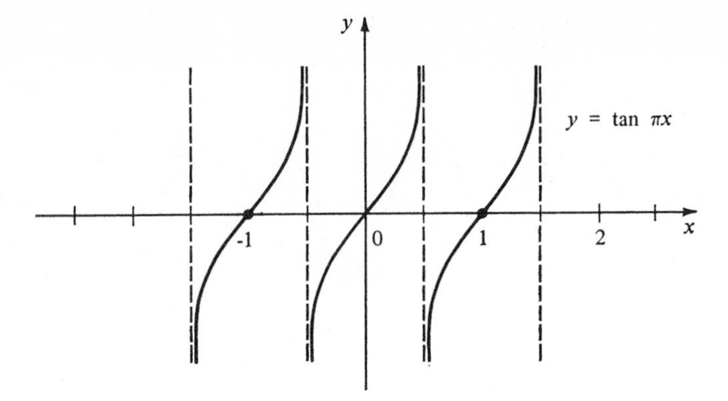

Fig. 3-25

Theorem 3. *If f is a periodic function with period p, and $a \neq 0$, then the function g defined by $g(x) = f(ax)$ is periodic with period $p/|a|$.*

Proof. To show that $p/|a|$ is a period of g, we need to establish the identity

$$g\left(x + \frac{p}{|a|}\right) = g(x)$$

for every x in the domain of g. This is done in the following sequence of equalities.

$$g\left(x + \frac{p}{|a|}\right) = f\left(a\left(x + \frac{p}{|a|}\right)\right) = f\left(ax + \frac{pa}{|a|}\right)$$
$$= f(ax \pm p) = f(ax) = g(x).$$

If p is the period of f we can also show that $p/|a|$ is the period of g, that is, the smallest positive number such that $g(x + p/|a|) = g(x)$. If $b > 0$, and $g(x + b) = g(x)$, then

$$f(x + |a|\, b) = g\left(\frac{x}{a} + \frac{|a|\, b}{a}\right)$$
$$= g\left(\frac{x}{a} \pm b\right) = g\left(\frac{x}{a}\right) = f(x).$$

Since p is the period of f, and $|a|\, b$ is also a period of f, we have $|a|\, b \geq p$, whence $b \geq p/|a|$. Thus $p/|a|$ is the period of g.

Example 3. Sketch the graph of $f(x) = \sin(-\pi x)$.

Solution. The function f is periodic with period 2, since sin is periodic with period 2π. Thus we know the complete graph of the function f once we know the graph in the interval from 0 to 2.

Using $\sin(-x) = -\sin x$, we get the graph in Fig. 3-26.

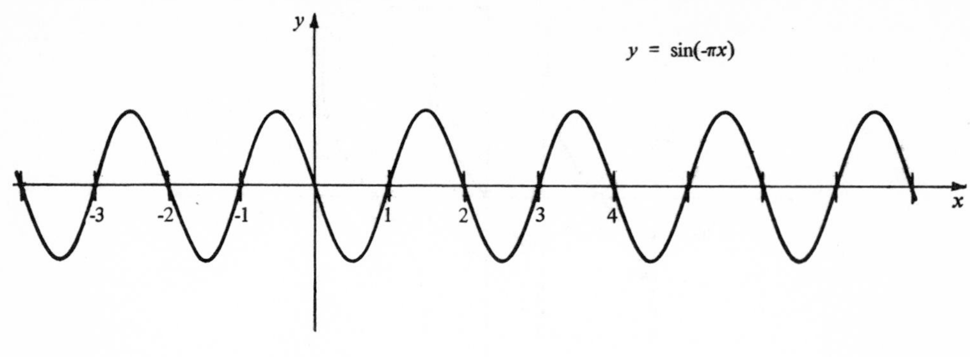

Fig. 3-26

Suppose f is a periodic function with period p. Let $g(x) = f(x + b)$, and $b > 0$. It is obvious that g is also periodic with period p. (Why?) Furthermore, the graph of g is the graph of f shifted b units to the left. Figure 3-27 illustrates this.

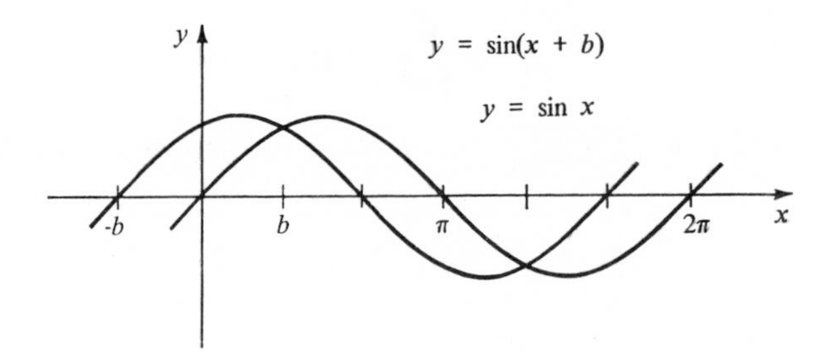

Fig. 3-27

More generally, if f is periodic with period p, and a and b are real numbers with $a \neq 0$, how is the function g defined by $g(x) = f(ax + b)$ related to f? First, we see that g is periodic with the same period as the function $h(x) = f(ax)$. By Theorem 2, this function has period $p/|a|$. Next notice that

$$g(x) = f(ax + b) = f\left(a\left(x + \frac{b}{a}\right)\right) = h\left(x + \frac{b}{a}\right).$$

Thus the graph of g is the graph of h shifted b/a units to the left. This is the same as $-b/a$ units to the right, as a negative shift to the left is a shift to the right, and vice versa. The number $-b/a$ is called the *phase shift*. It represents the number of units that the graph of $y = f(ax)$ must be shifted to the *right* in order to coincide with the graph of $y = f(ax + b)$. The graph of $y = f(ax)$ is easily obtainable from that of f, as we have seen.

Example 4. Sketch the graph of $y = \sin(2x + 1)$.

Solution. The function g defined by $g(x) = \sin(2x + 1)$ is periodic with period π. The phase shift is $-1/2$. Thus the graph of $y = \sin(2x + 1)$ is that of $y = \sin 2x$ shifted 1/2 units to the left. The graph is shown in Fig. 3-28.

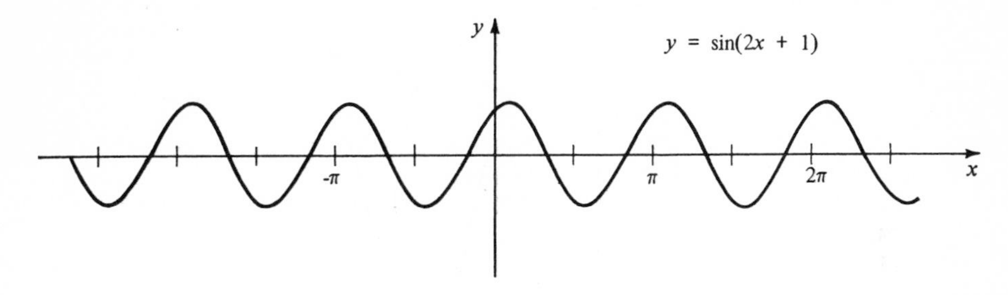

Fig. 3-28

A function f is *bounded above* if there is a number M such that $f(x) \leq M$ for all x in the domain of f. It is *bounded below* if there is a number m such that $f(x) \geq m$ for all x in the domain of f. A function is *bounded* if it is bounded above and below. For example, sin and cos are both bounded. In fact, $-1 \leq \sin x \leq 1$ for all x. However, tan is bounded neither above nor below.

When a function f is bounded above, there is a smallest number M such that $f(x) \leq M$ for all x in the domain of f. When f is bounded below, there is a largest m such that $m \leq f(x)$ for all x in the domain of f. M is called the *least upper bound* of f, and m the *greatest lower bound* of f. The least upper bound of cos is 1; the greatest lower bound is -1. The function tan has no least upper bound or greatest lower bound since it is bounded neither above nor below.

Definition. Let f be a bounded periodic function with least upper bound M and greatest lower bound m. The *amplitude* of f is $\frac{1}{2}(M - m)$.

The amplitude of sin is $\dfrac{1-(-1)}{2} = 1$. The function tan has no amplitude.

If f has amplitude a, then g defined by $g(x) = Af(x)$ has amplitude $|A|\,a$.

Example 5. Determine the amplitude and phase shift of the functions defined by (a) $f(x) = 6 \sin x$; (b) $F(x) = 6 \sin(8\pi x + 3)$.

Solution. (a) The amplitude of sin is 1. Thus the amplitude of f is 6. The phase shift of f is 0. (b) The amplitude of the function g defined by $g(x) = \sin(8\pi x + 3)$ is 1. Thus the amplitude of F is 6. The phase shift is $-3/8\pi$, that is, $3/8\pi$ units to the left (compared to the function $y = \sin 8\pi x$).

Example 6. Sketch the graph of the function f defined by $f(x) = 3\sin(2x + 4)$.

Solution. The function f is periodic with period π. It has amplitude 3 and phase shift -2 (compared to 3 sin). The graph of f then is the graph of $y = 3\sin 2x$ shifted 2 units to the left (Fig. 3-29).

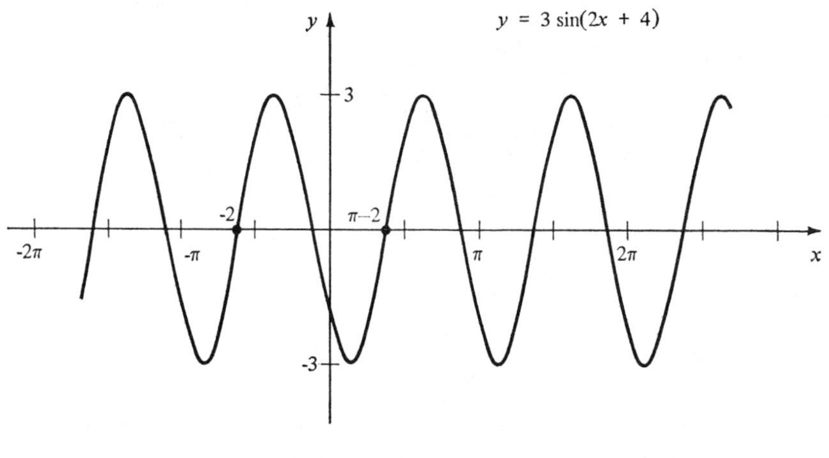

Fig. 3-29

The same procedure enables one to graph the function f defined by $f(x) = A\sin(ax + b)$.

The graphs of the trigonometric functions have certain symmetries. We make the notion of symmetry precise.

Definition. A set of points is *symmetric with respect to the origin*, if for each point (x, y) in the set, the point $(-x, -y)$ is also in the set. A set is *symmetric with respect to the y axis* if for each point (x, y) in the set, the point $(-x, y)$ is also in the set.

A function f is called *odd* if $f(-x) = -f(x)$; a function is *even* if $f(-x) = f(x)$. These names come from the fact that x^n is an odd function if n is an odd integer and an even function if n is an even integer. The graphs of odd functions are symmetric with respect to the origin. Indeed, if f is an odd function and (x, y) is in the graph of f, then $y = f(x)$ and so $-y = -f(x) = f(-x)$. Hence $(-x, -y)$ is in the graph of f. Similarly, the graphs of even functions are symmetric with respect to the y axis. We have seen that sin and tan are odd functions and cos is an even function. Knowing that a function is odd or even cuts the job of graphing it in half.

Example 7. Sketch the graph of $y = \sin x \cos x$.

Solution. The function f given by $f(x) = \sin x \cos x$ is periodic with period π, since $f(x + \pi) = \sin(x + \pi) \cos(x + \pi) = (-\sin x)(-\cos x) = \sin x \cos x = f(x)$. It is odd since $f(-x) = \sin(-x) \cos(-x) = (-\sin x) \cos x = -f(x)$. Thus the graph of f from 0 to $\pi/2$ tells all. That is, from the little bit of the graph sketched in Fig. 3-30, we can draw the rest of the graph. Symmetry with respect to the origin enables us to sketch in the graph from $-\pi/2$ to 0, giving the picture in Fig. 3-31. The rest of the graph may now be sketched in, since f has period π. (If you think this looks suspiciously like the graph of a sine function you are right. In Chapter 5 you will learn that $\sin x \cos x = \frac{1}{2} \sin 2x$.)

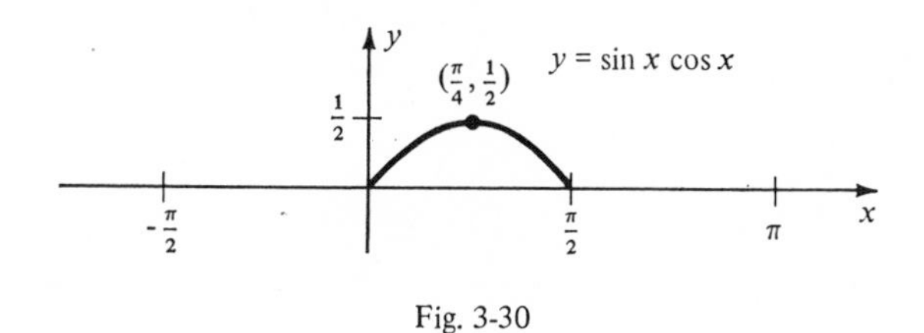

Fig. 3-30

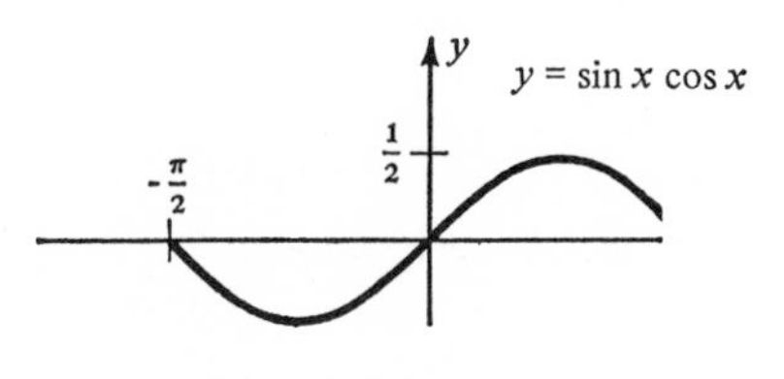

Fig. 3-31

Suppose f and g are functions with the same domain, and the function h is defined by $h(x) = f(x) + g(x)$. One method for graphing h is to graph f and g and from these graphs to draw the graph of h by adding y coordinates. This may be easier than graphing h directly, because f and g may be easy to graph while h is not. For example, f and g may be periodic and their graphs may have various symmetries which h does not have. We illustrate with an example.

Example 8. Graph the function f defined by $f(x) = \cos x + \sin 2x$.

Solution. We know the graphs of $y = \cos x$ and $y = \sin 2x$. They appear below as the broken-line curves.

The graph of $f(x) = \cos x + \sin 2x$ is obtained simply by adding the y coordinates of points on the two broken-line curves with the same x coordinate. The result is the solid-line curve in Fig. 3-32.

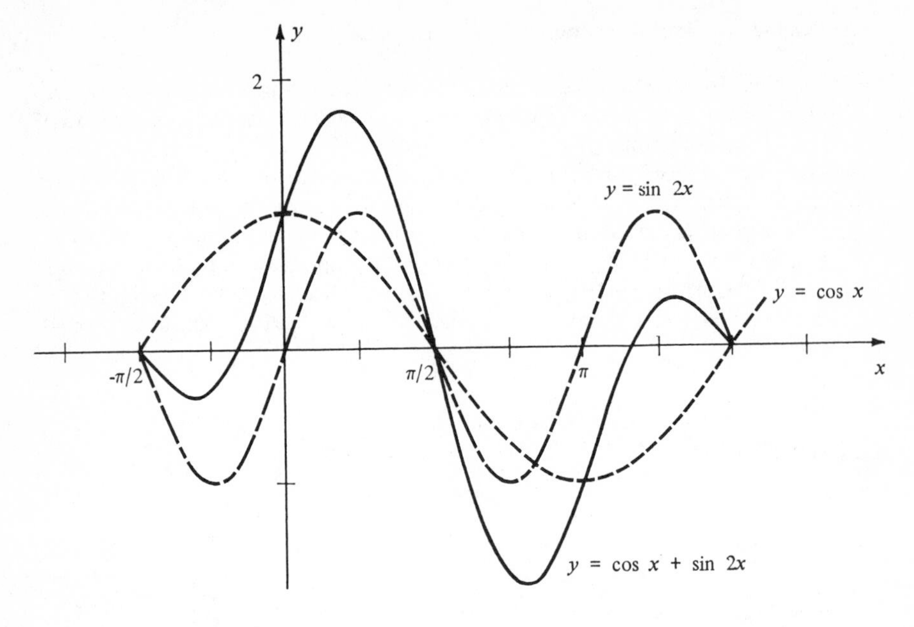

Fig. 3-32

Problems 3–4

Show that f defined by the following are periodic. Determine the period and sketch the graph of two periods of each.

1. $f(x) = \sin 2\pi x.$

2. $f(x) = \tan \pi x.$

3. $f(x) = |\sin x|.$

4. $f(x) = \frac{1}{2} \cos \frac{\pi}{3} x.$

Determine which of the following are periodic. If periodic, determine the period if it exists.

5. $f(x) = x \sin x.$

6. $f(x) = 1.$

7. $f(x) = \sin x - \cos 2x.$

8. $f(x) = \sin x - \cos \pi x.$

Graph the following, making use of the methods of this section.

9. $f(x) = \cos^2 x.$

10. $f(x) = \cos^2 x - \sin^2 x.$

11. $f(x) = 2 \cos \frac{\pi}{4} x.$

12. $f(x) = 2 \sin \left(x - \frac{\pi}{4}\right).$

13. $f(x) = 2 \sin \left(3x + \frac{\pi}{2}\right).$

14. $f(x) = x + \sin x.$

15. $f(x) = 3 \cos (2\pi x - 4\pi).$

4 Right Triangle Trigonometry

4–1 Angles

An angle is formed when a line segment L is rotated about one of its endpoints v as in Fig. 4-1.

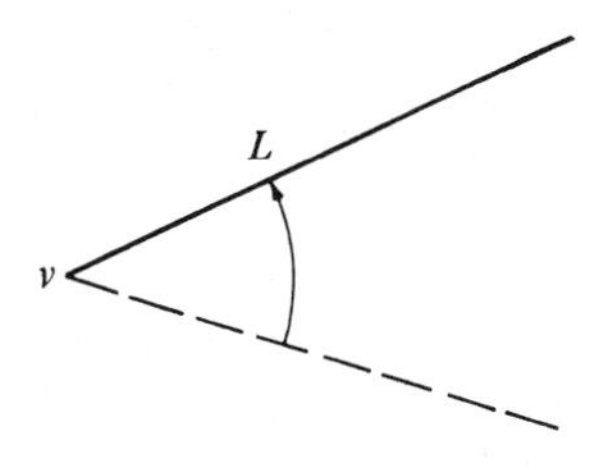

Fig. 4-1

The endpoint v is called the *vertex* of the angle. If the initial position of the line segment is along the positive x axis and the vertex is at the origin, then the angle is said to be in *standard position* (Fig. 4-2).

The most common way to measure angles is in *degrees*. We say that an angle is ninety degrees or 90°, if it is formed by rotating a line segment until it is perpendicular to its initial position. All other angles are measured in terms of this basic unit. Thus an angle of 1° is formed if a line segment is rotated one-ninetieth of the amount required to bring it perpendicular to its initial position.

The angles depicted in Fig. 4-3 were all formed by rotating a line segment *counterclockwise*, that is, in the direction opposite to that which the hands of

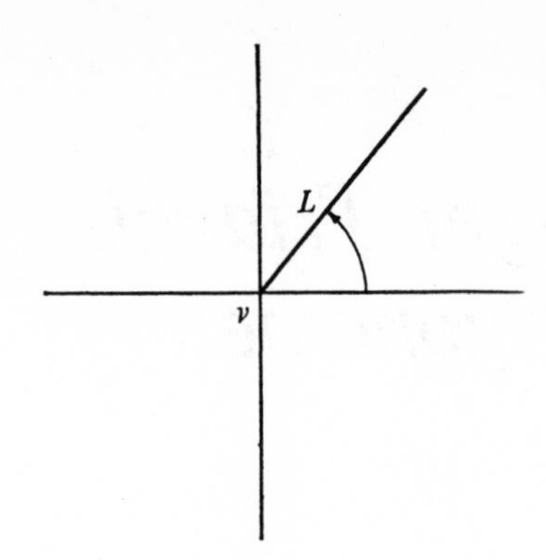

Fig. 4-2

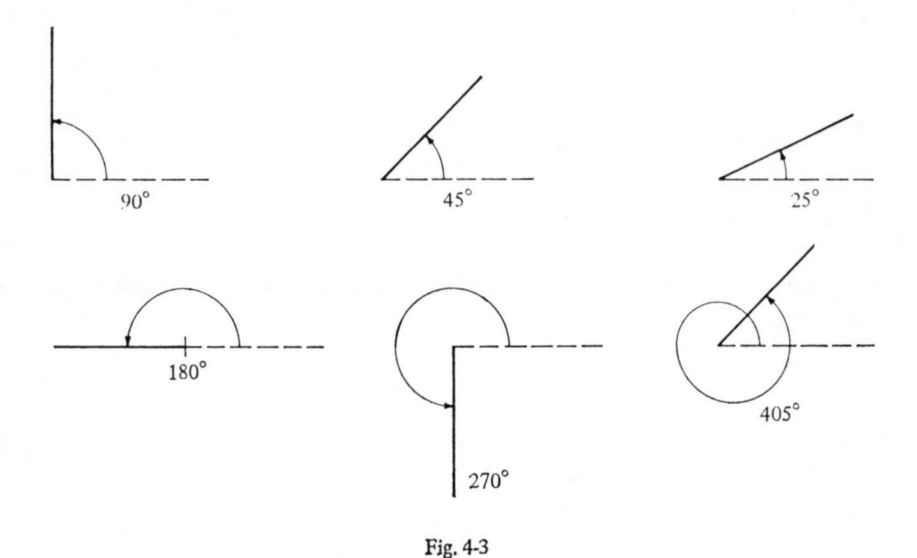

Fig. 4-3

a clock move. If a line segment is rotated *clockwise*, we say that the angle formed is negative and measure it in negative degrees. Some negative angles are depicted in Fig. 4-4.

Notice that if a line segment is rotated 360° or $-360°$, the final position coincides with the initial position. Thus the $-405°$ angle looks like the $-45°$ angle, since $-405° = -45° + (-360°)$. The distinction is illustrated by comparing how much time is required for the hour hand of a clock to move $-45°$ as compared to $-405°$.

Another important measure of angles is provided by the trigonometric point $P(t)$. As t varies, the line segment from the origin to $P(t)$ rotates about the origin, as in Fig. 4-5. The result of any such rotation may be described by specifying the number t corresponding to the final position of this

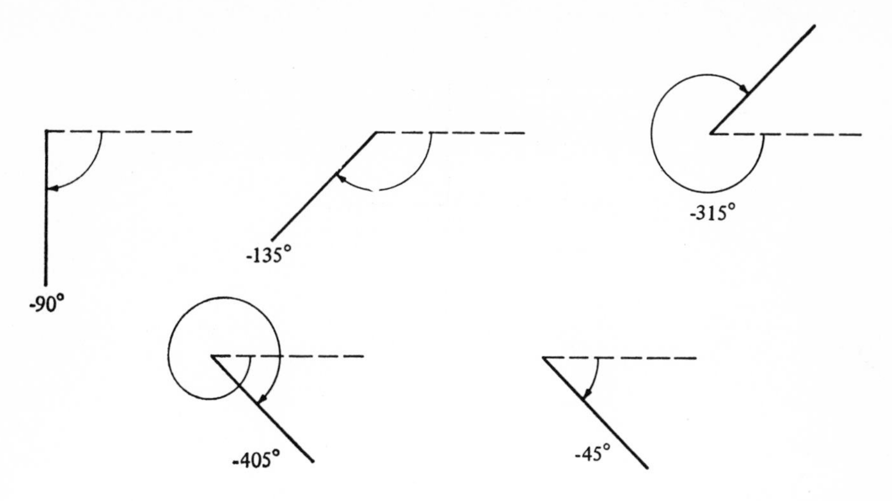

Fig. 4-4

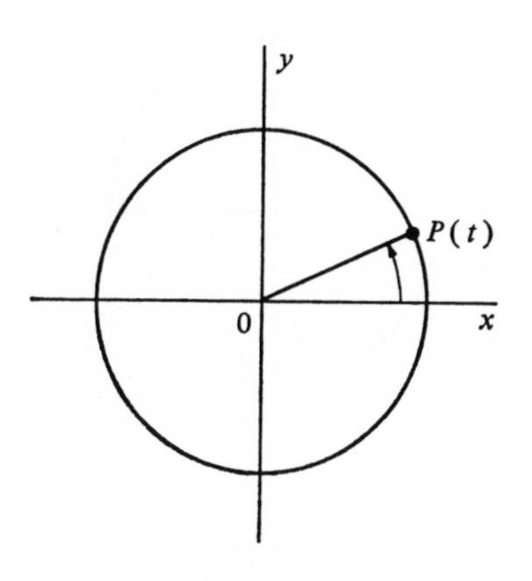

Fig. 4-5

segment. A rotation through an angle of 90° would correspond to $\pi/2$ (Fig. 4-6). Similarly, a rotation through an angle of $-45°$ would correspond to $-\pi/4$ (Fig. 4-7).

The unit used to describe this measure of an angle is called a *radian*. An angle of one radian is the angle corresponding to $P(1)$ (Fig. 4-8). Since π radians is the same as 180°, one radian is $180/\pi$ degrees or about 57.3°, and 1° is $\pi/180$ radians or about 0.01745 radians.

In general, one converts from degrees to radians, and vice-versa, by the rule:

$$\frac{\text{Number of degrees}}{180} = \frac{\text{Number of radians}}{\pi} \tag{1}$$

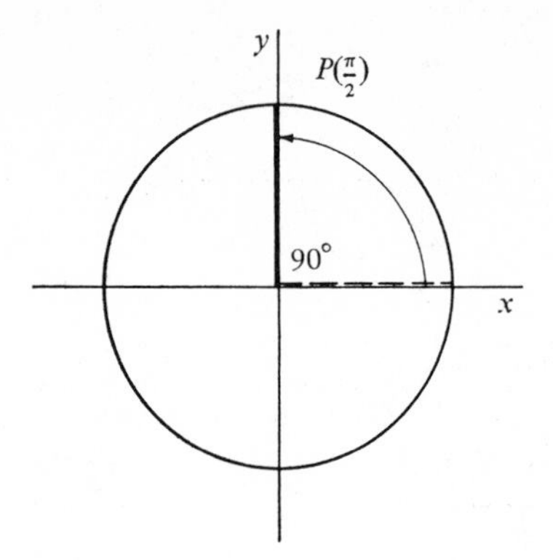

Fig. 4-6

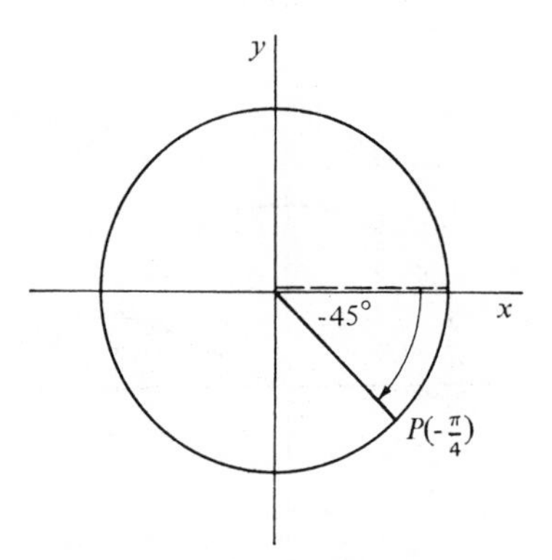

Fig. 4-7

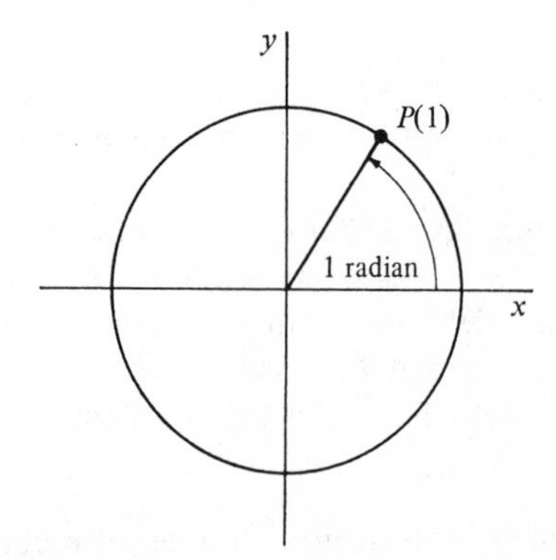

Fig. 4-8

Problems 4–1

1. Sketch an angle in standard position which measures:
a) $30°$, b) $1{,}000°$, c) $-120°$.

2. What are the measures of the angles in problem 1 in radians?

3. Give the measures of the following angles in radians.
a) $50°$, b) $835°$, c) $2.6°$.

4. If the measure of an angle in radians is one of the following, what is its measure in degrees?
a) $2\pi^2$, b) 2.5, c) 436.

5. If the measure of an angle in radians is one of the following, what is its measure in degrees?
a) 17, b) 1,000, c) -16π.

6. Complete the following table.

radian measure	0	$\frac{\pi}{6}$	$\frac{\pi}{4}$	$\frac{\pi}{3}$	$\frac{\pi}{2}$	$\frac{2\pi}{3}$	$\frac{5\pi}{6}$	π	$\frac{3\pi}{2}$	2π
degree measure	$0°$									

7. Find the angle between 0 and 2π radians that has the same standard position as each of the following.
a) $\frac{13\pi}{2}$, b) 17, c) $-\frac{11\pi}{4}$.

8. Find the angle between $0°$ and $360°$ that has the same standard position as each of the following.
a) $512°$, b) $4{,}687{,}205°$, c) $-4{,}307°$.

4–2 Trigonometric Functions as Ratios

The trigonometric functions have a natural interpretation as ratios of the lengths of sides of right triangles. Classically, they were defined in this manner. Suppose we have a right triangle, and we distinguish one of the acute angles θ (Fig. 4-9). The side adjacent to the angle θ is of length a, the side opposite, o, and the hypotenuse, h. To relate this situation to the trigonometric functions let us compare this figure with the trigonometric point corresponding to θ. For notational convenience we measure θ in radians (otherwise we would have to consider $P(\theta\pi/180)$). Figure 4-10 shows the case $h > 1$. The other cases are practically identical.

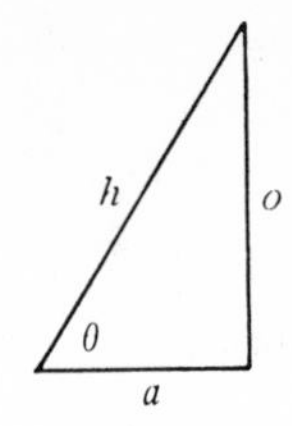

Fig. 4-9

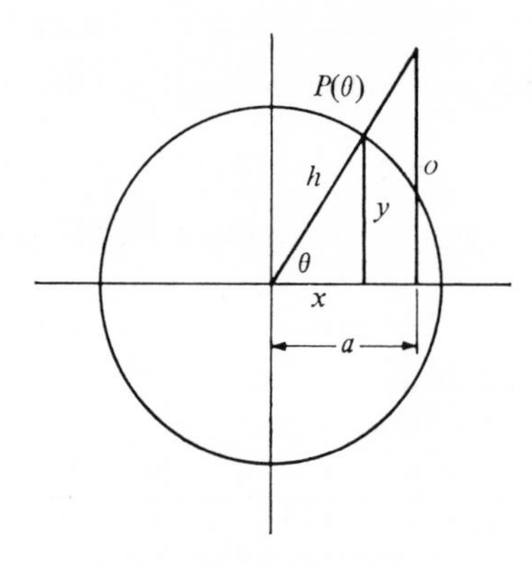

Fig. 4-10

Consider the two right triangles, one with sides o and a, and one with sides x and y. Elementary geometric considerations show that these triangles are similar, and so the ratios of corresponding sides are equal. Thus,

$$\begin{aligned}
\frac{\text{opposite}}{\text{hypotenuse}} &= \frac{o}{h} = \frac{y}{1} = \sin\theta,\\
\frac{\text{adjacent}}{\text{hypotenuse}} &= \frac{a}{h} = \frac{x}{1} = \cos\theta,\\
\frac{\text{opposite}}{\text{adjacent}} &= \frac{o}{a} = \frac{y}{x} = \tan\theta,\\
\frac{\text{adjacent}}{\text{opposite}} &= \frac{a}{o} = \frac{x}{y} = \cot\theta,\\
\frac{\text{hypotenuse}}{\text{adjacent}} &= \frac{h}{a} = \frac{1}{x} = \sec\theta,\\
\frac{\text{hypotenuse}}{\text{opposite}} &= \frac{h}{o} = \frac{1}{y} = \csc\theta.
\end{aligned} \tag{2}$$

The length of the hypotenuse of the smaller triangle is 1, because the trigonometric point is on the *unit* circle about the origin. These relations between the lengths of the sides of a right triangle and the trigonometric functions of its acute angles form the basis for the application of trigonometry to indirect distance measuring. An example is provided by the problem of measuring the height of a tall monument. It may be troublesome to attempt to measure this directly, but measuring the length of its shadow and the angle θ as depicted in Fig. 4-11 is relatively easy. To compute the height of the monument we use the relationship $\dfrac{\text{opposite}}{\text{adjacent}} = \tan\theta$. Thus $\dfrac{\text{height of monument}}{\text{length of shadow}} = \tan\theta$. If θ is 39° and the length of the shadow is 203 feet, then the height of the monument is 203 tan 39° feet. But how do we find out what tan 39° is? To do this from scratch requires fairly sophisticated mathematics and some laborious computation. Fortunately this has all been done, and we can simply look it up in a table. Here we would find that tan 39° to four places is 0.8098 and thus the height of the monument is $(203)\cdot(0.8098) = 164.3894$ feet. If the length of the shadow is known only to the nearest foot, the actual length of the shadow might be anywhere from 202.5 to 203.5 feet. Thus we would round this to 164. If the size of the angle is known only to the nearest degree, this answer might be off by as much as four feet. You can verify this, using the figures $\tan 38\frac{1}{2}° = 0.7954$ and $\tan 39\frac{1}{2}° = 0.8243$.

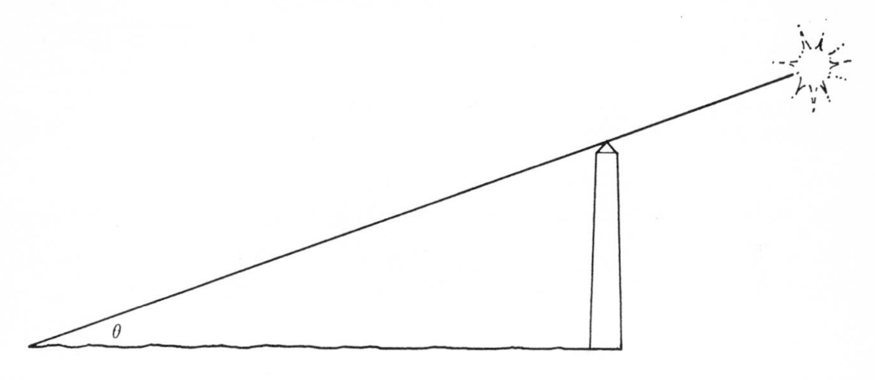

Fig. 4-11

Problems 4–2

1. The angle subtended to the ground from the top of a building at a distance x feet away from its base is 45°. The angle subtended at a distance 80 feet further away is 30°. What is the height h of the building?

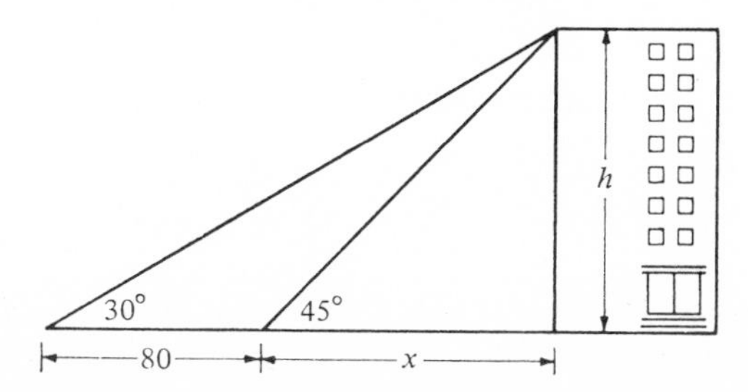

2. Benjamin measured the angle subtended by the top of a tall tree at the end of its shadow to be 60°. A few hours later he noticed the shadow was 50 feet longer and measured the angle at this time to be 30°. How tall was the tree?

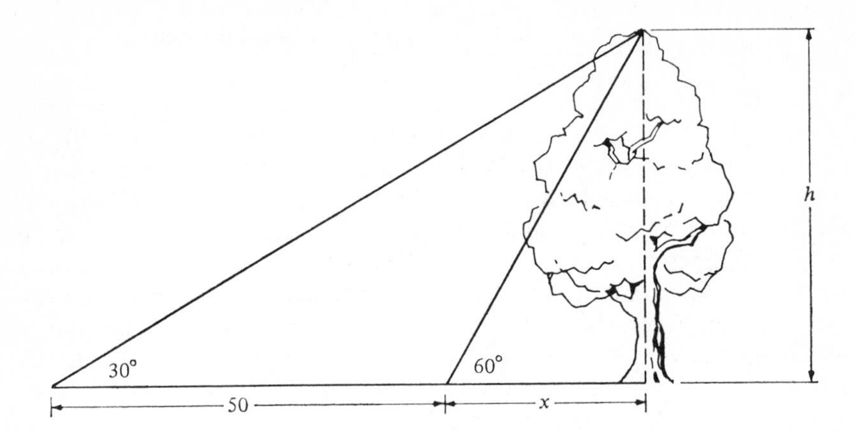

3. When a man 6 feet tall looks towards the top of a ladder, his line of vision makes an angle of 30° with the horizontal. When a child 4 feet tall stands in the same spot, his line of vision makes an angle of 45° with the horizontal. How tall is the ladder?

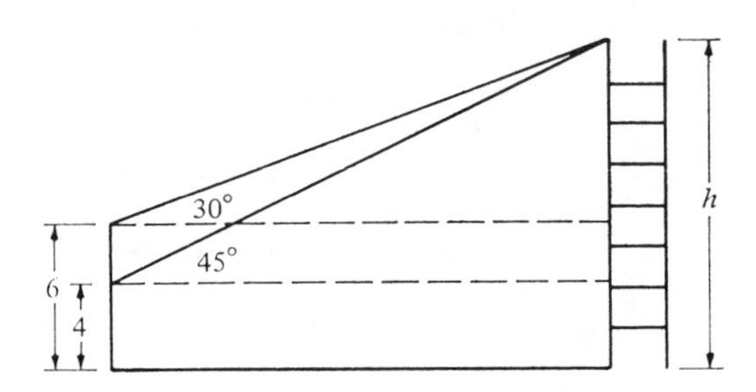

4. Complete the following table.

θ	0°	30°	45°	60°	90°	120°	135°	150°	180°
$\sin\theta$	0								
$\cos\theta$	1								
$\tan\theta$	0								

5. Find the angles of a right triangle if the lengths of two of the sides are
a) $a=8, b=8\sqrt{3}$, b) $a=b=19$, c) $a=5\sqrt{3}, b=5$.

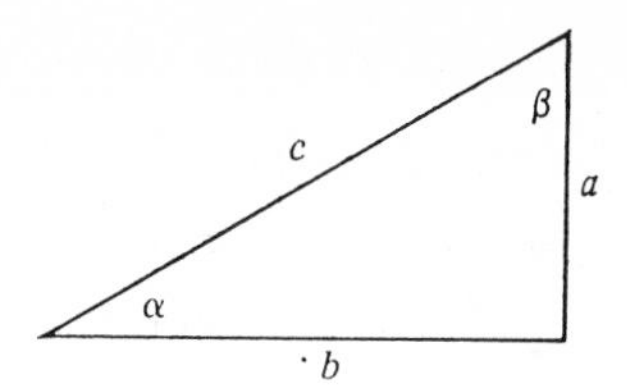

6. Find $\sin \theta$, $\cos \theta$, $\tan \theta$ for the right triangles with the following two sides.
a) $a = 8, b = 15$, b) $a = 4, c = 23$, c) $b = 9, c = 32$.

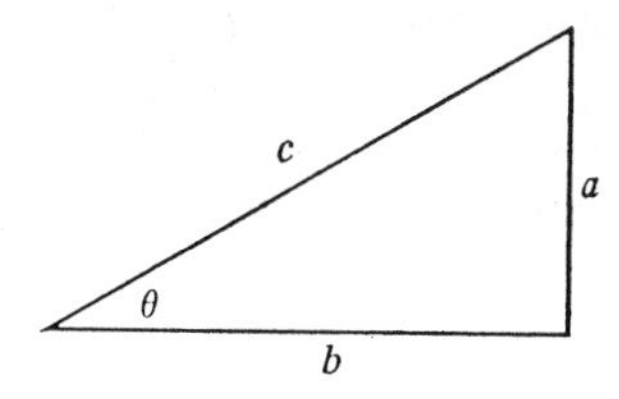

4–3 *Tables of Trigonometric Functions*

The usefulness of the trigonometric functions for solving practical problems led to the compilation of tables of their values. Since no table can list *all* possible values of the trig functions, each table lists the values of trig functions at certain selected points. Furthermore, since most of the values of the trig functions must be expressed by nonterminating decimal expansions we have to be content with approximations to the true values. This is no real hardship in practice; the numbers to which we apply the functions are usually the result of a measurement which is itself an approximation.

Angles are commonly measured in *degrees*. Degrees are further subdivided into *minutes*, there being 60 minutes in a degree. Thus we can talk about an angle of 23.5 degrees or equivalently, 23 degrees 30 minutes which we write $23°30'$. In Section 4–1 we determined that one radian is about $57.3°$. Since $0.3 \cdot 60 = 18$, we see that one radian is about $57°18'$. Ordinarily this is more than enough precision; we usually don't care whether an angle is $15°26'$ or $15°27'$. For those occasions when we do, the minute is divided into 60 seconds and an angle of 35 degrees 29 minutes 24 seconds is denoted by $35°29'24''$.

If we are no more precise in our measurement of angles than minutes, how precisely do we need to know the values of the trig functions? Suppose we measure an angle to be $22°12'$. Now $\sin 22°12'$ is 0.37784 to five decimal places. However, the true value of the angle which we measured may be anywhere from $22°11\frac{1}{2}'$ to $22°12\frac{1}{2}'$, since our measurement is only good "to the nearest minute." Let's compare the sines of these angles (to five places):

$$\begin{aligned}\sin 22°11\tfrac{1}{2}' &= 0.37771,\\ \sin 22°12' &= 0.37784,\\ \sin 22°12\tfrac{1}{2}' &= 0.37798.\end{aligned} \tag{3}$$

The sine of the true value of the angle may lie anywhere between 0.37771 and 0.37798. We thus have no real information about what the digit in the fifth decimal place is; we do have some about the fourth decimal place—it is either 7, 8, or 9. Hence it is natural to have only four decimal places in our table.

Table II which starts on page 160 gives the sine, tangent, cotangent, cosine, secant, and cosecant of angles from 0° to 45°. The angles from 0° to 45° are listed at ten-minute intervals down the first column of the table under the heading *angle*. A typical section of the table looks like this:

Angle	Sin	Cos	Tan	Cot	Sec	Csc	Coangle
37°00′	.6018	.7986	.7536	1.327	1.252	1.662	53°00′
10′	.6041	.7969	.7581	1.319	1.255	1.655	50′
20′	.6065	.7951	.7627	1.311	1.258	1.649	40′
30′	.6088	.7934	.7673	1.303	1.260	1.643	30′
40′	.6111	.7916	.7720	1.295	1.263	1.636	20′
50′	.6134	.7898	.7766	1.288	1.266	1.630	10′
38°00′	.6157	.7880	.7813	1.280	1.269	1.624	52°00′
Coangle	Cos	Sin	Cot	Tan	Csc	Sec	Angle

The first line tells us that sin 37° is 0.6018, cos 37° is 0.7986, tan 37° is 0.7536, cot 37° is 1.327, sec 37° is 1.252, csc 37° is 1.662, and the *co*mplementary *angle*, or *coangle*, of 37° is 53°. The coangle of an angle x is $(90° - x)$. If y is the coangle of x then:

$$\begin{aligned}\sin y &= \sin(90° - x) = \cos x,\\ \cos y &= \cos(90° - x) = \sin x,\\ \tan y &= \frac{\sin y}{\cos y} = \frac{\cos x}{\sin x} = \cot x.\end{aligned} \tag{4}$$

Similarly, $\cot y = \tan x$, $\sec y = \csc x$, and $\csc y = \sec x$. Hence the first line of the table also tells us that sin 53° = 0.7986, cos 53° = 0.6018, tan 53° = 1.327, cot 53° = 0.7536, sec 53° = 1.662, and csc 53° = 1.252. This information can be read off directly from the headings at the bottom of the page.

The second line of the table gives the information that sin 37°10′ is 0.6041, and so on. The coangle of 37°10′ is 52°50′ (*not* 53°50′). Thus this line also says that sin 52°50′ is 0.7969, and so on.

In this manner we may find sine, cosine, tangent, cotangent, secant, and cosecant of angles from 0° to 45° by locating the angle under the leftmost column, headed "angle," and reading across the line. To find the values of trig functions of angles from 45° to 90°, look up the angle under the rightmost column, headed "coangle," and read across the line, referring to the headings at the bottom of the page.

For example, suppose we want to know cos 72°20′. Since this angle is greater than 45°, we must look for it under the coangle column. Since we wish the cosine of a coangle, we find the required value in the sine column, i.e., 0.3035. This is the same as sin 17°40′.

The problem of finding the value of a trig function of an arbitrary angle may be reduced to finding the value of the trig function of an angle between 0° and 90°. The relevant identities are:

for any trigonometric function f and integer n

$$f(x + n(360°)) = f(x) = f(x - n(360°)). \tag{5}$$

$$\begin{aligned} \sin(-x) &= -\sin x, & \cos(-x) &= \cos x, \\ \tan(-x) &= -\tan x, & \cot(-x) &= -\cot x, \\ \sec(-x) &= \sec x, & \csc(-x) &= -\csc x, \end{aligned} \tag{6}$$

$$\begin{aligned} \sin(x + 90°) &= \cos x, & \cos(x + 90°) &= -\sin x, \\ \tan(x + 90°) &= -\cot x, & \cot(x + 90°) &= -\tan x, \\ \sec(x + 90°) &= -\csc x, & \csc(x + 90°) &= \sec x. \end{aligned} \tag{7}$$

Roughly speaking, we use (5) to get the angle between −180° and 180°; we use (6) to get the angle between 0° and 180°; and we use (7) to get the angle between 0° and 90°. (The identities in (5) and (6) were proved in Chapter 3. The identities of (7) will be proved in Chapter 5.)

Example 1. Find sin 140°.

Solution. Since 140° is already between 0° and 180°, we proceed directly to (7) to get it between 0° and 90°. By (7) we have sin 140° = sin (50° + 90°) = cos 50°, which we find in the table to be 0.6428.

Example 2. Find cos 470°.

Solution. Here we must use (5) to get the angle between −180° and 180°. In fact, cos 470° = cos (110° + 360°) = cos 110°. Since 110° is between 0° and 180°, we may skip (6) and apply (7). This yields cos 110° = cos (20° + 90°) = −sin 20° which we find in the table to be −0.3491.

Example 3. Find sin 950°.

Solution. We first apply (5) to get the angle between −180° and 180° by subtracting the appropriate integer multiple of 360°. In this case 3 · 360° = 1080° works, since 950° − 1080° = −130°, which is in the right range. Thus

$\sin(-130°) = \sin(950° - 3 \cdot 360°) = \sin 950°$. By (6) we have $\sin(-130°) = -\sin 130°$. Finally, by (7) we know that $\sin 130° = \sin(40° + 90°) = \cos 40°$ which we find in the table to be 0.7660. Collecting everything together we have $\sin 950° = -\cos 40° = -0.7660$.

Of course, any of the identities may be used at any time. In particular, we may always use (6) immediately to go from a negative angle to a positive one if we wish.

Problems 4–3

Find the values of the expressions in 1—6, using the table of trig functions.

1. a) $\sin 24°50'$, b) $\cos 79°20'$, c) $\tan 48°$, d) $\cot 36°50'$.

2. a) $\sec 48°30'$, b) $\cos 69°10'$, c) $\csc 83°10'$, d) $\cot 4°20'$.

3. a) $\sin 422°10'$, b) $\cos 4961°20'$, c) $\tan -86°40'$, d) $\cot 3859°20'$.

4. a) $\sin 689°$, b) $\sec 425°50'$, c) $\tan 666°$, d) $\csc -895°40'$.

5. a) $\sin -32°10'$, b) $\cos -5859°$, c) $\tan 130°20'$, d) $\cot 38{,}426°$.

6. a) $\sec -943°20'$, b) $\csc 3859°$, c) $\tan -130°$, d) $\cot 843{,}269°$.

7. The angle subtended to the ground from the top of a building, at some point on the ground, is 50°. At the point 60 feet further away from the base of the building, the angle subtended is 40°. What is the height of the building?

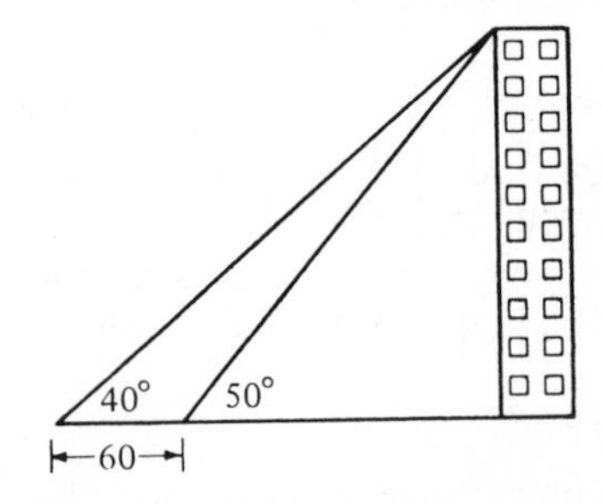

8. The angle from the ground to the top of a flagpole is 65° at one point. At another point 10 feet further away the angle is 53°. How tall is the flagpole?

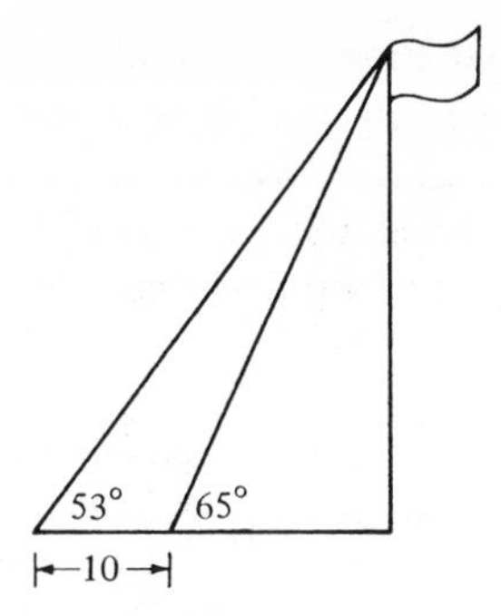

9. A building casts a shadow 80 feet long. The angle subtended from the top of the building to the end of the shadow is 36°50′. How tall is the building?

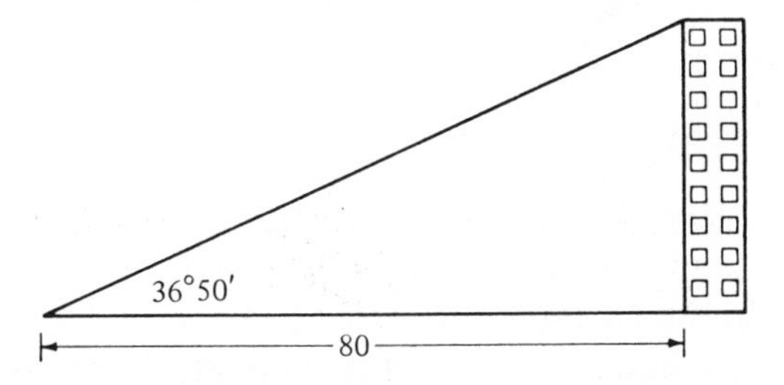

10. A telephone pole casts a shadow 36.5 feet long. The angle subtended from the top of the pole to the end of the shadow is 28°40′. How tall is the telephone pole?

4-4 Interpolation

Suppose we wish to know the sine of 32°46′. In our table we can find sin 32°40′ and sin 32°50′. In fact, we find

$$\begin{aligned} \sin 32°40' &= 0.5398, \\ \sin 32°50' &= 0.5422. \end{aligned} \tag{8}$$

Now it is clear that sin 32°46′ will lie somewhere between 0.5398 and 0.5422, but where? Observe that as the angle increases 10′, from 32°40′ to 32°50′, the value of the sine increases by 0.0024, from 0.5398 to 0.5422. Hence the sine increases 0.00024, on the *average*, for every increase in the angle of 1′. An increase of 6′ in the angle should then produce an increase of about 6 times 0.00024, or 0.00144, in the sine. Since sin 32°40′ = 0.5398, we might well expect sin 32°46′ to be about 0.5398 + 0.00144, or 0.54124. Rounding to four places, we conclude that sin 32°46′ = 0.5412, to four places. This, indeed, is the case.

The technique illustrated above for finding values of a function at points which lie between those listed in a table is called *linear interpolation.* The basic idea is best illustrated geometrically. Suppose we know the value of a function f at two points, a and b, and we wish to know $f(x)$ for some point x between a and b. Consider the graph of the relevant piece of the function (Fig. 4-12).

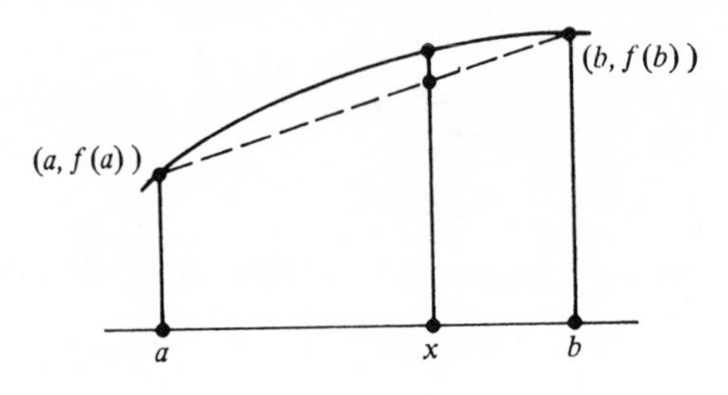

Fig. 4-12

All the table tells us about the function here is the location of the two points $(a, f(a))$ and $(b, f(b))$; we know nothing about what it looks like between. The idea of linear interpolation is to assume that the graph of the function does not differ significantly from the straight line drawn through the two known points $(a, f(a))$ and $(b, f(b))$. The approximate value of $f(x)$ can then be determined by computing where the vertical line through x intersects this line. Denoting by y the approximate value of f at x, we consider the triangle in Fig. 4-13.

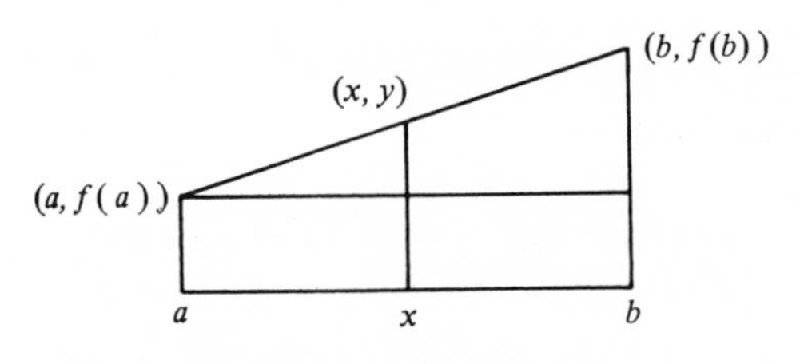

Fig. 4-13

Since the little triangle is similar to the big one their sides are proportional. The ratio of their bases is $(x - a)/(b - a)$; the ratio of their altitudes is $(y - f(a))/(f(b) - f(a))$. Thus

$$\frac{y - f(a)}{f(b) - f(a)} = \frac{x - a}{b - a}, \tag{9}$$

or

$$y = f(a) + \frac{f(b) - f(a)}{b - a}(x - a). \tag{10}$$

Notice that $(f(b) - f(a))/(b - a)$ is the average increase in the function f as we go from a to b, and $x - a$ is how far we go from a to x. Thus we are approximating the function f at x by taking the value at a and adding to that the distance from a to x times the average rate of increase from a to b. This is just what we did in the first paragraph of this section to find sin 32°46′.

It is easily seen that the accuracy of linear interpolation depends on how well the function in question is approximated by a straight line in the region of interest. It turns out that the trig functions we deal with behave reasonably well in the intervals in which we consider them, and hence linear interpolation will yield fairly accurate results.

Example 1. Find tan 15°21′.

Solution. In the table we find

$$\begin{aligned} \tan 15°20' &= 0.2742, \\ \tan 15°30' &= 0.2773. \end{aligned} \tag{11}$$

Here we observe that as the angle goes the 10′ from 15°20′ to 15°30′ the tangent increases by $0.2773 - 0.2742 = 0.0031$. This amounts to an average of 0.00031 per minute; thus we estimate tan 15°21′ by $0.2742 + 0.00031 = 0.27451$ which we round to 0.2745. Do you get the same thing by applying the formula given above?

Example 2. Find cos 27°13′.

Solution. In the table we find

$$\begin{aligned} \cos 27°10' &= 0.8897, \\ \cos 27°20' &= 0.8884. \end{aligned} \tag{12}$$

Thus, as the angle increases 10′ from 27°10′ to 27°20′, the cosine *decreases* from 0.8897 to 0.8884; that is, it decreases by 0.0013. This is an average decrease of 0.00013 per minute; we estimate cos 27°13′ by $0.8897 - 3 \cdot (0.00013) = 0.8897 - 0.00039 = 0.88931$ which we round to 0.8893. The reader should work this out by the formula also.

Problems 4–4

Find the values of the expressions in 1—6 to four places.

1. a) sin 32°35′, b) cos 42°28′,
c) tan 82°17′, d) cot 83°14′.

2. a) sin 39°46′, b) cos 89°18′,
c) tan 62°58′, d) cot 3°13′.

3. a) sin 389°14′, b) cos 286°29′,
c) tan 3864°54′, d) cot 1286°13′.

4. a) $\sin 689°24'$, b) $\cos 232°43'$,
c) $\tan 999°33'$, d) $\cot 333°55'$.

5. a) $\sin -32°14'$, b) $\cos -84°48'$,
c) $\tan -369°42'$, d) $\cot -18°18'$.

6. a) $\sin -97°27'$, b) $\cos -18°18'$,
c) $\tan -2965°25'$. d) $\cot -888°22'$.

7. The angle to the top of a mountain is 10°36′. From a point 500 feet further away the angle is 10°17′. How much higher is the top of the mountain than the observer? (Ignore the earth's curvature.)

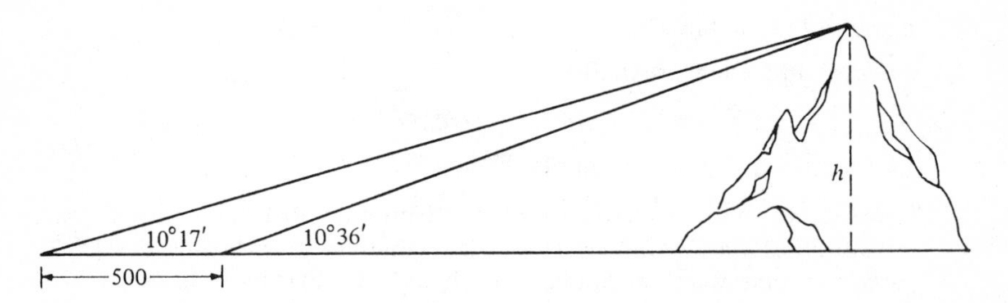

8. The angle to the top of a mountain is 2°28′. Measuring the angle from a point 500 feet further away gives an angle of 2°15′. How much higher is the top of the mountain than the observer? (Ignore the earth's curvature.)

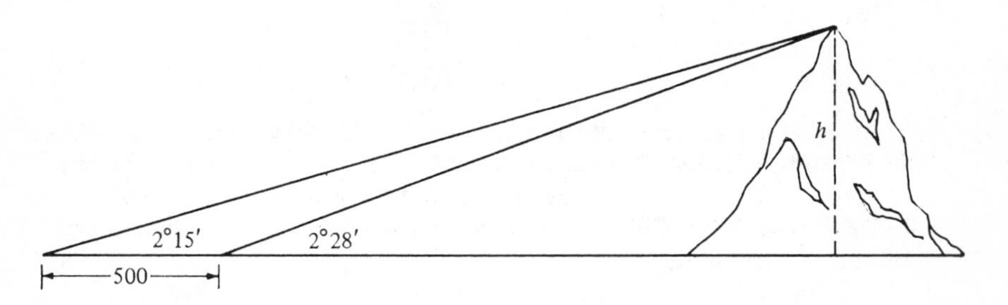

4–5 *Solving Right Triangles*

There are six numbers associated with every triangle: the lengths of the three sides and the measures (in degrees or radians) of the three angles. To *solve* a triangle means to determine all of these numbers. The simplest type of triangle to solve is one having an angle of 90°, that is, a right triangle.

Consider the right triangle in Fig. 4-14, with sides a, b, c and angles α, β, γ where $\gamma = 90°$.

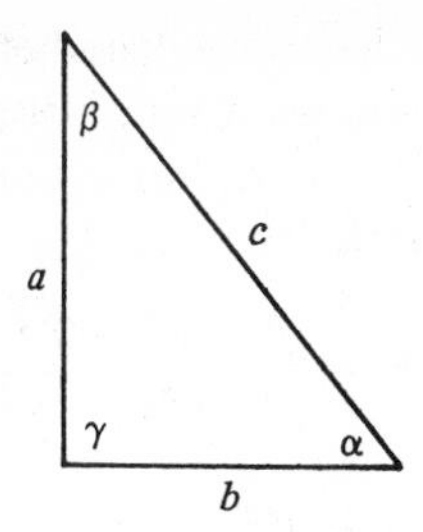

Fig. 4-14

Suppose we know that $c = 2$ and $\alpha = 20°$. This is enough information to enable us to solve the triangle. Elementary geometry tells us that $\alpha + \beta = 90°$; thus $\beta = 90° - \alpha = 90° - 20° = 70°$. To find a, we observe that $a/c = \sin \alpha$ so $a = c \sin \alpha = 2 \sin 20°$. Looking up sin 20°, we have $a = 2(0.3420) = 0.6840$. Similarly, $b/c = \cos \alpha$, so $b = c \cos \alpha = 2 \cos 20° = 2(0.9397) = 1.8794$. Thus we have completely solved the triangle:

$$\begin{aligned} a &= 0.6840, & \alpha &= 20°, \\ b &= 1.8794, & \beta &= 70°, \\ c &= 2, & \gamma &= 90°. \end{aligned} \tag{13}$$

The technique for solving a right triangle when you are given one side and one angle (other than the 90° one) is always the same: compute the other angle from the relation $\alpha + \beta = 90°$ and compute the other sides by forming their ratios with the known side.

Let us look at another example. Suppose we know that $\beta = 35°10'$ and $a = 5.362$; we must compute α, b and c. Since $\alpha + \beta = 90°$, we have $\alpha = 90° - \beta = 90° - 35°10' = 54°50'$. To compute b we must look at its ratio to the known side $a = 5.362$. But $b/a = \tan \beta$ so $b = a \tan \beta = 5.362 \tan 35°10' = (5.362) \cdot (0.7046) = 3.778$. To compute c we take its ratio with a and get $c/a = \sec \beta$ (or $\csc \alpha$) so $c = a \sec \beta = 5.362 \sec 35°10' = (5.362) \cdot (1.223) = 6.558$. (Generally, one should round to four significant digits when using numbers from a four-place table.)

You will notice that there is a certain amount of rather unpleasant arithmetic involved in solving these triangles. Later on you will be able to use a table of logarithms to make this task easier.

We have seen that one side and one (acute) angle is enough to determine a right triangle. Another way of determining a right triangle is by two sides. If we wish to solve such a triangle, we must compute the other side and the two acute angles.

Referring to Fig. 4-14 again, suppose we know that $a = 2$ and $b = 1$. The best way to proceed is to compute an angle first. Here we note that $\tan \beta = b/a = 1/2$. To find out what β is we look in the table under tan until we find an entry close to 0.5000. We notice that $\tan 26°30' = 0.4986$ and

$\tan 26°40' = 0.5022$. Hence β lies somewhere between $26°30'$ and $26°40'$. If we didn't need to be overly precise, we would just say $\beta = 26°30'$ since 0.4986 is closer to 0.5000 than 0.5022 is. If we wanted as much precision as possible, we would interpolate, obtaining

$$\begin{aligned}\beta &= 26°30' + \left(\frac{0.5000 - 0.4986}{0.5022 - 0.4986}\right) \cdot 10' \\ &= 26°30' + \left(\frac{14}{36}\right) \cdot 10' \\ &= 26°34'.\end{aligned}$$

Now that we know an acute angle and two sides, we can use either of the sides and this angle to compute the other quantities with the techniques developed earlier. In this case, $\alpha = 90° - 26°34' = 63°26'$, and since $\sin \beta = b/c$, $c = b/\sin \beta = 1/0.4472 = 2.236$ (or directly applying the Pythagorean law, $c = \sqrt{a^2 + b^2} = \sqrt{5} = 2.236$, to three places). Thus we have again completely solved the triangle:

$$\begin{aligned} a &= 2, & \alpha &= 63°26', \\ b &= 1, & \beta &= 26°34', \\ c &= 2.236, & \gamma &= 90°. \end{aligned}$$

Problems 4–5

Solve the following right triangles in 1 through 10, each having sides and angles labeled as in Fig. 4-14, with $\gamma = 90°$.

1. a) $\alpha = 22°$ and $a = 14$,
b) $\alpha = 39°30'$ and $a = 3.596$,
c) $\alpha = 16°10'$ and $a = 376$.

2. a) $\alpha = 37°$ and $a = 19$,
b) $\alpha = 62°20'$ and $a = 32$,
c) $\alpha = 6°50'$ and $a = 4.937$.

3. a) $\alpha = 72°$ and $b = 96$,
b) $\alpha = 37°35'$ and $b = 13.9$,
c) $\beta = 49°13'$ and $a = 432$.

4. a) $\alpha = 16°$ and $c = 42$,
b) $\beta = 73°20'$ and $c = 23.9$,
c) $\alpha = 47°47'$ and $c = 5.936$.

5. a) $\alpha = 63°$ and $b = 8.7$,
b) $\alpha = 13°23'$ and $b = 13.23$,
c) $\beta = 57°57'$ and $a = 5.73$.

6. a) $\alpha = 61°$ and $c = 24$,
b) $\beta = 37°40'$ and $c = 93.2$,
c) $\alpha = 23°13'$ and $c = 2.963$.

7. a) $a = 5$ and $b = 2$,
b) $a = 36.9$ and $b = 9$,
c) $a = 762$ and $b = 267$.

8. a) $a = 9$ and $b = 5$,
b) $a = 47.96$ and $b = 19.1$,
c) $a = 964$ and $b = 469$.

9. a) $a = 9$ and $c = 14$,
b) $b = 20.5$ and $c = 30.5$,
c) $a = 19.27$ and $c = 37.83$.

10. a) $a = 19$ and $c = 23$,
b) $a = 43$ and $c = 143$,
c) $b = 34.9$ and $c = 78.5$.

11. The angle subtended to the ground from the top of a building at a distance 30 feet away from its base is 50°14′. How tall is the building?

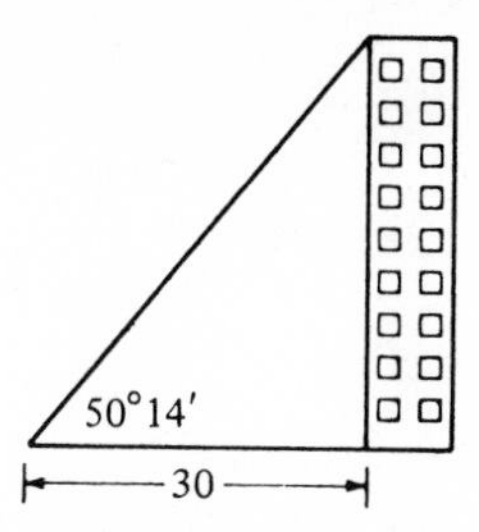

12. At the High City airport, an airplane is required to be at an altitude of at least 800 feet above ground when it has attained a horizontal distance of one mile from take-off. What must be the (minimum) average angle of ascent?

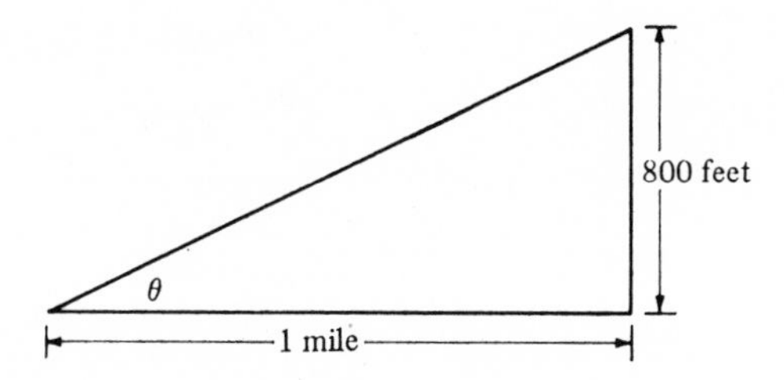

5 *Trigonometric Identities*

5–1 The Fundamental Trigonometric Identities

An *identity* is an equation which is true for *all* values of the variable for which both sides of the equation are defined. Thus $(x + 1)(x - 1) = x^2 - 1$ is an identity since no matter what number we substitute for x in the equation we get a true statement: substituting 9 for x gives us $(9 + 1)(9 - 1) = 9^2 - 1$, which is true since both sides evaluate to 80; substituting 5 for x gives $(5 + 1)(5 - 1) = 5^2 - 1$, which is true since both sides equal 24; and so on. Similarly, $\cos^2 x + \sin^2 x = 1$ and $\tan x \cdot \cot x = 1$ are identities (note that $\tan x \cdot \cot x$ is undefined if x is an integer multiple of $\pi/2$; for all other values of x both sides of the equation are defined and are equal). On the other hand, equations like $x^3 = 8$, $\sin x = 0.3$, and $2x^2 - 5x + 1 = 0$ are satisfied for *some* but not *all* values of x. Such equations are called *conditional equations.*

Since identities are true no matter what *number* we substitute for the variable, we may create new identities by substituting *expressions* for the variable in identities we already have. Take the identity $\cos^2 x + \sin^2 x = 1$ as an example. Since it is true for *any* value of x, it will be true, in particular if $x = 3\pi y$, no matter what the value of y is. Thus substituting $3\pi y$ for x results in the identity $\cos^2 3\pi y + \sin^2 3\pi y = 1$, which holds for any value of y. Similarly, $\tan(\phi + 2)\cot(\phi + 2) = 1$ and $\cos^2(4t^2 + 5t - 1) + \sin^2(4t^2 + 5t - 1) = 1$ are true for all values of ϕ and t for which the terms are defined.

Trigonometric identities are used frequently in simplifying trigonometric expressions. They are also used in solving conditional equations, allowing one to translate expressions into terms of known quantities. These and other applications will be illustrated in examples.

To prove the validity of a trigonometric identity one may use previously proved identities together with standard algebraic or geometric manipulations. The fundamental identities were proved in an earlier chapter, and we will review them briefly.

The first trigonometric functions introduced were the sine and cosine functions. These functions are related by the Pythagorean identity

$$\cos^2\theta + \sin^2\theta = 1. \tag{1}$$

This identity allows us to compute $\cos\theta$ from $\sin\theta$ and vice versa; i.e., $\cos\theta = \pm\sqrt{1-\sin^2\theta}$ and $\sin\theta = \pm\sqrt{1-\cos^2\theta}$. The choice of sign is determined by the quadrant in which θ lies. You will frequently find this identity useful in simplifying trigonometric expressions.

Example 1. Simplify $(\cos\theta + \sin\theta)^2$.

Solution. $(\cos\theta + \sin\theta)^2 = \cos^2\theta + 2\cos\theta\sin\theta + \sin^2\theta = 1 + 2\cos\theta\sin\theta$.

Example 2. Simplify $20\sin^2\theta + 20\cos^2\theta$.

Solution. $20\sin^2\theta + 20\cos^2\theta = 20(\sin^2\theta + \cos^2\theta) = 20$.

The definitions of the other trigonometric functions provide us with the following identities:

$$\begin{aligned} \tan\theta &= \frac{\sin\theta}{\cos\theta}, \\ \cot\theta &= \frac{\cos\theta}{\sin\theta}, \\ \sec\theta &= \frac{1}{\cos\theta}, \\ \csc\theta &= \frac{1}{\sin\theta}. \end{aligned} \tag{2}$$

Combining (1) and (2), we obtain two additional Pythagorean identities. Dividing both sides of (1) by $\cos^2\theta$ and by $\sin^2\theta$ yields the two identities:

$$\begin{aligned} \tan^2\theta + 1 &= \sec^2\theta, \\ \cot^2\theta + 1 &= \csc^2\theta. \end{aligned} \tag{3}$$

Example 3. Simplify $(\tan x + \sec x)(\tan x - \sec x)$.

Solution. $(\tan x + \sec x)(\tan x - \sec x) = \tan^2 x - \sec^2 x$
$= \tan^2 x - (\tan^2 x + 1) = -1.$

Example 4. If $\sec t = 2$ and $0 \le t \le \pi/2$, what are the values of $\tan t$, $\cot t$, and $\csc t$?

Solution.

$$\tan t = \pm\sqrt{\sec^2 t - 1} \quad \text{(by (3))}$$
$$= \pm\sqrt{3}.$$
$$\cot t = \frac{1}{\tan t} \quad \text{(by (2))}$$
$$= \pm\frac{\sqrt{3}}{3}.$$
$$\csc t = \pm\sqrt{\cot^2 t + 1} \quad \text{(by (3))}$$
$$= \pm\sqrt{\frac{4}{3}} = \pm\frac{2\sqrt{3}}{3}.$$

To complete the solution we look at the quadrant of t. For $0 \le t \le \pi/2$, $\tan t \ge 0$, $\cot t \ge 0$, and $\csc t \ge 0$. Thus $\tan t = \sqrt{3}$, $\cot t = \sqrt{3}/3$, and $\csc t = 2\sqrt{3}/3$ are the correct answers.

Some additional properties of the sine and cosine functions have already been established. It was shown that the sine and cosine functions are odd and even, respectively.

$$\sin(-\theta) = -\sin\theta, \qquad \cos(-\theta) = \cos\theta. \tag{4}$$

It was shown that the sine and cosine functions are periodic of period 2π.

$$\sin\theta = \sin(\theta + 2\pi n), \qquad \cos\theta = \cos(\theta + 2\pi n). \tag{5}$$

In the above identities, n is any integer. The following identities were also established.

$$\sin(\theta \pm \pi) = -\sin\theta, \qquad \cos(\theta \pm \pi) = -\cos\theta. \tag{6}$$

Problems 5–1

1. Give the possible values for $\cos\theta$ and $\tan\theta$, given the following:
a) $\sin\theta = 1/5$, b) $\csc\theta = 8$, c) $\sin\theta = \sqrt{3}/3$.

2. Give the possible values for $\sin\theta$ and $\tan\theta$, given the following:
a) $\cos\theta = 2/9$, b) $\cos\theta = 3/\pi$, c) $\sec\theta = 5\sqrt{2}$.

3. Give the possible values for $\sin\theta$ and $\cot\theta$, given the following:
a) $\cos\theta = 4/7$, b) $\sec\theta = 21/4$, c) $\cos\theta = 1/3$.

4. Give the possible values for $\cos\theta$ and $\cot\theta$, given the following:
   a) $\sin\theta = 5/19$, b) $\csc\theta = \sqrt[3]{9}$, c) $\csc\theta = \pi^2 + 1$.

5. Simplify $1 + \tan^2\theta\cos^2\theta - \sin^2\theta$.

6. Simplify $\sin^2\theta - \sin^4\theta - \sin^2\theta\cos^2\theta$.

7. Simplify $\sin^4\theta + 2\sin^2\theta\cos^2\theta + \cos^4\theta$.

8. Simplify $\dfrac{4}{\tan\theta} + \dfrac{5}{\cot\theta}$.

9. Simplify $\sin\theta + \sin(\theta + \pi)$.

10. Simplify $3\sin^2(2\theta + \pi/2) - 3\cos(2\theta + 5\pi/2)\cos(2\theta - \pi/2)$.

11. Simplify $5\csc^2(\theta + \pi/2) - 5\cot(\theta + \pi/2)\cot(\theta - \pi/2)$.

12. Simplify $2\sec 3\theta\sec(3\theta + \pi) - 2\tan 3\theta\sin 3\theta\csc 3\theta$.

13. If $\csc x = y$, what are the possible values for
    a) $\sec x$, b) $\tan x$?

14. Evaluate the following expressions for $\phi + \theta = \pi$.
    a) $\sin^2\phi + \cos^2\theta$, b) $\sin\phi - \sin\theta$.

15. If $\csc x = 2$ and $\pi/2 \le x \le \pi$, what are the values of the following?
    a) $\cos x$, b) $\cot x$.

16. If $\sec t = 1000$ and $0 \le t \le \pi/2$, what are the values of the following?
    a) $\sin t$, b) $\cot t$.

5–2 *The Addition Formulas*

In this section we will derive two more fundamental trigonometric identities called the addition formulas.

$$\begin{aligned}\sin(\phi + \theta) &= \sin\phi\cos\theta + \cos\phi\sin\theta,\\ \cos(\phi + \theta) &= \cos\phi\cos\theta - \sin\phi\sin\theta.\end{aligned} \tag{7}$$

The other identities which occur can be derived from these together with the basic list of identities in Section 5–1. As you can see from the identities, knowing the values of sine and cosine at ϕ and θ will enable us to compute the values of sine and cosine at $\phi + \theta$. The reader should verify that for $\theta = 2\pi n$ or $\pm\pi$ these formulas agree with those listed in Section 5–1.

In order to express $\sin(\phi + \theta)$ and $\cos(\phi + \theta)$ in terms of $\sin\phi$, $\sin\theta$, $\cos\phi$, and $\cos\theta$, we first express $P(\phi + \theta)$ in terms of the coordinates of $P(\phi)$ by looking at rotations of the plane.

Suppose that we take the cartesian plane and rotate it counterclockwise through an angle θ, as in Fig. 5-1. What happens to a point (x, y)? For certain points this question is easily answered. Let us indicate by $T(x, y)$

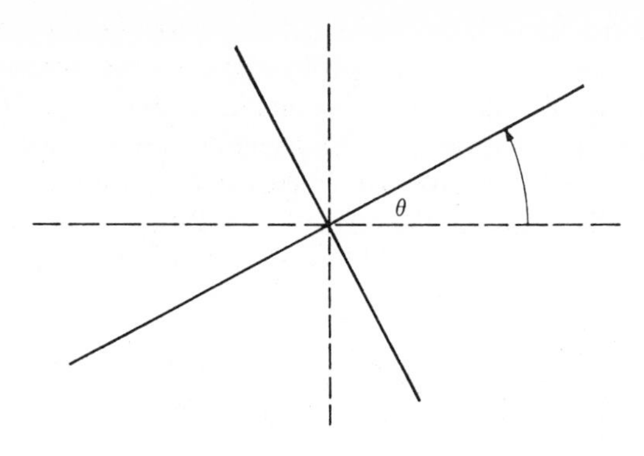

Fig. 5-1

the position of the point (x, y) after the rotation. Then $T(0, 0) = (0, 0)$; i.e., the origin is unaffected by the rotation. $T(1, 0)$ is simply the trigonometric point $P(\theta)$ as is easily seen in the sketch in Fig. 5-2 (θ being measured in

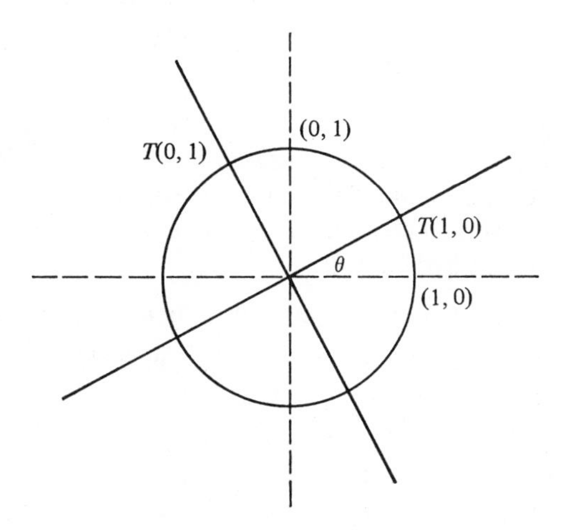

Fig. 5-2

radians). Thus $T(1, 0) = (\cos\theta, \sin\theta)$. Similarly, $T(x, 0) = (x\cos\theta, x\sin\theta)$ for any real number x. We also note that $T(0, 1)$ is the trigonometric point $P(\theta + \pi/2)$. Thus $T(0, 1) = (\cos(\theta + \pi/2), \sin(\theta + \pi/2))$. Similarly, $T(0, y) = (y\cos(\theta + \pi/2), y\sin(\theta + \pi/2))$ for any real number y. The two expressions

$$T(x, 0) = (x\cos\theta, x\sin\theta),$$
$$T(0, y) = \left(y\cos\left(\theta + \frac{\pi}{2}\right), y\sin\left(\theta + \frac{\pi}{2}\right)\right) \tag{8}$$

tell us where the points on the x and y axes go. To pass from these expressions to a general expression for $T(x, y)$ we make the following observation.

Consider a rectangle in the plane with one corner at the origin (Fig. 5-3). We have written in the coordinates of two of the other three corners of the rectangle. Can we compute the coordinates of the third corner? A little thought will convince you that the coordinates are $(a + c, b + d)$. Observe that the third corner is situated with respect to (c, d) just as (a, b) is situated with respect to $(0, 0)$, and $(a, b) = (a + 0, b + 0)$.

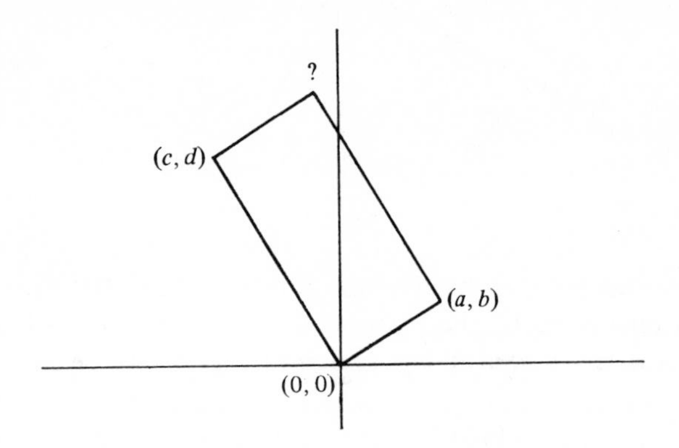

Fig. 5-3

To compute $T(x, y)$ we fix our attention on Fig. 5-4. When the plane is rotated, this changes to the situation depicted in Fig. 5-5. But we know that $T(x, 0) = (x \cos \theta, x \sin \theta)$ and $T(0, y) = (y \cos (\theta + \pi/2), y \sin (\theta + \pi/2))$. Thus by the argument given above,

$$T(x, y) = (x \cos \theta + y \cos (\theta + \pi/2), x \sin \theta + y \sin (\theta + \pi/2)). \qquad (9)$$

If $(x, y) = P(\phi) = (\cos \phi, \sin \phi)$, then $T(x, y) = P(\phi + \theta)$ since rotation by θ takes $P(\phi)$ to $P(\phi + \theta)$. Thus we have

$$P(\phi + \theta) = (\cos (\phi + \theta), \sin (\phi + \theta)) = T(\cos \phi, \sin \phi)$$

$$= \left(\cos \phi \cos \theta + \sin \phi \cos \left(\theta + \frac{\pi}{2}\right), \cos \phi \sin \theta + \sin \phi \sin \left(\theta + \frac{\pi}{2}\right)\right)$$

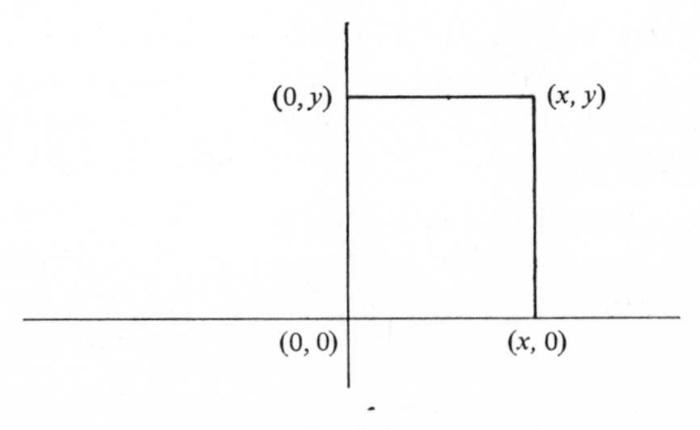

Fig. 5-4

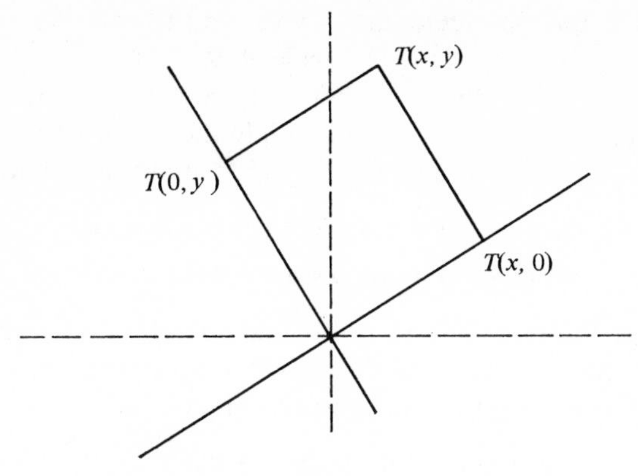

Fig. 5-5

from which we get the formulas

$$\begin{aligned} \cos(\phi+\theta) &= \cos\phi\cos\theta + \sin\phi\cos\left(\theta+\frac{\pi}{2}\right), \\ \sin(\phi+\theta) &= \cos\phi\sin\theta + \sin\phi\sin\left(\theta+\frac{\pi}{2}\right). \end{aligned} \tag{10}$$

If $\theta = \pi/2$, these become

$$\begin{aligned} \cos\left(\phi+\frac{\pi}{2}\right) &= \cos\phi\cos\frac{\pi}{2} + \sin\phi\cos\pi = -\sin\phi, \\ \sin\left(\phi+\frac{\pi}{2}\right) &= \cos\phi\sin\frac{\pi}{2} + \sin\phi\sin\pi = \cos\phi. \end{aligned} \tag{11}$$

Replacing ϕ by $-x$ we get the important identities below:

$$\begin{aligned} \cos\left(\frac{\pi}{2}-x\right) &= \sin x, \\ \sin\left(\frac{\pi}{2}-x\right) &= \cos x. \end{aligned} \tag{12}$$

For $0 < x < \pi/2$ these last formulas have an immediate geometric meaning. Consider the right triangle of Fig. 5-6. Since the sum of the angles

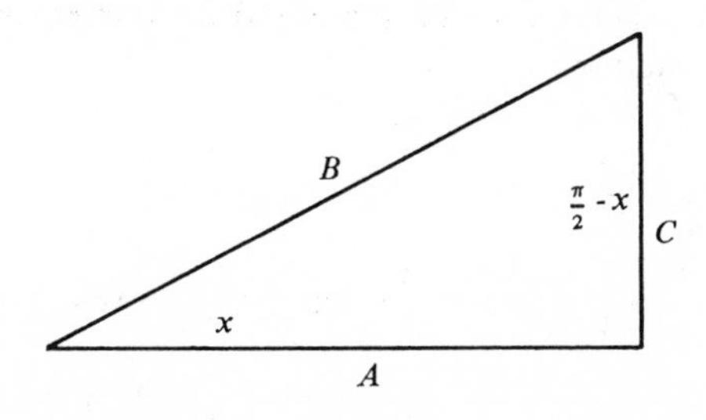

Fig. 5-6

in a triangle is π, the two acute angles must add to $\pi/2$. We have seen that $\cos x = A/B$ and also that $\sin(\pi/2 - x) = A/B$. Thus $\sin(\pi/2 - x) = \cos x$. Since $\pi/2 - x$ was called the complementary angle of x, $\sin(\pi/2 - x)$ was called the complementary sine of x, or simply the cosine of x.

With equations (11) we may simplify (10) to get the addition formulas.

$$\begin{aligned} \cos(\phi + \theta) &= \cos\phi\cos\theta - \sin\phi\sin\theta, \\ \sin(\phi + \theta) &= \cos\phi\sin\theta + \sin\phi\cos\theta. \end{aligned} \tag{13}$$

Using these formulas one can also find subtraction formulas, namely, $\sin(\phi - \theta) = \sin(\phi + (-\theta)) = \cos\phi\sin(-\theta) + \sin\phi\cos(-\theta) = -\cos\phi\sin\theta + \sin\phi\cos\theta$. Combining the two formulas gives

$$\sin(\phi \pm \theta) = \sin\phi\cos\theta \pm \cos\phi\sin\theta. \tag{14}$$

You are asked to establish the subtraction formula for cosine in the problems. The resulting formula will be

$$\cos(\phi \pm \theta) = \cos\phi\cos\theta \mp \sin\phi\sin\theta. \tag{15}$$

Finally, let us look at $\tan(\phi + \theta)$. Applying the addition formulas for sine and cosine gives

$$\tan(\phi + \theta) = \frac{\sin\phi\cos\theta + \cos\phi\sin\theta}{\cos\phi\cos\theta - \sin\phi\sin\theta}. \tag{16}$$

Dividing numerator and denominator by $\cos\phi\cos\theta$ we are able to express this entirely in terms of the tangent function, since the equation

$$\tan(\phi + \theta) = \frac{\dfrac{\sin\phi\cos\theta}{\cos\phi\cos\theta} + \dfrac{\cos\phi\sin\theta}{\cos\phi\cos\theta}}{\dfrac{\cos\phi\cos\theta}{\cos\phi\cos\theta} - \dfrac{\sin\phi\sin\theta}{\cos\phi\cos\theta}} \tag{17}$$

simplifies to

$$\tan(\phi + \theta) = \frac{\tan\phi + \tan\theta}{1 - \tan\phi\tan\theta}. \tag{18}$$

Again, you are asked to find the subtraction formula in the problems.

The addition formulas provide a method for computing more values of the trigonometric functions.

Example. Find $\sin\dfrac{5\pi}{12}$.

Solution. $\dfrac{5\pi}{12} = \dfrac{\pi}{6} + \dfrac{\pi}{4}$; thus $\sin\dfrac{5\pi}{12} = \sin\dfrac{\pi}{6}\cos\dfrac{\pi}{4} + \cos\dfrac{\pi}{6}\sin\dfrac{\pi}{4}$

$$= \frac{1}{2}\cdot\frac{\sqrt{2}}{2} + \frac{\sqrt{3}}{2}\cdot\frac{\sqrt{2}}{2} = \frac{\sqrt{2}}{4}(1 + \sqrt{3}).$$

Problems 5–2

1. Verify the identity $\cos(x-y) = \cos x \cos y + \sin x \sin y$.

2. Find an expression for $\tan(x-y)$ in terms of $\tan x$ and $\tan y$.

3. Find an expression for $\sin(x+y+z)$ in terms of trigonometric functions of x, y, and z.

4. Find $\cos\dfrac{\pi}{12}$. $\left(\text{Hint: } \dfrac{\pi}{12} = \dfrac{\pi}{3} - \dfrac{\pi}{4}\right)$

5. Find $\sin\dfrac{7\pi}{12}$.

6. Find $\sin\dfrac{\pi}{12}$.

7. Find $\cos\dfrac{11\pi}{12}$.

8. Fill in the following table.

	$-\theta$	$\frac{\pi}{2} \pm \theta$	$\pi \pm \theta$	$\frac{3\pi}{2} \pm \theta$	$2\pi n \pm \theta$
sin ___	$-\sin\theta$	$+\cos\theta$	$\pm\sin\theta$		
cos ___					
tan ___					$\pm\tan\theta$
cot ___				$\pm\tan\theta$	
sec ___			$-\sec\theta$		
csc ___		$+\sec\theta$			

Simplify the expressions in 9—14.

9. $3\sin^2\alpha + 3\sin^2\left(\alpha + \dfrac{\pi}{2}\right)$.

10. $2\sec\left(\dfrac{\pi}{2} + \theta\right)\csc(\pi + \theta) + \cot(\pi - \theta)\tan\left(\dfrac{3\pi}{2} - \theta\right) + \tan^2\left(\dfrac{\pi}{2} + \theta\right)$.

11. $15\csc\left(\dfrac{\pi}{2} + \theta\right)\csc\left(\dfrac{\pi}{2} - \theta\right) + 15\tan(-\theta)\cot\left(\dfrac{\pi}{2} - \theta\right)$.

12. $\cos(\alpha - \beta) - \cos(\alpha + \beta)$.

13. $3\cos(\theta + \phi) + 3\cos(\theta - \phi)$.

14. $2\sin(\alpha + \beta) + 2\sin(\alpha - \beta)$.

5–3 *Double and Half Angle Formulas*

An important special case of the addition formulas occurs when $\phi = \theta$. Substituting θ for ϕ, we get the *double angle* formulas.

$$\begin{aligned} \cos 2\theta &= \cos^2 \theta - \sin^2 \theta, \\ \sin 2\theta &= 2 \cos \theta \sin \theta. \end{aligned} \tag{19}$$

The formula for $\cos 2\theta$ admits two useful modifications using the fact that $\cos^2 \theta + \sin^2 \theta = 1$. Replacing $\cos^2 \theta$ by $1 - \sin^2 \theta$, we get

$$\cos 2\theta = 1 - 2 \sin^2 \theta. \tag{20}$$

Replacing $\sin^2 \theta$ by $1 - \cos^2 \theta$, we get

$$\cos 2\theta = 2 \cos^2 \theta - 1. \tag{21}$$

We may solve these expressions for $\sin \theta$ and $\cos \theta$:

$$\begin{aligned} \sin \theta &= \pm\sqrt{\frac{1 - \cos 2\theta}{2}}, \\ \cos \theta &= \pm\sqrt{\frac{1 + \cos 2\theta}{2}}. \end{aligned} \tag{22}$$

Substituting $x/2$ for θ, we get the *half angle formulas*:

$$\begin{aligned} \sin \frac{x}{2} &= \pm\sqrt{\frac{1 - \cos x}{2}}, \\ \cos \frac{x}{2} &= \pm\sqrt{\frac{1 + \cos x}{2}}. \end{aligned} \tag{23}$$

The choice of sign depends, of course, upon the quadrant in which $x/2$ lies, sine being positive in the first and second quadrants and negative in the third and fourth quadrants, and cosine being positive in the first and fourth quadrants and negative in the second and third quadrants.

To illustrate the use of these formulas we compute $\sin \pi/8$. We have

$$\sin \frac{\pi}{8} = \sin \frac{\pi/4}{2} = \pm\sqrt{\frac{1 - \cos \pi/4}{2}} = \pm\sqrt{\frac{1 - \sqrt{2}/2}{2}}$$

$$= \pm\sqrt{\frac{\frac{2 - \sqrt{2}}{2}}{2}} = \pm\sqrt{\frac{2 - \sqrt{2}}{4}} = \pm\tfrac{1}{2}\sqrt{2 - \sqrt{2}}.$$

Since $\sin \pi/8$ is positive, $\sin \pi/8 = \frac{1}{2}\sqrt{2 - \sqrt{2}}$.

Problems 5–3

1. Find $\cos \pi/8$ by the half angle formula.

2. Find $\cos 3\pi/8$ and $\sin 3\pi/8$ by the half angle formulas.

3. Find $\sin \pi/12$ by the half angle formula.

4. Show that $\tan \frac{x}{2} = \frac{1 - \cos x}{\sin x} = \frac{\sin x}{1 + \cos x} = \pm\sqrt{\frac{1 - \cos x}{1 + \cos x}}$.

5. Develop a formula for $\tan 2\theta$.

6. Develop a formula for $\cot 2\theta$.

7. Use the identities in problem 4 to find

a) $\tan \frac{\pi}{8}$, b) $\tan \frac{\pi}{12}$, c) $\tan \frac{5\pi}{8}$.

8. Develop formulas for $\sin 3\theta$ and $\cos 3\theta$ in terms of $\sin \theta$ and $\cos \theta$, respectively.

9. If $\sin \theta = 4/5$, what are the possible values of the following?

a) $\cos^2 \theta$, b) $\cos \theta$, c) $\sin 2\theta$,

d) $\sin \frac{\theta}{2}$, e) $\cos 2\theta$, f) $\sin 3\theta$.

10. If $\sin \theta = 3/8$, what are the possible values of the following?

a) $\cos^2 \theta$, b) $\cos \theta$, c) $\sin 2\theta$,

d) $\sin \frac{\theta}{2}$, e) $\cos 2\theta$, f) $\sin 3\theta$.

11. Use the double angle formula to find three different numbers t, with $0 \leq t < 2\pi$, for which $\cos 2t = \cos t$.

12. Use the double angle formula to find a number t for which $\sin t \neq 0$ and $\sin 2t = \sin t$.

Simplify the expressions in 13—20.

13. $\cos^2 \theta + \frac{1}{4} \sin^2 2\theta - \sin^2 \theta \cos^2 \theta + 2 \sin^2 \theta$.

14. $2 \sin \frac{\alpha}{2} \cos \frac{\alpha}{2}$.

15. $\sec \theta \, (1 + \cos 2\theta)$.

16. $\sin 2\theta \tan \theta + \cos 2\theta$.

17. $\frac{\tan 2\theta}{\tan \theta} - \frac{1}{\cos 2\theta}$.

18. $\tan\frac{\theta}{2}\sin\frac{\theta}{2}+\cos\frac{\theta}{2}-2\csc\theta\sin\frac{\theta}{2}$.

19. $(\cos 3\alpha+3\cos\alpha)\sec\alpha$.

20. $\sin 3\alpha+4\sin^3\alpha$.

5–4 Miscellaneous Formulas

It must be clear by now that no trigonometry book is large enough to develop all possible trigonometric identities, and we shall consider only a few more. Those developed in previous sections constitute what might be considered a minimal list of fundamental identities. In fact, all other identities which you might need can be derived from these through purely algebraic manipulations. This is also true of those we will develop in this section. However, for the sake of better insight we will give a partially geometric development.

We are looking for formulas for $\sin\phi+\sin\theta$ and $\cos\phi+\cos\theta$. These occur as the coordinates of the point $P(\phi)+P(\theta)=(\cos\phi+\cos\theta,\ \sin\phi+\sin\theta)$. Geometrically this occurs as the fourth vertex of the parallelogram having (0, 0), $P(\phi)$, and $P(\theta)$ as the other three vertices (see Fig. 5-7). The diagonal of this parallelogram connecting (0, 0) and $P(\phi)+P(\theta)$ bisects the interior angle $\phi-\theta$; thus it intersects the circle at $P\left(\theta+\frac{\phi-\theta}{2}\right)=P\left(\frac{\phi+\theta}{2}\right)$. (See Fig. 5-8.)

On the other hand, this diagonal intersects the circle at the point whose coordinates are obtained by dividing the coordinates of $P(\phi)+P(\theta)$ by the length of the diagonal, i.e., the distance from $P(\phi)+P(\theta)$ to (0, 0). (This is

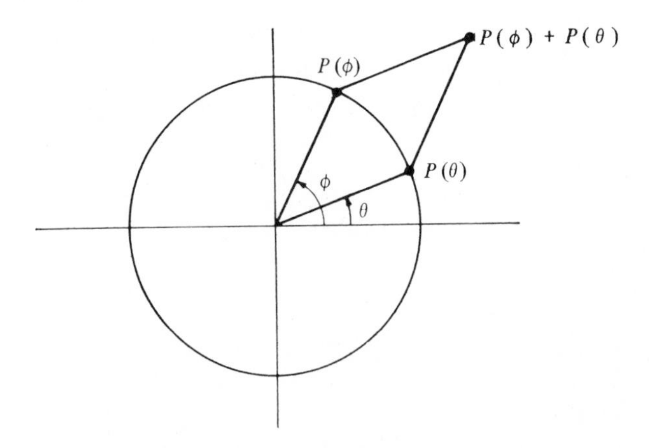

Fig. 5-7

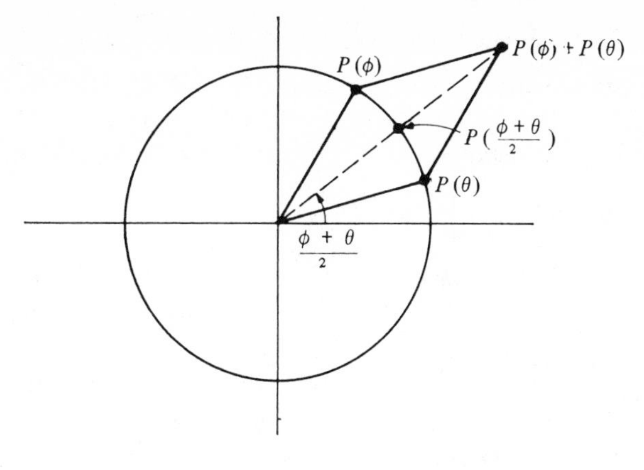

Fig. 5-8

the point on the diagonal having distance 1 from (0, 0).) Using the identity $\sin^2 x + \cos^2 x = 1$ and the formulas for $\cos(\phi - \theta)$ and $\cos(\phi - \theta)/2$ we can find the distance from $P(\phi) + P(\theta)$ to (0, 0).

$$\sqrt{(\cos\phi + \cos\theta)^2 + (\sin\phi + \sin\theta)^2}$$

$$= \sqrt{\cos^2\phi + 2\cos\phi\cos\theta + \cos^2\theta + \sin^2\phi + 2\sin\phi\sin\theta + \sin^2\theta}$$

$$= \sqrt{2 + 2\cos\phi\cos\theta + 2\sin\phi\sin\theta}$$

$$= \sqrt{2 + 2\cos(\phi - \theta)}$$

$$= 2\sqrt{\frac{1 + \cos(\phi - \theta)}{2}} = 2\cos\left(\frac{\phi - \theta}{2}\right).$$

Now we have two expressions for $P\left(\frac{\phi + \theta}{2}\right)$, and they must be equal.

$$\left(\cos\frac{\phi + \theta}{2}, \sin\frac{\phi + \theta}{2}\right) = \left(\frac{\cos\phi + \cos\theta}{2\cos\frac{\phi - \theta}{2}}, \frac{\sin\phi + \sin\theta}{2\cos\frac{\phi - \theta}{2}}\right). \tag{24}$$

Equating coordinates gives the following two formulas.

$$\begin{aligned} \cos\phi + \cos\theta &= 2\cos\frac{\phi + \theta}{2}\cos\frac{\phi - \theta}{2}, \\ \sin\phi + \sin\theta &= 2\sin\frac{\phi + \theta}{2}\cos\frac{\phi - \theta}{2}. \end{aligned} \tag{25}$$

Problems 5–4

Verify the following identities.

1. $\sin \phi - \sin \theta = 2 \cos \dfrac{\phi + \theta}{2} \sin \dfrac{\phi - \theta}{2}$.

2. $\cos \phi - \cos \theta = -2 \sin \dfrac{\phi + \theta}{2} \sin \dfrac{\phi - \theta}{2}$.

3. $\sin 3\theta = 3 \sin \theta - 4 \sin^3 \theta$.

4. $\cos 3\theta = 4 \cos^3 \theta - 3 \cos \theta$.

5. $\sin^2 \theta = \frac{1}{2}(1 - \cos 2\theta)$.

6. $\sin^3 \theta = \frac{1}{4}(3 \sin \theta - \sin 3\theta)$.

7. $\cos^2 \theta = \frac{1}{2}(1 + \cos 2\theta)$.

8. $\cos^3 \theta = \frac{1}{4}(\cos 3\theta + 3 \cos \theta)$.

9. $\sin \alpha \sin \beta = \frac{1}{2} \cos (\alpha - \beta) - \frac{1}{2} \cos (\alpha + \beta)$.

10. $\cos \alpha \cos \beta = \frac{1}{2} \cos (\alpha - \beta) + \frac{1}{2} \cos (\alpha + \beta)$.

11. $\sin \alpha \cos \beta = \frac{1}{2} \sin (\alpha + \beta) + \frac{1}{2} \sin (\alpha - \beta)$.

12. $2 \cos^2 \theta\, (1 + 2 \cos \theta) = 1 + 3 \cos \theta + \cos 2\theta + \cos 3\theta$.

Bonus: Show that $\sin 54° - \sin 18° = \sin 30°$. (Using the tables is not fair, as this only shows they are the same to four decimal places.)

6 *Complex Numbers*

6–1 *The Square Root of Minus One*

There are many different kinds of numbers. The numbers with which we count are 1, 2, 3, 4, 5, ..., etc. These are called the *counting numbers* or the *natural numbers*; they are used to count oranges, people, grains of sand, and so on.

If we wish to measure lengths we need other numbers like 3/4, $\sqrt{2}$, and π. We call the numbers we measure with *real numbers.*

Yet another kind of number arose from consideration of equations that could not be solved by real numbers. These numbers, the *complex numbers,* have come to play a central role both in pure mathematics and for describing many physical phenomena.

The complex numbers are built up from the real numbers and a number called i. The number i, like $\sqrt{2}$, is specified by describing how it behaves. The number $\sqrt{2}$ has the property that its square is 2; the number i has the property that its square is -1; i.e.,

$$i^2 = -1. \tag{1}$$

Clearly i is not a real number because the square of any real number is positive or zero. Equation (1) is all you have to know to be able to deal with complex numbers.

We said that the complex numbers are *built up* from the real numbers and i. This is done by the familiar operations of addition, subtraction, multiplication, and division. Thus we get numbers like $3 + i$, $7 - i$, $3i$, $4 - 2i$, and so on. In general, if a and b are any two real numbers, then $a + bi$ is a complex number (note that $7 - i$ may be written $7 + (-1)i$). The number a is called the *real part*, and the number bi is called the *imaginary part* of the complex number $a + bi$.

We can add, subtract, and multiply complex numbers almost as easily as real numbers.

Example 1. Find $(3 + 2i) + (-6 + i)$.

Solution. $(3 + 2i) + (-6 + i) = 3 + 2i - 6 + i = 3 - 6 + 2i + i = -3 + 3i$.

Example 2. Find $(7 - 3i) - (4 - 2i)$.

Solution. $(7 - 3i) - (4 - 2i) = 7 - 3i - 4 + 2i = 7 - 4 - 3i + 2i = 3 - i$.

Example 3. Find $(2 + i)(3 + 2i)$.

Solution.
$$\begin{aligned}(2 + i)(3 + 2i) = (2 + i)3 + (2 + i)2i &= 6 + 3i + 4i + 2i^2\\ &= 6 + 7i + 2i^2.\end{aligned}$$
But $i^2 = -1$, and we get $6 + 7i - 2 = 4 + 7i$.

Example 4. Find $(1 - i)(-2 + 3i)$.

Solution. $(1 - i)(-2 + 3i) = (1 - i)(-2) + (1 - i)3i = -2 + 2i + 3i - 3i^2 = -2 + 5i - 3i^2$. But since $i^2 = -1$ we get $-2 + 5i + 3 = 1 + 5i$.

These examples illustrate that to add, subtract, and multiply complex numbers you use the ordinary rules of arithmetic and the one extra fact that $i^2 = -1$.

What about division? We said that the complex numbers were built up from the real numbers and i, using addition, subtraction, multiplication, *and division*. However, it turns out that division does not get us anything new. Suppose we wish to divide $3 - 2i$ by $1 + 4i$; that is, we wish to find the number $\dfrac{3 - 2i}{1 + 4i}$. The trick here is to multiply the numerator and the denominator by $1 - 4i$. This gives

$$\frac{3 - 2i}{1 + 4i} = \frac{(3 - 2i)(1 - 4i)}{(1 + 4i)(1 - 4i)} = \frac{-5 - 14i}{17} = \frac{-5}{17} - \frac{14}{17}i.$$

The purpose of the mysterious multiplication by $\dfrac{1 - 4i}{1 - 4i}$ is to get a *real* number in the denominator; we *know* how to divide by real numbers.

Example 5. Find $\dfrac{6 + i}{1 + i}$.

Solution. Multiply numerator and denominator by $1 - i$. We get $\dfrac{6 + i}{1 + i} = \dfrac{(6 + i)(1 - i)}{(1 + i)(1 - i)} = \dfrac{7 - 5i}{2} = \dfrac{7}{2} - \dfrac{5}{2}i.$

Example 6. Find $\dfrac{2+i}{3-i}$.

Solution. Multiply numerator and denominator by $3-(-i)=3+i$. We get

$$\frac{2+i}{3-i}=\frac{(2+i)(3+i)}{(3-i)(3+i)}=\frac{5+5i}{10}=\frac{1}{2}+\frac{1}{2}i.$$

Example 7. Find $\dfrac{1}{a+bi}$.

Solution. Multiply numerator and denominator by $a-bi$ getting $\dfrac{1}{a+bi}=$

$$\frac{a-bi}{(a+bi)(a-bi)}=\frac{a-bi}{a^2+b^2}=\frac{a}{a^2+b^2}-\frac{b}{a^2+b^2}i.$$

The number $a-bi$ is called the *conjugate* of $a+bi$. If w is a complex number we denote its conjugate by $\bar{w}$. Thus $\overline{3+i}=3-i$, $\overline{2-3i}=2+3i$, $\bar{i}=-i$, $\bar{6}=6$, and so on. We have seen that to evaluate a complex fraction w/z we multiply numerator and denominator by $\bar{z}$. The notion of a conjugate is important in the study of roots of polynomial equations.

Problems 6–1

Perform the indicated operations.

1. $(1+i)+(1-i)$.

2. $(3-i)+(6+4i)$.

3. $(3+2i)-(2+3i)$.

4. $(i+5)+(2-4i)$.

5. $2i+(6+3i)$.

6. $(1+i)+(2-3i)+(i-4)$.

7. $(10+i)-(7+2i)$.

8. $(8-2i)-(3+i)$.

9. $(2-4i)-(i-4)$.

10. $(i-5)-(2i-4)$.

11. $(8-3i)-(2+i)$.

12. $13-(6-2i)$.

13. $(1+i)(2+3i)$.

14. $(2+i)(2-i)$.

15. $(1+2i)(1-2i)$.

16. $i(i+1)$.

17. $(2-4i)(7+3i)$.

18. $(4-2i)(i-1)$.

19. $(2+6i)(2-5i)$.

20. $(1+i)(2+i)(3+i)$.

21. $(1-i)(2-i)(3-i)$.

22. i^{5280}.

23. $1/i$.

24. $1/2i$.

25. $1/(1+i)$.

26. $i/(1+i)$.

27. $(2+2i)/(4+3i)$.

28. $(a+bi)/i$.

29. $(1+i)^2$.

30. $(1+i)^3$.

31. $(2-9i)/(2-3i)$.

32. $(1+2i)/(i-1)$.

33. $(1+i)/(1-i)$.

34. $(1-i)/(1+i)$.

35. $1/(3-i)$.

36. $1/(5-i)$.

37. $(i^2+1)/(i+1)$.

38. $i^2(1-i)/(i^5+i^6)$.

6–2 *Graphical Representation of Complex Numbers*

A complex number $a+bi$ is specified by the two real numbers a and b. If we associate with $a+bi$ the point (a, b) of the rectangular cartesian coordinate system we get a geometric representation of complex numbers.

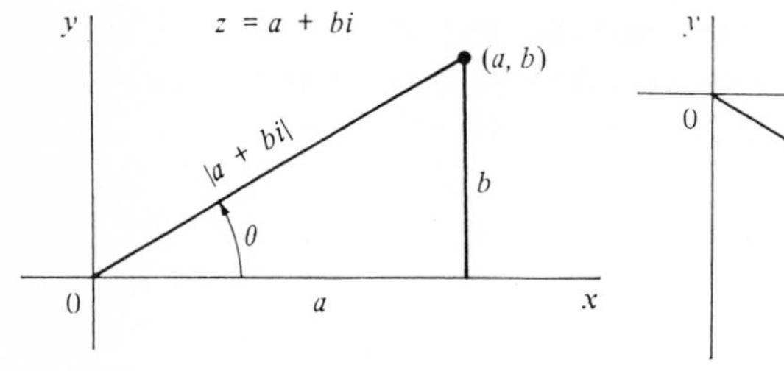

Fig. 6-1

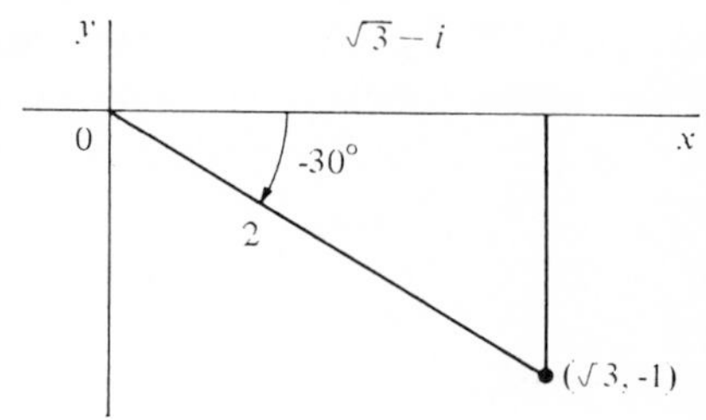

Fig. 6-2

The distance from the origin to the point (a, b) is called the *absolute value* or *modulus* of the complex number $a+bi$, and is denoted $|a+bi|$. From Fig. 6-1 and the Pythagorean theorem we have

$$|a+bi| = \sqrt{a^2+b^2}. \tag{2}$$

If θ is the angle in standard position having the line from the origin to the point (a, b) as its terminal side (Fig. 6-1) and $r = |a+bi|$,

$$a = r\cos\theta, \quad b = r\sin\theta. \tag{3}$$

Thus

$$a+bi = r(\cos\theta + i\sin\theta). \tag{4}$$

Since sin and cos are both periodic with period 360°, we have also that for any integer k,

$$a+bi = r(\cos(\theta + k360^\circ) + \sin(\theta + k360^\circ)).$$

Whenever $a+bi = r(\cos\theta + i\sin\theta)$, the expression $r(\cos\theta + i\sin\theta)$ is called a *trigonometric form* for the complex number $a+bi$. Thus

$$2(\cos(-30^\circ) + i\sin(-30^\circ)) \quad \text{and} \quad 2(\cos 330^\circ + i\sin 330^\circ)$$

are trigonometric forms for $\sqrt{3} - i$ (Fig. 6-2). The angle θ in a trigonometric form $r(\cos\theta + i\sin\theta)$ for a complex number is called an *amplitude* or *argument* of that number. Hence an argument for $1 + i$ is $45°$ or $\pi/4$ radians.

Example 1. Express $-3 + 3i$ in trigonometric form.

Solution. $r = \sqrt{(-3)^2 + 3^2} = \sqrt{9+9} = 3\sqrt{2}$. So $-3 = r\cos\theta = 3\sqrt{2}\cos\theta$ and $3 = r\sin\theta = 3\sqrt{2}\sin\theta$. Thus $\sin\theta = \sqrt{2}/2$ and $\cos\theta = -\sqrt{2}/2$. Hence $\theta = 135°$. The trigonometric form for $-3 + 3i$ is thus $3\sqrt{2}(\cos 135° + i\sin 135°)$.

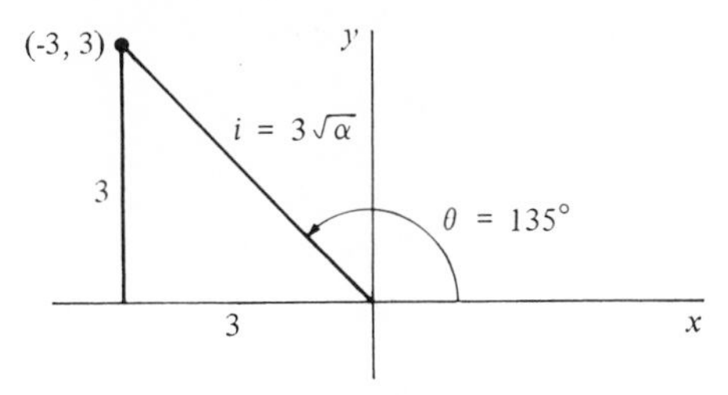

Fig. 6-3

Addition and subtraction of complex numbers have very nice interpretations in the graphical representation of complex numbers. Examine Fig. 6-4. P is the point which represents $a + bi$, and Q is the point which represents $c + di$. From the figure we see that $(a + c) + (b + d)i$ is represented by the point R. Thus, if we associate with $a + bi$ the vector $\overline{OP}$ and with $c + di$ the vector $\overline{OQ}$, we find that addition of complex numbers corresponds to vector addition as given by the parallelogram law. That is, the sum of the two vectors $\overline{OP}$ and $\overline{OQ}$ is the diagonal $\overline{OR}$ of the parallelogram $OPRQ$. Thus the sum of $a + bi$ and $c + di$ is represented by the point at the end of the diagonal $\overline{OR}$ of the parallelogram determined by $\overline{OP}$ and $\overline{OQ}$. Since $(a + bi) - (c + di) = (a + bi) + (-c - di)$, this also gives a graphical representation of subtraction of complex numbers.

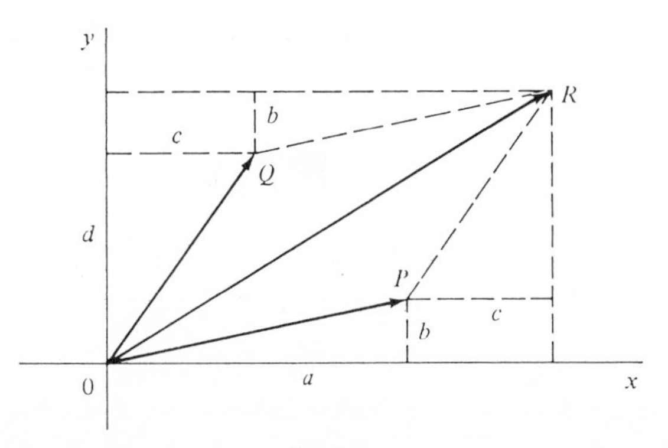

Fig. 6-4

Example 2. Find $(3-2i)+(2+i)$ and $(3-2i)-(2+i)$ graphically.

Solution. In Fig. 6-5, $(3-2i)+(2+i)$ is represented by the point B which is seen to be $(5, -1)$. Thus $(3-2i)+(2+i)=5-i$. Similarly, $(3-2i)-(2+i)=(3-2i)+(-2-i)$ is represented by the point E which is seen to be $(1, -3)$. Thus $(3-2i)-(2+i)=1-3i$.

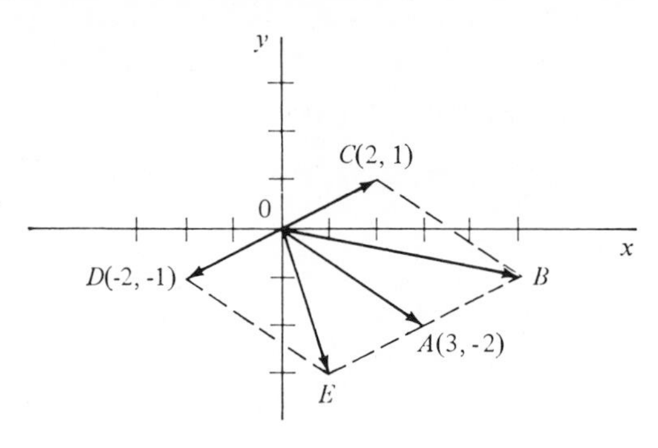

Fig. 6-5

Problems 6–2

In 1—10 plot the point that represents the given complex number and the point that represents its conjugate.

1. $1+2i$.

2. $-1+2i$.

3. 0.

4. 1.

5. $-i$.

6. $\sqrt{2}(\frac{1}{2}-\frac{1}{2}i)$.

7. $4-3i$.

8. $-4+3i$.

9. $\sqrt{3}+3i$.

10. $-\sqrt{3}-3i$.

In 11—20 write the trigonometric form of the given complex number and also of its conjugate.

11. $1+i$.

12. i.

13. 1.

14. $\sqrt{2}+i\sqrt{2}$.

15. $-1+i\sqrt{3}$.

16. $3(\cos 60° + i \sin 60°)$.

17. $3(\cos 60° - i \sin 60°)$.

18. $3(\cos 60° + i \cos 60°)$.

19. $-3 \cos(-41°) + 3i \sin(-41°)$.

20. $-2 \cos(-41°) + 2i \sin(-41°)$.

In 21—26 express each of the given complex numbers in the form $a+bi$.

21. $17(\cos 0° + i \sin 0°)$.

22. $4(\cos 135° + i \sin 135°)$.

23. $2(\cos 270° + i \sin 270°)$.

24. $5(\cos 90° + i \sin 90°)$.

25. $3(\cos(-45°) + i \sin(-45°))$.

26. $6(\cos(-765°) + i \sin(-765°))$.

In 27—30 find $z + w$ and $z - w$ both graphically and algebraically.

27. $z = 1 - i$, $w = 4 + 2i$.

28. $z = 5 - 6i$, $w = -2 + 3i$.

29. $z = 3(\cos 30° - i \sin 30°)$, $w = 2(\cos 120° + i \sin 120°)$.

30. $z = 4(\cos 240° + i \sin 240°)$, $w = -2(\cos \pi/4 + i \sin \pi/4)$.

6–3 Powers and Roots of Complex Numbers

The greatest advantage of using the trigonometric form for complex numbers is that multiplication and division become extremely simple.

Theorem 4. (a) $r_1(\cos\theta_1 + i\sin\theta_1)r_2(\cos\theta_2 + i\sin\theta_2)$
$= r_1r_2(\cos(\theta_1+\theta_2) + i\sin(\theta_1+\theta_2))$.

(b) $r_1(\cos\theta_1 + i\sin\theta_1)/r_2(\cos\theta_2 + i\sin\theta_2)$
$= (r_1/r_2)(\cos(\theta_1-\theta_2) + i\sin(\theta_1-\theta_2))$.

Proof.

$$r_1(\cos\theta_1 + i\sin\theta_1)r_2(\cos\theta_2 + i\sin\theta_2)$$
$$= r_1r_2((\cos\theta_1\cos\theta_2 - \sin\theta_1\sin\theta_2) + i(\cos\theta_1\sin\theta_2 + \cos\theta_2\sin\theta_1)).$$

But from the addition formulas (7) of Section 5–2, we have that $\cos\theta_1\cos\theta_2 - \sin\theta_1\sin\theta_2 = \cos(\theta_1+\theta_2)$, and $\cos\theta_1\sin\theta_2 + \cos\theta_2\sin\theta_1 = \sin(\theta_1+\theta_2)$. Therefore, $r_1(\cos\theta_1 + i\sin\theta_1)r_2(\cos\theta_2 + i\sin\theta_2) = r_1r_2(\cos(\theta_1+\theta_2) + i\sin(\theta_1+\theta_2))$, and (a) is proved. We now prove (b).

$$\frac{r_1(\cos\theta_1 + i\sin\theta_1)}{r_2(\cos\theta_2 + i\sin\theta_2)} = \frac{r_1(\cos\theta_1 + i\sin\theta_1)(\cos\theta_2 - i\sin\theta_2)}{r_2(\cos\theta_2 + i\sin\theta_2)(\cos\theta_2 - i\sin\theta_2)}$$
$$= \frac{r_1}{r_2}\left(\frac{(\cos\theta_1\cos\theta_2 + \sin\theta_1\sin\theta_2) + i(\cos\theta_2\sin\theta_1 - \cos\theta_1\sin\theta_2)}{\cos^2\theta_2 + \sin^2\theta_2}\right).$$

But

$$\cos\theta_1\cos\theta_2 + \sin\theta_1\sin\theta_2 = \cos(\theta_1-\theta_2)$$

and

$$\cos\theta_2\sin\theta_1 - \cos\theta_1\sin\theta_2 = \sin(\theta_1-\theta_2)$$

by equations (15) and (14) of Section 5–2. Thus $\dfrac{r_1(\cos\theta_1 + i\sin\theta_1)}{r_2(\cos\theta_2 + i\sin\theta_2)} = \dfrac{r_1}{r_2}(\cos(\theta_1-\theta_2) + i\sin(\theta_1-\theta_2))$, and (b) is proved.

Thus to multiply two complex numbers given in trigonometric form we just multiply the absolute values and add the arguments of the two numbers. To divide two such numbers we divide the absolute values and subtract the arguments.

Example 1. Find $2(\cos 60° + i \sin 60°)3(\cos 30° + i \sin 30°)$.

Solution. $2(\cos 60° + i \sin 60°)3(\cos 30° + i \sin 30°) = 6(\cos 90° + i \sin 90°) = 6i$.

Example 2. Use the trigonometric form to find $\dfrac{1+\sqrt{3}\cdot i}{1-i}$.

Solution. $1+\sqrt{3}\cdot i = 2(\cos 60° + i \sin 60°)$,

and $1 - i = \sqrt{2}(\cos(-45°) + i \sin(-45°))$.

Thus

$$\frac{1+\sqrt{3}\cdot i}{1-i} = \frac{2(\cos 60° + i \sin 60°)}{\sqrt{2}(\cos(-45°) + i \sin(-45°))} = \sqrt{2}(\cos 105° + i \sin 105°).$$

From Theorem 4(a), we have

$$[r(\cos\theta + i\sin\theta)]^2 = r(\cos\theta + i\sin\theta)r(\cos\theta + i\sin\theta) = r^2(\cos 2\theta + i\sin 2\theta),$$

$$\begin{aligned}[r(\cos\theta + i\sin\theta)]^3 &= [r(\cos\theta + i\sin\theta)]^2 r(\cos\theta + i\sin\theta)\\ &= r^2(\cos 2\theta + i\sin 2\theta)r(\cos\theta + i\sin\theta)\\ &= r^3(\cos 3\theta + i\sin 3\theta), \text{ etc.}\end{aligned}$$

Thus we see that the following very famous theorem is true.

DeMoivre's Theorem. *For any positive integer n,*

$$[r(\cos\theta + i\sin\theta)]^n = r^n(\cos n\theta + i\sin n\theta).$$

Example 3. Find $(1+i)^{10}$.

Solution.
$$\begin{aligned}(1+i)^{10} &= (\sqrt{2}(\cos 45° + i\sin 45°))^{10}\\ &= (\sqrt{2})^{10}(\cos 450° + i\sin 450°) = 32(\cos 90° + i\sin 90°)\\ &= 32i.\end{aligned}$$

If r is a positive real number, then there is precisely one positive real number s such that $s^n = r$. This number s is called the nth root of r and is denoted $\sqrt[n]{r}$. We may talk about nth roots of complex numbers in exactly the same way. However, unlike the situation for positive real numbers, any nonzero complex number has n nth roots. DeMoivre's Theorem may be used to find them.

Theorem 5. *If n is a positive integer, the nth roots of $r(\cos\theta + i\sin\theta)$ are given by*

$$\sqrt[n]{r}\left(\cos\left(\frac{\theta + k360°}{n}\right) + i\sin\left(\frac{\theta + k360°}{n}\right)\right),$$

$k = 0, 1, 2 \ldots, n-1$.

Proof. We verify that these are nth roots of $r(\cos\theta + i\sin\theta)$ by raising them to the nth power. Using DeMoivre's Theorem, we find that the nth powers are $r(\cos(\theta + k360°) + i\sin(\theta + k360°)) = r(\cos\theta + i\sin\theta)$. To show that there are no other nth roots, suppose $s(\cos\alpha + i\sin\alpha)$ is an nth root of $r(\cos\theta + i\sin\theta)$. Then, from DeMoivre's Theorem, $s^n(\cos n\alpha + i\sin n\alpha) = r(\cos\theta + i\sin\theta)$. Thus $s^n = r$, and $\cos n\alpha + i\sin n\alpha = \cos\theta + i\sin\theta$. Hence $s = \sqrt[n]{r}$, $\cos n\alpha = \cos\theta$, and $\sin n\alpha = \sin\theta$. These last two equations imply that the trigonometric points for $n\alpha$ and θ are the same. Thus $n\alpha = \theta + k360°$ for some integer k, and hence $\alpha = (\theta + k360°)/n$. Since $k = n$ gives the same trigonometric point as $k = 0$, it suffices to look at $k = 0, 1, 2, \ldots, n-1$.

Example 3. Find the cube roots of $-\sqrt{2} + i\sqrt{2}$.

Solution. $-\sqrt{2} + i\sqrt{2} = 2(\cos 135° + i\sin 135°)$. By Theorem 5, the three cube roots of $-\sqrt{2} + i\sqrt{2}$ are $\sqrt[3]{2}\left(\cos\left(\frac{135° + k360°}{3}\right) + i\sin\left(\frac{135° + k360°}{3}\right)\right)$, $k = 0, 1, 2$. These three values of k gives $\sqrt[3]{2}(\cos 45° + i\sin 45°)$ for $k = 0$, $\sqrt[3]{2}(\cos 175° + i\sin 175°)$ for $k = 1$, and $\sqrt[3]{2}(\cos 285° + i\sin 285°)$ for $k = 2$.

Example 4. Find the fifth roots of -32.

Solution. $-32 = 32(\cos 180° + i\sin 180°)$. By Theorem 5, the fifth roots of -32 are given by

$$2\left(\cos\left(\frac{180° + k360°}{5}\right) + i\sin\left(\frac{180° + k360°}{5}\right)\right), \quad k = 0, 1, 2, 3, 4.$$

These five values of k give

$$\begin{aligned}
&2(\cos 36° + i\sin 36°) \quad \text{for } k = 0,\\
&2(\cos 108° + i\sin 108°) \quad \text{for } k = 1,\\
&2(\cos 180° + i\sin 180°) = -2 \quad \text{for } k = 2,\\
&2(\cos 252° + i\sin 252°) \quad \text{for } k = 3, \text{ and}\\
&2(\cos 324° + i\sin 324°) \quad \text{for } k = 4.
\end{aligned}$$

We see from Theorem 5 that the nth roots of a complex number $r(\cos\theta + i\sin\theta)$ all have the same absolute value $\sqrt[n]{r}$, and that the arguments are the angles $\frac{\theta}{n}, \frac{\theta}{n} + \frac{360°}{n}, \frac{\theta}{n} + \frac{2(360°)}{n}, \frac{\theta}{n} + \frac{3(360°)}{n}, \ldots$, and $\frac{\theta}{n} + \frac{(n-1)360°}{n}$. Therefore, graphically the nth roots of $r(\cos\theta + i\sin\theta)$ will be equally spaced on the circle with center at the origin and radius $\sqrt[n]{r}$, with one of them having argument θ/n.

Problems 6–3

In 1—10 perform the indicated operations by using trigonometric forms. Give your answers in trigonometric form.

1. $(\cos 5^\circ + i \sin 5^\circ)(\cos 6^\circ + i \sin 6^\circ)$.

2. $\sqrt{\pi}(\cos 300^\circ + i \sin 300^\circ)\sqrt{\pi}(\cos(-300^\circ) + i \sin(-300^\circ))$.

3. $(2 + 2i\sqrt{3})(5 - 5i)$.

4. $\dfrac{3\sqrt{5} + 3i\sqrt{5}}{4 - 4i}$.

5. $\dfrac{(7 - 7i)(9 - 3i\sqrt{3})}{5i - 5}$.

6. $(\cos 181^\circ - i \sin(-1^\circ))(\cos 179^\circ + i \sin 1^\circ)$.

7. $\dfrac{(\sqrt{3} - i)(1 + i)}{(1 - i\sqrt{3})(2\sqrt{3} + 2i)}$.

8. $\dfrac{2 \cos 33^\circ + 2i \sin 33^\circ}{\cos 22^\circ + i \sin 22^\circ}$.

9. $\dfrac{7(\cos 570^\circ + i \sin 210^\circ)}{14(-\cos 421^\circ + i \sin 241^\circ)}$.

10. $(1 + i)(1 - i)(-1 - i)(-1 + i)$.

Perform the indicated operations in 11—20.

11. i^{541}.

12. i^{-541}.

13. $(\cos 1^\circ + i \sin 1^\circ)^{90}$.

14. $(\cos 1^\circ + i \sin 1^\circ)^{-90}$.

15. $\left(\dfrac{1 + i\sqrt{3}}{2}\right)^{-6}$.

16. $\dfrac{(1 - i)^5(5 + 12i)^4}{\left(-\frac{1}{2} + \frac{i}{2}\right)^6}$.

17. $[2(\cos 15^\circ + i \sin 15^\circ)]^6$.

18. $\dfrac{[3(\cos 36^\circ + i \sin 36^\circ)]^{10}}{[6(\cos 45^\circ + i \sin 45^\circ)]^8}$.

19. $(\sin 210^\circ + i \sin 300^\circ)^5$.

20. $(\cos 144^\circ - i \sin 144^\circ)^5$.

21. Find the fifth roots of 5, and graph them.

22. Find the cube roots of 3, and graph them.

23. Find the cube roots of i, and graph them.

24. Find the fourth roots of $16(\cos 120^\circ + i \sin 120^\circ)$.

25. Find the fourth roots of $-16(\cos 120^\circ + i \sin 120^\circ)$.

26. Solve $z^4 = 1$.

27. Solve $z^4 = -i$.

28. Solve $64z^6 + 1 = 0$.

7 Exponents and Logarithms

7–1 Exponential Functions

If b is a positive real number we may speak of b^n, where n is an integer, according to the scheme:

$$\begin{aligned}
&\vdots \\
b^{-3} &= \frac{1}{b \cdot b \cdot b} \\
b^{-2} &= \frac{1}{b \cdot b} \\
b^{-1} &= \frac{1}{b} \\
b^{0} &= 1 \\
b^{1} &= b \\
b^{2} &= b \cdot b \\
b^{3} &= b \cdot b \cdot b \\
&\vdots
\end{aligned} \tag{1}$$

One can readily check that the following equations, called the *laws of exponents*, are true.

$$\begin{aligned}
b^m b^n &= b^{m+n}, \\
(b^m)^n &= b^{m \cdot n}, \\
(bc)^m &= b^m c^m.
\end{aligned} \tag{2}$$

We read b^n as "b to the nth power" or simply as "b to the n." The number n is referred to as the *exponent*. The expressions b^{-1}, b^2, and b^3 are usually read as "b inverse," "b squared," and "b cubed," respectively.

It is possible to extend the use of exponents to include rational numbers simply by demanding that the laws of exponents continue to be true. For example, what would $b^{1/2}$ have to be? If the second law of exponents is to hold we must have

$$(b^{1/2})^2 = b^{1/2 \cdot 2} = b^1 = b.$$

Thus $b^{1/2}$ must be $\sqrt{b}$, the square root of b. More generally, if n is any positive integer, the laws of exponents require that

$$(b^{1/n})^n = b^{1/n \cdot n} = b^1 = b. \tag{3}$$

Thus we must define $b^{1/n}$ to be the nth root of b for the laws of exponents to hold.

Now, if m/n is any rational number we must have

$$(b^{m/n})^n = b^{m/n \cdot n} = b^m. \tag{4}$$

So if n is positive, which we can always arrange, $b^{m/n}$ must be defined as the nth root of b^m.

For example, $8^{2/3}$ is the cube root of 64, which is 4 since $4^3 = 64$. An easier way for obtaining $8^{2/3}$ is as the square of the cube root of 8, i.e., 2^2. To evaluate $8^{2/3}$ we either square and then take the cube root, or we take the cube root and then square. It is usually easier to extract the root first because then one deals with smaller numbers. To see that this always works consider $b^{m/n}$ again. If r is the nth root of b, then $r^n = b$. By the laws of exponents for integers, $(r^m)^n = r^{mn} = r^{nm} = (r^n)^m = b^m$ and so r^m is the nth root of b^m; i.e., $r^m = b^{m/n}$. What we have shown (since $r = b^{1/n}$) is that $(b^{1/n})^m = (b^m)^{1/n}$. This is necessary for the laws of exponents to hold for rational numbers. (Why?) We shall not prove that these laws are always true for this definition of $b^{m/n}$ but will content ourselves with a couple of examples.

Consider $8^{2/3} \cdot 8^{1/3}$. Now $8^{2/3} = 4$ and $8^{1/3}$ is the cube root of 8 which is 2. Thus $8^{2/3} \cdot 8^{1/3} = 4 \cdot 2 = 8 = 8^1 = 8^{2/3+1/3}$. Again, what is $64^{2/3} \cdot 64^{1/2}$? We have $64^{2/3} = 4^2 = 16$ since $4^3 = 64$, and $64^{1/2} = 8$ since $8^2 = 64$. Thus $64^{2/3} \cdot 64^{1/2} = 16 \cdot 8 = 128$. But $64^{2/3+1/2} = 64^{7/6} = 2^7$ since $2^6 = 64$. But $2^7 = 128$ and so $64^{2/3} \cdot 64^{1/2} = 64^{2/3+1/2}$.

Lastly, we may allow any real number in the exponent by approximating. What should 2^π mean? Intuitively, if we get a rational number r very close to π, then 2^r should be very close to 2^π. Now 3 is somewhat close to π so 2^π shouldn't be far from $2^3 = 8$. The rational number 3.1 or 31/10 is even closer to π so $2^{31/10}$ will be closer to 2^π. Now $2^{31/10}$ is the tenth root of 2 to the 31st power, an awesome computation. Using techniques we shall develop later, we find that $2^{31/10}$ is 8.574 to three places; i.e., $8.5735 \le 2^{31/10} \le 8.5745$.

Continuing in this manner, using the expansion $\pi = 3.14159265\ldots$, we get (to three places)

$$\begin{aligned}
2^3 &= 8,\\
2^{3.1} &= 8.574,\\
2^{3.14} &= 8.815,\\
2^{3.141} &= 8.821,\\
2^{3.1415} &= 8.824,\\
2^{3.14159} &= 8.825.
\end{aligned}$$

But $2^{3.14160}$ is 8.825 to three places also, and $3.14159 < \pi < 3.14160$. Thus 2^π must be 8.825 to three places. In a like manner we could compute 2^π to as many places as we wished (in theory). Other real exponents are done the same way. That the laws of exponents still hold is a consequence of the fact that any number can be approximated as closely as needed by a fraction.

For each positive real number b, the rule which assigns to each real number x the number b^x is a function. This gives us an important family of functions, known as the *exponential functions.*

In order to understand these functions more thoroughly we will sketch the graphs of some of them.

Example 1. Let $f(x) = 10^x$. For every x, $10^x > 0$. If x is a rational number this is obvious from the definition, and if x is any real number it can be approximated as closely as needed by rationals to show that $10^x > 0$. Thus the graph will lie entirely in the first and second quadrants. (See Fig. 7-1.) If $x < y$ then

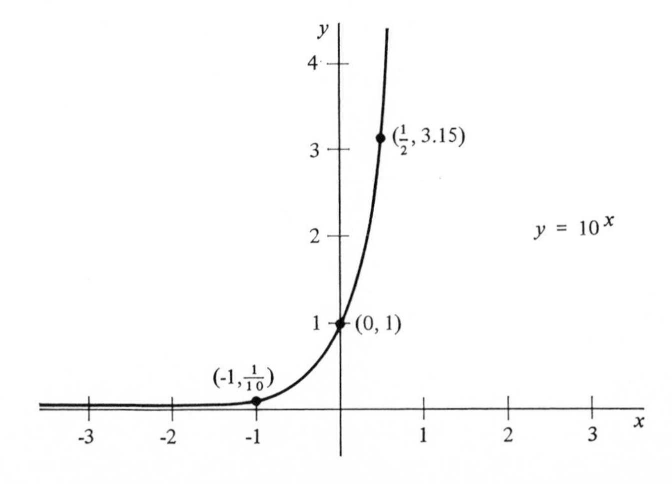

Fig. 7-1

$10^x < 10^y$. This again follows from the fact that it is true when x and y are rationals, a fact you will find easy to check.

x	-2	-1	0	1	2	3
10^x	$\frac{1}{100}$	$\frac{1}{10}$	1	10	100	1000

This information together with the table above indicates that the graph crosses the y axis at the point $y = 1$ and rises rapidly on the right. However, moving to the left of the y axis it decreases from 1 towards 0, remaining above the x axis. It is helpful for the part of the graph we will sketch to observe that $10^{1/2}$ is approximately 3.15.

As long as $b > 1$, the graph of $y = b^x$ will appear similar to this one.

Example 2. $f(x) = 2^x$. The general observations made for 10^x are still valid here. (See Fig. 7-2.)

x	-3	-2	-1	0	1	2	3	4
2^x	$\frac{1}{8}$	$\frac{1}{4}$	$\frac{1}{2}$	1	2	4	8	16

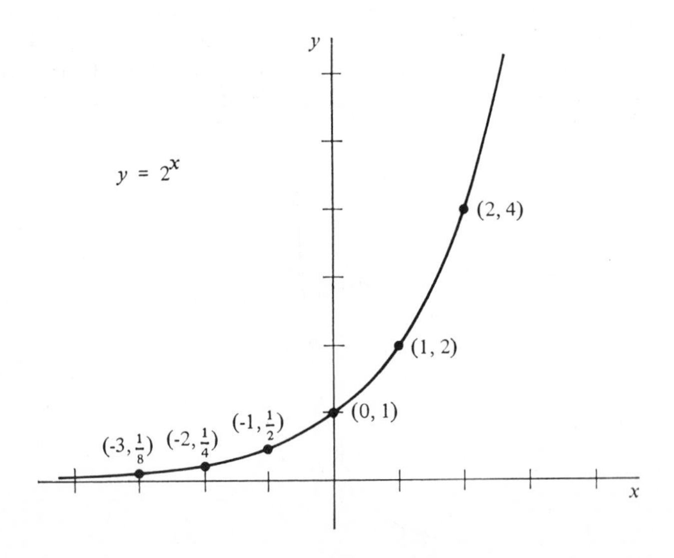

Fig. 7-2

For $b = 1$, $b^x = 1$ for all x, giving the straight line $y = 1$.

For $0 < b < 1$, $x < y$ implies $b^x > b^y$; i.e., the inequality is reversed. This changes the appearance of the graph drastically.

Example 3. $f(x) = (1/2)^x$. (Since $1/2 = 2^{-1}$, $(1/2)^x = (2^{-1})^x = 2^{-1 \cdot x} = 2^{-x}$, and this function is usually written in the form, $f(x) = 2^{-x}$.)

x	-3	-2	-1	0	1	2	3
2^{-x}	8	4	2	1	$\frac{1}{2}$	$\frac{1}{4}$	$\frac{1}{8}$

The resulting graph (Fig. 7-3) is simply a reflection about the y axis of the graph for $y = 2^x$.

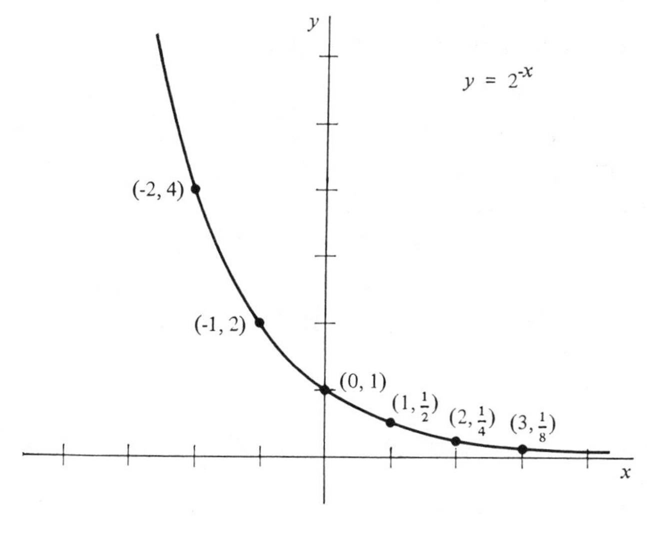

Fig. 7-3

The number b is called the *base* for the exponential function $y = b^x$. One of the most common bases is 10. The other is a number called e which defies elementary description but arises frequently and naturally in calculus. (The numbers $(1 + 1/2)^2$, $(1 + 1/3)^3$, $(1 + 1/4)^4$, $(1 + 1/5)^5, \ldots$ approximate e arbitrarily closely; e.g., if you want a number which approximates e with an error of at most 0.0001, then you can find an integer n such that $(1 + 1/n)^n$ does the trick.) Its decimal expansion to 5 places is 2.71828 . . . . The graph of e^x is very similar to that of 2^x, shown in Fig. 7-2.

Problems 7–1

1. Sketch graphs of $y=3^x$ and $y=3^{-x}$.

2. Sketch graphs of $y=3(2^x)$ and $y=-2^x$.

3. Using the graph for $y=2^x$ in Fig. 7-2, find approximate values for each of the following:
   a) $2^{1/4}$, b) $2^{\pi/4}$, c) $2^{-1/2}$, d) $2^{\sqrt{3}/2}$.

4. Sketch a graph of $y=(3/2)^x$, and find approximate values for each of the following:
   a) $(3/2)^{\sqrt{2}}$, b) $(3/2)^{1/2}$, c) $(3/2)^{-1/4}$.

5. Sketch graphs for $y=e^x$ and $y=e^{-x}$.

6. Sketch graphs for $y=2^x3^x$ and $y=2^{3x}$.

7. If f is an exponential function, show that $f(x+y)=f(x)f(y)$ for all x and y.

8. If f is an exponential function, show that $f(xy)=f(x)^y$ for all x and y.

9. Let f and g be exponential functions. Let k be the function defined by $k(x)=f(x)g(x)$. Show that k is an exponential function.

10. Let f and g be exponential functions. Let k be the function defined by $k(x)=f(x)/g(x)$. Show that k is an exponential function.

11. Which of the following are exponential functions? For those which are exponential functions, find the number b for which $f(x)=b^x$.
    a) $f(x)=2^x3^x$, b) $f(x)=2^{3x}$,
    c) $f(x)=1$, d) $f(x)=2$.

12. Which of the following are exponential functions? For those which are exponential functions, find the number b for which $f(x)=b^x$.
    a) $f(x)=2^{x^2}$, b) $f(x)=2^{4x}3^{6x}$,
    c) $f(x)=2^{6x}3^{-4x}$, d) $f(x)=-2^x$.

13. What exponential functions contain the following points in their graphs?
    a) $(2, 4)$, b) $(2, -4)$, c) $(0, 1)$.

14. What exponential functions contain the following points in their graphs?
    a) $(-3, 6)$, b) $(3, 6)$, c) $(1, 0)$.

15. The amount of radioactivity remaining in a substance after t days is given by ka^t, where k is the number of units of radioactivity present at the beginning and a is the percentage of radioactivity remaining after one day. (This percentage seems to depend only on the substance involved, not on how radioactive it is at the time or on how much of the substance is present.) Suppose you have a substance which loses ten percent of its radiation each day and which begins with 50 units of radiation. The amount of radiation at the beginning of the nth day will then be $50\left(\frac{90}{100}\right)^n$. The *half-life* of the substance is the number of days it

takes to get down to one-half of the original units, i.e., the n for which $50\left(\frac{90}{100}\right)^n = 50\left(\frac{1}{2}\right)$. Since the 50's cancel this is seen to be independent of the amount of radiation involved, and we have the equation $\left(\frac{9}{10}\right)^n = \frac{1}{2}$.

a) Sketch a graph for the equation $f(x) = \left(\frac{9}{10}\right)^x$.

b) Estimate from the graph for what value of x, $\left(\frac{9}{10}\right)^x = \frac{1}{2}$; i.e., estimate the half-life of the substance.

16. Suppose you have a substance which loses five percent of its radiation each day. Use the methods of Problem 15 to estimate the half-life of this substance.

7–2 Inverse Functions

Consider the function $f(x) = x + 3$. It takes a number and adds 3 to it. To "undo" this function we must subtract 3; that is, the "undoing" function is $g(x) = x - 3$. The relation between f and g is provided by the equalities

$$g(f(x)) = g(x + 3) = (x + 3) - 3 = x,$$
$$f(g(x)) = f(x - 3) = (x - 3) + 3 = x.$$

Thus $f(x)$ is the number such that $g(f(x)) = x$ and $g(x)$ is the number such that $f(g(x)) = x$. We say that g is the *inverse* of f and write $g = f^{-1}$ (read "g equals f inverse"). Similarly, we say that f is the inverse of g and write $f = g^{-1}$.

Many functions arise as the inverses of other functions. An example of this is the square root which arises from the function $f(x) = x^2$. The square root of y solves the equation $f(?) = y$. Let $g(x) = \sqrt{x}$. Then

$$f(g(x)) = (\sqrt{x})^2 = x,$$
$$g(f(x)) = \sqrt{x^2} = x.$$

We have been a little careless here. First of all, not every number has a square root. The domain of $\sqrt{x}$ is the nonnegative numbers. Secondly, $\sqrt{x^2}$ is not x but $|x|$. Remember that $\sqrt{y}$ means the *nonnegative* square root of y. In order to consider the function $\sqrt{x}$ as the inverse of x^2 we must restrict the domain of x^2 to the nonnegative numbers. With this restriction both $\sqrt{x}$ and x^2 have domain and range equal to the set of nonnegative numbers, and the equalities $f(g(x)) = x$ and $g(f(x)) = x$ are true.

We make precise the notion of inverse functions.

Definition. Let f be a function. A function g is the *inverse* of f if g satisfies:

1) $f(g(x)) = x$ for all x in the domain of g,
2) $g(f(x)) = x$ for all x in the domain of f.

Example 1. $f(x) = 5x$, $g(x) = \frac{1}{5}x$. We have $f(g(x)) = f\left(\frac{1}{5}x\right) = 5\left(\frac{1}{5}x\right) = x$ and $g(f(x)) = g(5x) = \frac{1}{5}(5x) = x$ for every real number x.

Example 2. $f(x) = \frac{1}{1+x}$. Can we find an inverse for f? If g were an inverse of f, then by the first property of inverse functions we would have $f(g(x)) = x$ for all x in the domain of g. Hence we must find a function g satisfying

$$\frac{1}{1+g(x)} = x,$$

for x in the domain of g. Solving this for $g(x)$ we obtain

$$g(x) = \frac{1}{x} - 1 = \frac{1-x}{x}.$$

Thus the only function that could be an inverse of f is $g(x) = \frac{1-x}{x}$, on some domain. The set of real numbers on which g is defined consists of all nonzero real numbers. We check that g with this domain is the inverse of f. In fact,

$$f(g(x)) = f\left(\frac{1-x}{x}\right) = \frac{1}{1+\dfrac{1-x}{x}} = x,$$

$$g(f(x)) = g\left(\frac{1}{1+x}\right) = \frac{1-\dfrac{1}{1+x}}{\dfrac{1}{1+x}} = x.$$

The first equation is true for every nonzero x. The second holds for all $x \neq -1$ which is the domain of f.

When does a function f have an inverse? The key to this question lies in the notion of a 1–1 function (read "one-to-one").

Definition. A function f is 1–1 if $f(x) \neq f(y)$ for any two distinct numbers x and y in the domain of f.

Example 1. $f(x) = 3x - 5$ is a 1–1 function with domain the set of real numbers. In fact, if $f(x) = f(y)$, then $3x - 5 = 3y - 5$ so $3x = 3y$ and $x = y$ (and so x and y are not *distinct*).

Example 2. $f(x) = \dfrac{1}{1+x}$ is a 1-1 function with domain the set of real numbers different from -1. Again, if $\dfrac{1}{1+x} = \dfrac{1}{1+y}$, then $1 + x = 1 + y$ and thus $x = y$.

Example 3. $f(x) = x^2$ is *not* a 1-1 function if its domain is taken to be the set of real numbers. It *is* a 1-1 function on the domain of nonnegative real numbers. Indeed $f(2) = 4 = f(-2)$ which shows that f is not 1-1 on the set of real numbers. However, if x and y are nonnegative and $f(x) = f(y)$, then $x^2 = y^2$ and so $x^2 - y^2 = 0$. Factoring this we get $(x - y)(x + y) = 0$ and so either $x - y = 0$ or $x + y = 0$. The former equality says that $x = y$; the latter can only hold if $x = y = 0$ (why?). In either event $x = y$.

The connection between 1-1 functions and functions with inverses is provided by:

Theorem 1. *A function f has an inverse if and only if it is* 1-1.

Proof. There are two things to prove. First, suppose f has an inverse g; we must show that f is 1-1. If $f(x) = f(y)$, then $g(f(x)) = g(f(y))$ and so $x = y$. Thus f is 1-1.

On the other hand, suppose f is 1-1. We must find an inverse g for f. We take the domain of g to be the image of f. If z is in the image of f, then $f(x) = z$ for some x in the domain of f. This x is unique because if $f(y) = z = f(x)$ then, since f is 1-1, we have $x = y$. Define $g(z)$ to be x. Then $f(g(z)) = f(x) = z$ for all z in the domain of g. Moreover, since $f(x) = z$ we have $g(f(x)) = g(z) = x$ for all x in the domain of f. Thus g is the inverse of f.

The graph of the inverse of f is closely related to the graph of f. We get the graph of f by plotting all points of the form (x, y), where x is in the domain of f and $y = f(x)$. Suppose $g = f^{-1}$. To say that $y = f(x)$ is the same as saying that $g(y) = x$, for if $y = f(x)$, then $g(y) = g(f(x)) = x$ and if $x = g(y)$ then $f(x) = f(g(y)) = y$. Thus if (x, y) is in the graph of f, then (y, x) is in the graph of g and conversely. We get the graph of g from the graph of f by interchanging the roles of the x and y coordinates.

Consider the graph of $f(x) = x^2$, $x \geq 0$, depicted in Fig. 7-4. To the gentleman standing on the y axis and looking out at us, the y axis appears to be the x axis and vice-versa. Where we see (x, y) he sees (y, x). He thinks he is looking at the graph of $g(x) = \sqrt{x}$. Indeed, he is seeing the graph of the equation $y = x^2$ which is the same as $x = \sqrt{y}$. He sees the graph in Fig. 7-5, which (to him) is the graph of $g(x) = \sqrt{x}$.

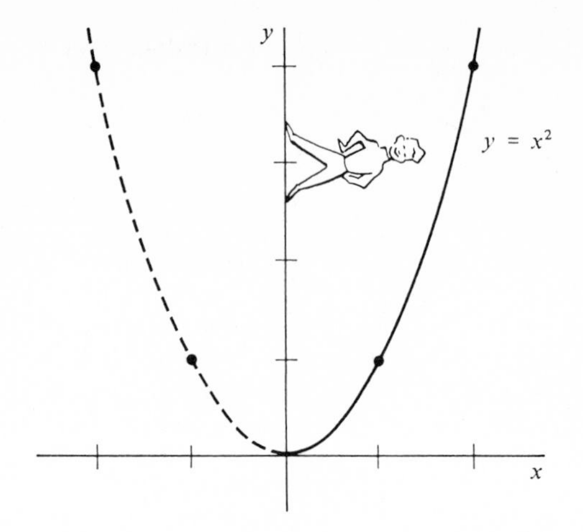

Fig. 7-4

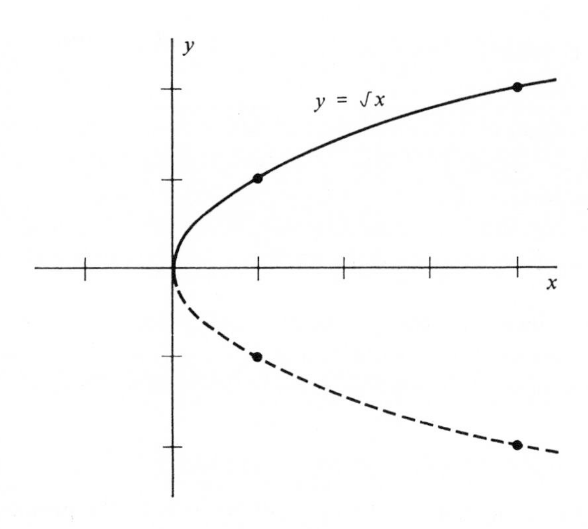

Fig. 7-5

Problems 7–2

In 1—14 find inverses for the functions and specify the domains.

1. $f(x) = x - 7.$

2. $f(x) = x + 15.$

3. $f(x) = 2x - 1.$

4. $f(x) = 2(x - 1).$

5. $f(x) = x^2 + 3, x \geq 0.$

6. $f(x) = x^2 - 4, x \geq 0.$

7. $f(x) = (x + 3)^2, x \geq -3.$

8. $f(x) = 1 - x.$

9. $f(x) = 1/x$.

10. $f(x) = 1/(x + 3)$.

11. $f(x) = 3/(x + 1)$.

12. $f(x) = 3/(2x - 5)$.

13. $f(x) = 5/(1 - 2x)$.

14. $f(x) = 1/x^2$, $x > 0$.

Determine from the graphs in 15—20 whether the functions have inverses and, if so, sketch the graph of the inverse function.

15.

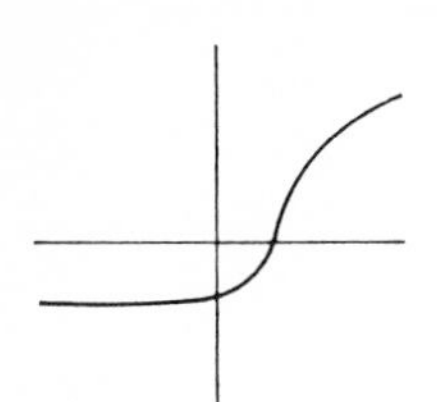

16.

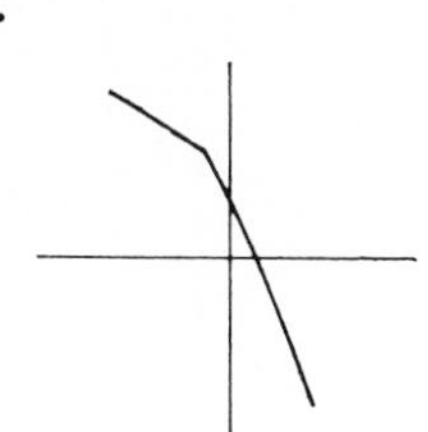

17.

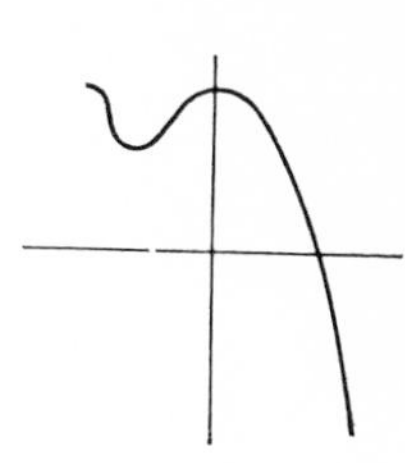

18.

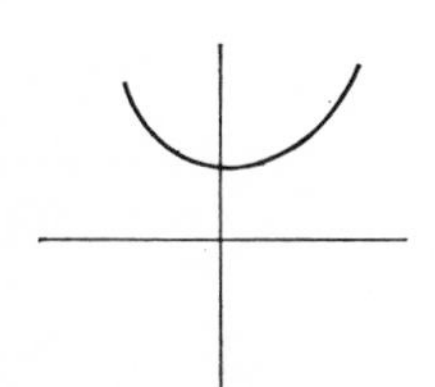

19.

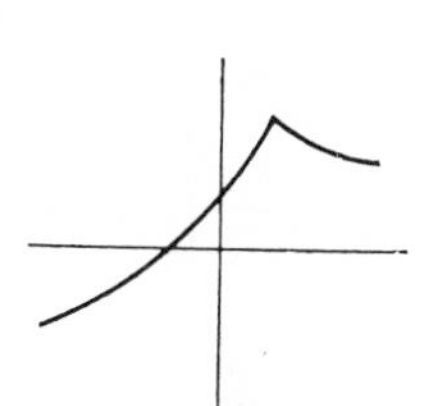

20.

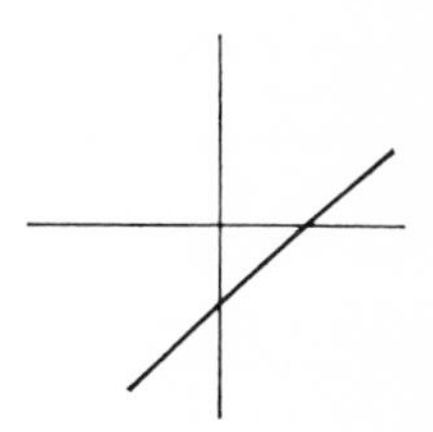

7–3 *Logarithmic Functions*

Suppose b is a positive real number. Then we can talk about b^x for any real number x. Thus the function $f(x) = b^x$ has domain the set of all real numbers, and as we have seen earlier, the range is the set of positive real numbers. If $b \neq 1$, the image of f is the set of all positive real numbers. If $b = 1$, $f(x) = 1$ for all x and the function f is uninteresting. So suppose that $b \neq 1$. Then if $x_1 \neq x_2$, $b^{x_1} \neq b^{x_2}$. In fact, if $b > 1$, then $b^{x_1} > b^{x_2}$ when $x_1 > x_2$; and if $b < 1$, $b^{x_1} < b^{x_2}$ if $x_1 > x_2$. This just expresses the fact that f is one-to-one. Therefore, for $b \neq 1$, the function $f(x) = b^x$ has an inverse. (Keep in mind that $b > 0$.) The domain of the inverse of f is the set of positive real numbers. Its image is the set of all real numbers. One of the most important cases is when $b = 10$. The graph of $f(x) = 10^x$ appears in Fig. 7-6.

Reflecting the graph of $f(x) = 10^x$ about the line $y = x$ we obtain the graph of the inverse of f, shown in Fig. 7-7.

What does the inverse of f do to a positive real number x? It assigns to it the number y such that $10^y = x$. This number is called the *logarithm* of x to the *base* 10. More generally, the inverse of the function f defined by $f(x) = b^x$ ($b > 0$, $b \neq 1$) is denoted $\log_b$ and called the *logarithm* to the *base* b. The

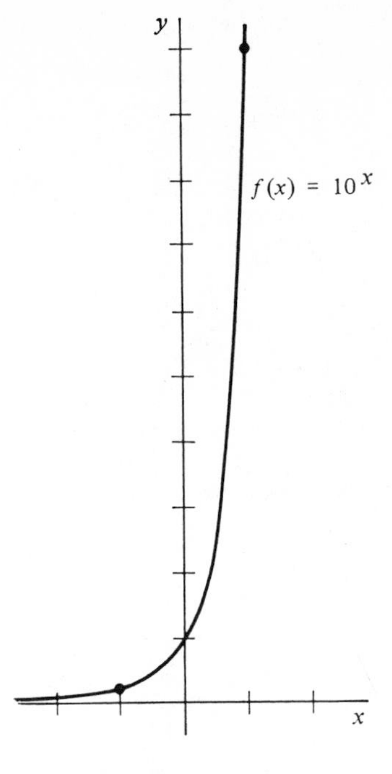

Fig. 7-6

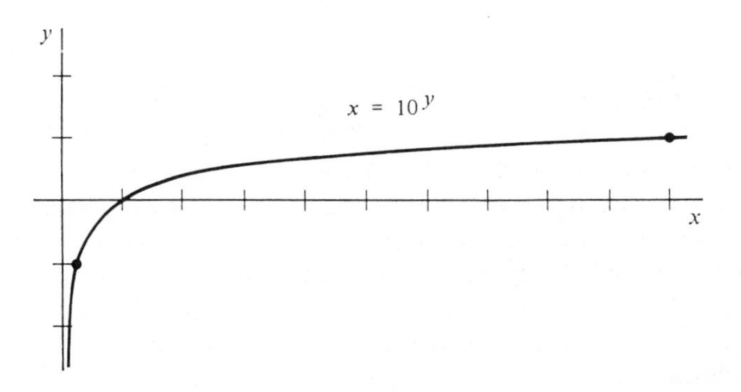

Fig. 7-7

domain of $\log_b$ is the set of positive real numbers. The image is the set of all real numbers.

Since the function $g(y) = \log_b y$ is the inverse of the function $f(x) = b^x$ we have the following characteristic properties of $\log_b$:

$$\begin{aligned} \log_b b^x &= x, \\ b^{\log_b x} &= x. \end{aligned} \tag{5}$$

These properties enable us to work with logs using our knowledge of exponents. Thus $\log_{10} 100 = \log_{10} 10^2 = 2$, $\log_b 1 = \log_b b^0 = 0$. If $y = \log_b x$, then $b^y = b^{\log_b x} = x$. Conversely, if $b^y = x$, then $y = \log_b b^y = \log_b x$. Thus the equations

$$\begin{aligned} y &= \log_b x, \\ b^y &= x \end{aligned} \tag{6}$$

say the same thing. Hence any statement about logs may be translated to a statement about exponents.

The laws of exponents give us corresponding properties of logarithms. For example, $\log_b xy = \log_b x + \log_b y$. This is proved as follows: $x = b^{\log_b x}$ and $y = b^{\log_b y}$. Thus $xy = (b^{\log_b x})(b^{\log_b y}) = b^{\log_b x + \log_b y}$. But $xy = b^{\log_b xy}$. By the definition of $\log_b$, $\log_b xy = \log_b x + \log_b y$. We list in the theorem below the basic properties of logarithms.

Theorem 2. (a) $\log_b b^x = x$.
(b) $b^{\log_b x} = x$.
(c) $\log_b xy = \log_b x + \log_b y$.
(d) $\log_b x/y = \log_b x - \log_b y$.
(e) $\log_b x^y = y \log_b x$.
(f) $\log_b x = \dfrac{\log_a x}{\log_a b}$.

Proof. Parts (a) and (b) are just equations (5), and we just proved part (c). Part (d) is proved similarly. To prove (e) we require that $x^y = b^{y \log_b x}$. But $b^{y \log_b x} = (b^{\log_b x})^y = x^y$. Part (f) shows the relation between the logarithms of x to different bases. To prove it, take $\log_a$ of both sides of $x = b^{\log_b x}$. We get $\log_a x = \log_a (b^{\log_b x})$. Applying (e) this becomes $\log_a x = (\log_b x)(\log_a b)$, so that $\log_b x = \log_a x / \log_a b$.

The laws of logarithms given above in Theorem 2 are used to manipulate expressions involving logarithms. We illustrate with some examples.

Example 1. Solve $\log_b x = \log_b \dfrac{21}{11} + \log_b \dfrac{22}{7} - \log_b 6$ for x.

Solution. $\log_b x = \log_b \left(\dfrac{21}{11} \cdot \dfrac{22}{7} \cdot \dfrac{1}{6}\right) = \log_b 1$. Thus $x = 1$.

Example 2. If $\log_b y = 3x - \log_b x$, express y as a function of x.

Solution. $\log_b y + \log_b x = 3x = \log_b xy$. Thus $xy = b^{3x}$, so $y = x^{-1} b^{3x}$.

Example 3. Simplify $\log_b (b/\sqrt{x}) - \log_b \sqrt{x/b}$.

Solution. $\log_b (b/\sqrt{x}) - \log_b \sqrt{x/b} = \log_b \left(\dfrac{b}{\sqrt{x}} \cdot \dfrac{\sqrt{b}}{\sqrt{x}}\right) = \log_b \dfrac{b^{3/2}}{x} = \log_b b^{3/2}$ $- \log_b x = 3/2 - \log_b x$.

Problems 7–3

Find the value of each of the expressions in 1—8.

1. $\log_b b$.

2. $\log_3 9$.

3. $\log_a \sqrt{a}$.

4. $\log_{10} (.01)$.

5. $\log_6 (1/6)$.

6. $\log_b b^b$.

7. $\log_b 1$.

8. $\log_3 9^2$.

Solve for x in 9—15.

9. $\log_b x = 0$.

10. $3^{\log_3 x} = 5$.

11. $\log_b b^4 = x + \log_b b^2$.

12. $x^{\log_x x} = 2$.

13. $\log_x 3^2 = 2$.

14. $\log_5 x = -2$.

15. $4^{\log_x 7} = 7$.

Simplify the expressions in 16—21.

16. $\log_b x^2 - \log_b \sqrt[3]{x}$.

17. $\log_b (x^2 - 1) - \log_b (x - 1)^2$.

18. $\log_b (2x + 3) + \log_b (2x - 3)$.

19. $\log_b \sqrt{\dfrac{x + y}{x - y}} + \log_b \sqrt{x - y}$.

20. $\log_b \dfrac{(x - y)^r}{(x - z)^s} + s \log_b (x - z)$.

21. $\log_b (x^3 + x^2 - 2x) - \log_b (x - 1) - \log_b (x + 2)$.

22. Show that $\log_{b^2} a = \dfrac{1}{2} \log_b a$.

23. Show that $(\log_a b^2 - \log_a b) \log_b a = 1$.

24. Show that $\log_{1/a} b = \log_a (1/b)$.

25. Show that $a^{(\log_b c)(\log_b a)} = c^{(\log_b a)^2}$.

7–4 Computations with Logarithms

There are two logarithmic functions of special interest, $\log_{10}$ and $\log_e$. Logarithms to the base 10 are called *common logarithms*, and $\log_{10} x$ is frequently written simply as $\log x$. Logarithms to the base 10 are helpful in simplifying long numerical computations, but the use of desk calculators and computing machines has almost removed the need to do routine numerical computations by hand. However, we will briefly indicate how to use logarithms in such computations to increase your understanding of logarithms, and to provide for the day you can't find a computer but can find a table of logarithms.

To find $\log N$, we must solve the equation $10^x = N$ for x. If N is an integral power of 10, it is easy. That is, $\log 10 = 1$, $\log 100 = 2$, $\log \frac{1}{10} = -1$, etc. How does one solve $10^x = 69$? Because we use the decimal notation in writing numbers, to find the logarithm (to the base 10) of any number, it suffices to know the logarithm of numbers between 1 and 10. Any number $N > 0$ can be written in the form $n \cdot 10^c$, where $1 \leq n < 10$ and c is an integer. For example, $69 = (6.9) \cdot 10^1$, $5280 = (5.280) \cdot 10^3$, $0.0312 = (3.12) \cdot 10^{-2}$, and $0.0001217 = (1.217) \cdot 10^{-4}$. If $N = n \cdot 10^c$ with $1 \leq n < 10$ and c is an integer, then $\log N = \log(n \cdot 10^c) = \log n + \log 10^c = \log n + c \log 10 = \log n + c$. So we know $\log N$ if we know $\log n$ and c. The log of any positive N is the log of a number between 1 and 10 plus an integer c. To find c, just write $N = n \cdot 10^c$ where $1 \leq n < 10$, which is easy to do if N is given in decimal form. But how do we find logs of numbers $1 \leq n < 10$? We look them up in tables. Table I on pages 158–159 is a table of common logarithms, that is, a table of logarithms to the base 10.

To find the log of a number N between one and 10 (given to three significant digits, say), find the first two digits of N in the first column of the table, and the third digit of N in the top row of the table. The number at the intersection of the row and column determined by these two entries is the log of N to four places. For example, $\log 1.16$ is 0.0645; $\log 5.33$ is 0.7267; $\log 9.89$ is 0.9952. Keep in mind that $\log 9.89$, for example, is not exactly 0.9952, but 0.9952 is accurate to 4 places. We will write $\log 9.89 = 0.9952$, however, this being customary practice.

To find $\log 5280$, we write $5280 = (5.28) \cdot 10^3$. Thus $\log 5280 = \log 5.28 + 3$. From our table we get $\log 5.28 = 0.7226$. Thus $\log 5280 = 3.7226$.

To find $\log 0.00535$ we write $0.00535 = (5.35) \cdot 10^{-3}$. From our table $\log 5.35 = 0.7284$, so $\log 0.00535 = 0.7284 - 3 = -2.2716$.

For any $N > 0$, $\log N$ may be written in the form $\log N = m + c$, where $0 \leq m < 1$ and c is an integer. The number m is called the *mantissa*, and c the *characteristic*, of $\log N$. The mantissa of $\log 0.00535$ is 0.7284, and the characteristic is -3. The mantissa of $\log 10$ is 0.0000 and the characteristic is 1. When we write $N = n \cdot 10^c$ with $1 \leq n < 10$ and c is an integer, we say that N is written in *scientific notation*. When we write $\log N = m + c$ with $0 \leq m < 1$ and c an integer, we say that $\log N$ is written in *standard form*. Our table is a table of mantissas.

We know now how to find the log of a number. Given $\log N$, how do we find N? We use our table backwards. To illustrate, let's find N given that $\log N = 3.0682$. First write $\log N$ in standard form: $\log N = 0.0682 + 3$. Find 0.0682 in the table. We see that it is $\log 1.17$. So $\log N = \log 1.17 + 3$. But $3 = \log 10^3$. Hence $\log N = \log 1.17 + \log 10^3 = \log((1.17) \cdot 10^3)$, and thus $N = (1.17) \cdot 10^3 = 1170$. In practice, we would not go to this much trouble. $\operatorname{Log} N = 0.0682 + 3$, and our table tells us that $0.0682 = \log 1.17$. The 3 tells us to move the decimal 3 places to the right in 1.17 to get N. That is, $N = 1170$.

Another example is in order. Let's find N when $\log N = -3.2668$. First write this in standard form: $\text{Log } N = -3.2668 = 0.7332 - 4$. From our table $0.7332 = \log 5.41$. Move the decimal four places to the left in 5.41 to get N. That is, $N = 0.000541$. This works because $\log N = \log 5.41 - 4 = \log 5.41 - \log 10^4 = \log (5.41/10^4) = \log 0.000541$.

From our table we can immediately find log 5.14 and the number whose log is 0.7110. But log 5.143 and the number whose log is 0.7112 are not in the table. The simplest way to get an approximation of log 5.143 is to round off 5.143 to 3 significant digits, that is, to 5.14. We would round off 5.146 to 5.15. When rounding off a number whose last significant digit is 5, we have adopted the convention that the rounded number end in an even digit. That is, 5.145 would be rounded to 5.14, and 5.135 would be rounded to 5.14. If we want to find N when $\log N = 0.7112$, the simplest approximation is to find the number N whose log is the number in the table nearest to 0.7112. In this case $N = 5.14$. If $\log N = 0.9937$, $N = 9.86$ by this scheme, and if $\log N = 0.9928$, $N = 9.84$.

Now, let's see how logs are used in computation. Here is a scheme to multiply two (positive) numbers. Suppose we want to find $N = xy$. Since we have a table of logs, we will know what N is if we know what $\log N$ is. So we'll find $\log N$. But $\log N = \log xy = \log x + \log y$. So look up $\log x$ and $\log y$ in a table and add them to get $\log N$. Then the table tells us what N is. The problem of multiplying x and y has been reduced to one of adding $\log x$ and $\log y$ and using a table. That is the general idea. Fancier things can be done, such as taking roots. A couple of examples will illuminate matters.

Example 1. Calculate $N = \dfrac{(501)(109)}{(996)}$.

Solution. $\dfrac{(501)(109)}{(996)} = \dfrac{(5.01)(1.09)(10^2)}{(9.96)}$.

$\log N = \log 5.01 + \log 1.09 + 2 - \log 9.96 = 0.6998 + 0.0374 + 2 - 0.9983 = 0.7389 + 1$. From our table 5.48 is the number whose log is closest to 0.7389. Thus $N = 54.8$.

Example 2. Find $N = \sqrt[4]{9830}$.

Solution.

$$\log N = \log (9830)^{1/4} = \frac{\log 9830}{4} = \frac{(\log 9.83) + 3}{4} = \frac{3.9926}{4} = 0.9982.$$

Thus $N = 9.96$.

Example 3. Find $N = \dfrac{(333)(0.01778)^{1/2}}{(22.2)(0.1125)^{11}}$.

Solution.

$$\begin{aligned}\log N &= \log 333 + \tfrac{1}{2} \log 0.01778 - \log 22.2 - 11 \log 0.1125\\ &= \log 3.33 + 2 + \tfrac{1}{2}(\log 1.778 - 2) - (\log 2.22 + 1) - 11(\log 1.125 - 1).\end{aligned}$$

Round 1.778 to 1.78 and 1.125 to 1.12. We get $\log N = 0.5224 + 2 + \frac{1}{2}(0.2504 - 2) - (0.3464 + 1) - 11(0.0492 - 1) = 0.5224 + 0.1252 - 0.3464 - 0.5312 + 11 = -0.2300 + 11 = 0.770 + 10$. To three digits, 5.89 is the number whose log is 0.7700. Thus $N = 58{,}900{,}000{,}000$.

A more accurate way to approximate the logarithm of a number not listed in the table is by *linear interpolation*, which was discussed in Section 4–4. Let's illustrate it here. The principles are the same. Suppose we want to find $\log 5.315$. Up to now, we would round 5.315 to 5.32 and approximate $\log 5.315$ by $\log 5.32 = 0.7259$, which we can get from our table of logs. A more accurate approximation may be obtained as follows: $\log 5.31 = 0.7251$ and $\log 5.32 = 0.7259$. If the function log were linear, then $\log 5.315$ would be halfway between $\log 5.31$ and $\log 5.32$. The function log is not linear, but treating it as if it were linear between points as close together as 5.31 and 5.32 yields good approximations. Thus a good approximation to $\log 5.315$ is halfway between $\log 5.31 = 0.7251$ and $\log 5.32 = 0.7259$. Thus $\log 5.315$ is about 0.72545, which we round to $\log 5.315 = 0.7254$. Similarly, $\log 5.312$ is about 0.2 the way from $\log 5.31 = 0.7251$ to $\log 5.32 = 0.7259$. Thus $\log 5.312$ is about $0.7251 + 0.2(0.0008) = 0.72516$, or 0.7252. One can easily derive a formula to use in such interpolations, but in this case the principle is easier to remember than the formula.

Suppose now that we know that $\log N = 0.5698$. From the log table we find that $\log 3.71 = 0.5694$ and $\log 3.72 = 0.5705$. We then estimate that N is 4/11 of the way from 3.71 to 3.72, which to three places is 3.714. Similarly, if $\log N = 0.5699$, we would estimate that N is 5/11 of the way from 3.71 to 3.72, or 3.716.

Let's redo Example 3, interpolating at the appropriate places.

Example 4. Find $N = \dfrac{(333)(0.01778)^{1/2}}{(22.2)(0.1125)^{11}}$.

Solution.

$$\begin{aligned}\log N &= \log 3.33 + 2 + \tfrac{1}{2}\log(1.778 - 2) - (\log 2.22 + 1) - 11\log(1.125 - 1)\\ &= 0.5224 + 2 + \tfrac{1}{2}(0.2499 - 2) - (0.3464 + 1) - 11(0.0512 - 1)\\ &= -0.2587 + 11 = 0.7413 + 10.\end{aligned}$$

Thus $N = 55{,}110{,}000{,}000$.

Using our table of common logarithms we can find $\log_b N$ for any base b. We simply use Theorem 2 (f), which asserts $\log_b N = \dfrac{\log N}{\log b}$. For example, to solve $5^x = 42$, we have $x = \log_5 42 = \dfrac{\log 42}{\log 5} = \dfrac{1.6232}{0.6990} = 2.3222$.

Problems 7–4

1. Write the following numbers in scientific notation.
a) 69, b) 696, c) 0.001, d) 10^3, e) -10^{-3}.

2. Write the following numbers in scientific notation.
a) 5.2314, b) 0.2314, c) $(55.2) \cdot 100^2$, d) 1, e) -235.6.

3. Write the following logarithms in standard form.
a) log 52.1, b) log 5.21, c) log 0.521, d) $\log((8.11) \cdot 10^{-6})$.

4. Write the following logarithms in standard form.
a) $\log \pi$, b) $\log 10^{\pi}$, c) $\log 10^{-2}$, d) log 5280, e) log 0.0001011.

Use the table of common logarithms and linear interpolation as necessary to make the computations in 5—15.

5. $\dfrac{(468)(21.5)}{(3680)(0.00119)}$.

6. $\dfrac{81}{\sqrt[5]{31}}$.

7. 2^{50}.

8. $\left(\dfrac{99}{100}\right)^{69}$.

9. $3^{\sqrt{2}}$.

10. $\sqrt[100]{1000}$.

11. $\log_3 96$.

12. $\log_{14} (715)^{2/3}$.

13. $\log_e 9e^{10}$.

14. $\log_2 (0.00555)^{-5}$.

15. $\log_{(\log_3 4)} 5$.

Solve 16—22 for x and give the answer in decimal form.

16. $10^x = 2.12$.

17. $5^x = 2.12$.

18. $2^{-x} = 50$.

19. $3^{4x-4} = 49(2^{3x-1})$.

20. $16 \cdot 2^{5x} = 17 \cdot 5^{2x}$.

21. $\log(x^2 - 1) - \log(x + 1) = 6$.

22. $2^{\log x} = 2x$.

7–5 Logarithms of the Trigonometric Functions

In solving numerical problems involving the trigonometric functions, especially in solving triangles, it is sometimes necessary to evaluate expressions such as

$$b = \frac{231.2 \sin 26°10'}{\sin 51°20'}.$$

As noted earlier, computations involving multiplication and division can often be simplified by the use of logarithms. In this case, taking logs of both sides we get $\log b = \log 231.2 + \log(\sin 26°10') - \log(\sin 51°20')$.

The value of log (sin 26°10′) may be found by finding sin 26°10′ in Table II, and the logarithm of that number in Table I. However, tables have been constructed which give the common logarithms of the trigonometric functions directly. Table III is such a table. There the values of the logarithm of the sine, cosine, tangent, and cotangent of angles between 0° and 90° are given. We write log (sin x) simply as log sin x and similarly for the other functions.

Most of these logarithms are negative, and for those the characteristic appears after the mantissa. For example, if $0° < x < 90°$, then $0 < \sin x < 1$, so that the characteristic of log sin x is less than or equal to -1. In Table III, we see that log sin 26°10′ = 0.6444 − 1, and log sin 51°20′ = 0.8925 − 1.

Notice that Table III is arranged so that angles from 45° to 90° are on the right side of the page, and for these angles we use the headings at the bottom of the page. This was done in finding log sin 51°20′.

Example 1. Find log tan 33°35′.

Solution. From Table III we find

$$\log \tan 33°30' = 0.8208 - 1,$$
$$\log \tan 33°40' = 0.8235 - 1.$$

We use linear interpolation as before. Since 33°35′ is halfway between 33°30′ and 33°40′, log tan 33°35′ is about halfway between 0.8208 − 1 and 0.8235 − 1. Thus we get

$$\log \tan 33°35' = 0.8222 - 1.$$

Example 2. Find log cos 83°23′.

Solution. From Table III we find

$$\log \cos 83°20' = 0.0641 - 1,$$
$$\log \cos 83°30' = 0.0539 - 1.$$

Since 83°23′ is 0.3 the way from 83°20′ to 83°30′, log 83°23′ is about 0.3 the way from 0.0641 − 1 to 0.0539 − 1. That distance is 0.3(0.0102) = 0.00306. Subtracting this from 0.0641 − 1 (since log cos x decreases as x goes from 83°20′ to 83°30′), we get

$$\log \cos 83°23' = 0.0610 - 1.$$

If we know log sin x, we can use Table III to find x, provided that x is between 0° and 90°.

Example 3. Find the value of x between 0° and 90° such that $\log \sin x = -1.1679$.

Solution. First, write −1.1679 in the form 0.8321 − 2. From our table we find

$$\log \sin 3°50' = 0.8251 - 2,$$
$$\log \sin 4° \quad = 0.8436 - 2.$$

Now, $0.8436-2-(0.8251-2)=0.0185$ and $0.8321-2-(0.8251-2)=0.0070$. Thus x is about 70/185 of the way from $3°50'$ to $4°$. But 70/185 of $10'$ is $4'$, to the nearest minute. Thus $x=3°54'$.

Example 4. In the right triangle in Fig. 7-8, given that $A=63°15'$, $a=24.33$, find the values of each of the unknown parts of the triangle.

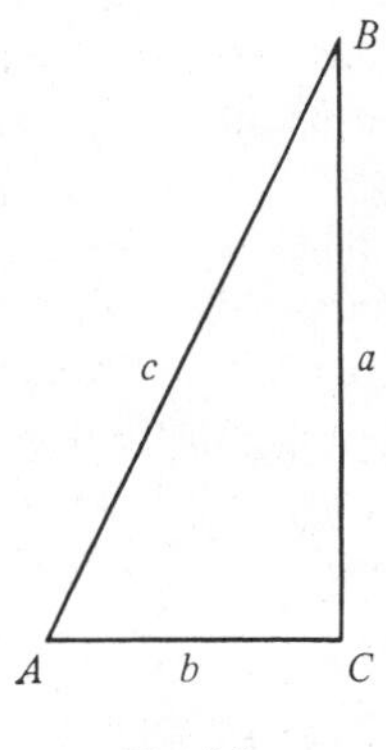

Fig. 7-8

Solution. A and B are complementary angles, so $B=90°-A=36°45'$. Since $\tan A=a/b$, we have

$$\tan 63°15' = \frac{24.33}{b}.$$

Hence

$$\log \tan 63°15' = \log 24.33 - \log b,$$
$$\log b = \log 24.33 - \log \tan 63°15' = 1.3861 - 0.2976 = 1.0885.$$

Thus

$$b = 12.27.$$

To find c we use $\sin A = a/c$. Hence

$$c = \frac{24.33}{\sin 63°15'},$$

$$\log c = \log 24.33 - \log \sin 63°15' = 1.3861 - (0.9508 - 1)$$
$$= 1.4353.$$

Thus

$$c = 27.24.$$

You will have an opportunity for further use of the logarithms of the trigonometric functions in the solution of general triangles in Chapter 8.

Problems 7–5

Use Table III to find the value of the logarithms in 1—12.

1. log sin 35°10′. **2.** log cos 24°20′.

3. log tan 58°40′. **4.** log cot 18°30′.

5. log sin 5°5′. **6.** log sin 40°15′.

7. log cos 48°13′. **8.** log cos 73°47′.

9. log sec 75°13′. **10.** log csc 33°36′.

11. log tan 136°52′. **12.** log sin 482°35′.

Use Table III to find the smallest positive value of A in 13—20.

13. $\log \cos A = -0.2778$. **14.** $\log \tan A = 0.1958$.

15. $\log \cot A = 1.1826$. **16.** $\log \cot A = -1.1989$.

17. $\log \csc A = 0.1830$. **18.** $\log \sec A = 2.0000$.

19. $\log \sin A = 0.8588 - 1$. **20.** $\log \sin A = -0.3333$.

Use Table III to solve the right triangles with the parts given in 21—28. (See Fig. 7-8.)

21. $A = 36°10′$, $a = 176$. **22.** $B = 51°50′$, $a = 15.1$.

23. $a = 31.35$, $b = 16.7$. **24.** $A = 15°25′$, $c = 111.2$.

25. $A = 45°26′$, $b = 1000$. **26.** $a = 5280$, $b = 5280$.

27. $a = 85.3$, $c = 131.5$. **28.** $B = 66°14′$, $a = 0.0214$.

8 Solution of General Triangles

8–1 The Law of Sines

We have seen in Chapter 4 how to "solve" a right triangle by capitalizing on the fact that the ratios of the sides may be expressed as trigonometric functions of the angles. In an arbitrary triangle the relationships are not quite so simple. The tools that enable us to solve general triangles are the *law of sines* and the *law of cosines*. We shall treat the law of sines in this section.

In any triangle the longer sides are opposite the larger angles. Another way of looking at it is that the longer sides are opposite the angles with the larger *sines*. In fact, if we fix our attention on any one triangle, the lengths of the sides are exactly proportional to the sines of the opposite angles—this is the law of sines.

Law of Sines. *If A, B, and C are the lengths of the sides of a triangle and α, β, and γ are the opposite angles, then*

$$\frac{A}{\sin \alpha} = \frac{B}{\sin \beta} = \frac{C}{\sin \gamma}.$$

Proof. What this statement says is that the expression

$$\frac{\text{length of a side}}{\sin \text{(opposite angle)}}$$

is the same for every side in a given triangle. We shall show that $A/\sin \alpha = B/\sin \beta$. The same argument shows that $B/\sin \beta = C/\sin \gamma$. There are two possible figures, one with both angles less than 90° and one with one of the angles greater than 90°, but the arguments are identical (Fig. 8-1 and Fig. 8-2).

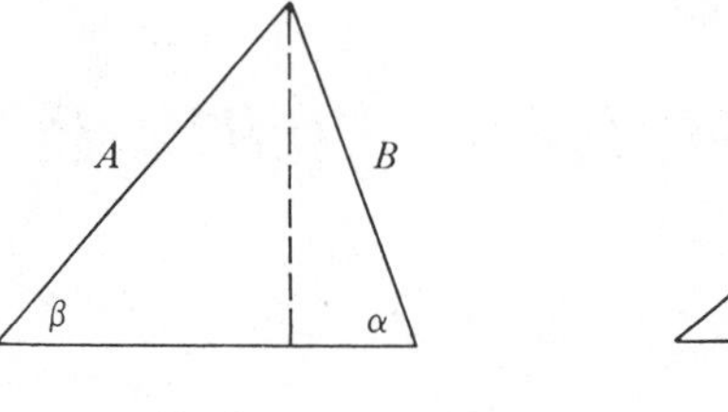

Fig. 8-1

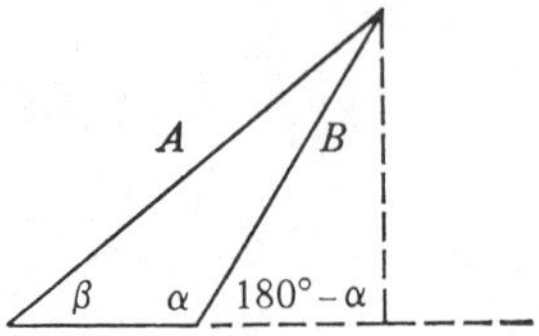

Fig. 8-2

The dashed line is dropped perpendicular to the third side. The length of the dashed line is seen to be $A \sin \beta$. In Fig. 8-1 it is also clear that the length of the dashed line is $B \sin \alpha$. This is true for Fig. 8-2 also, recalling that $\sin \alpha = \sin (180° - \alpha)$. Thus in either case $A \sin \beta = B \sin \alpha$, and we have $A/\sin \alpha = B/\sin \beta$.

There are several comments that should be made here concerning the law of sines and its proof. For one thing, we don't have a figure in the proof for the case when one of the angles is 90°. You should verify directly that if one of the angles is 90°, then the law of sines is a simple consequence of the facts about right triangles. Another (apparent) gap in the argument is the failure to consider the case when B is longer than A. This may be rectified by relabeling (call the longer side A instead of B). Finally, the law of sines says that the three numbers $A/\sin \alpha$, $B/\sin \beta$, and $C/\sin \gamma$ are all the same. If we call this number k, we have:

$$A/\sin \alpha = k \quad \text{or} \quad A = k \sin \alpha,$$

$$B/\sin \beta = k \quad \text{or} \quad B = k \sin \beta,$$

$$C/\sin \gamma = k \quad \text{or} \quad C = k \sin \gamma.$$

Thus the lengths of the sides are proportional to the sines of the opposite angles. We shall investigate the geometric meaning of the number k after looking at a few examples of the application of the law of sines.

Example 1. Solve the triangle where $\alpha = 20°$, $\beta = 40°$, and $C = 8$ (see Fig. 8-3).

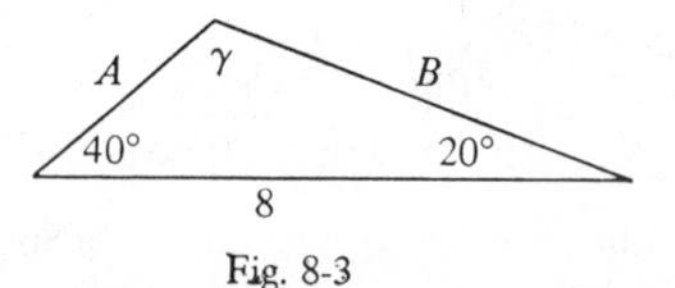

Fig. 8-3

Solution. Since the sum of the angles in any triangle is 180° we have $\gamma = 120°$. The law of sines tells us that $A/\sin 20° = B/\sin 40° = 8/\sin 120°$. In particular, $A = 8 \sin 20°/\sin 120° = 8 \sin 20°/\sin 60°$. Taking logarithms yields the equation $\log A = \log 8 + \log \sin 20° - \log \sin 60° = 0.9031 + 0.5341 - 1 - (0.9375 - 1) = 0.4997$ so $A = 3.16$. Similarly, $\log B = \log 8 + \log \sin 40° - \log \sin 60° = 0.9031 + 0.8081 - 1 - (0.9375 - 1) = 0.7737$ so $B = 5.94$.

Example 2. Solve the triangle, where $A = 5$, $C = 10$, and $\gamma = 110°$ (see Fig. 8-4).

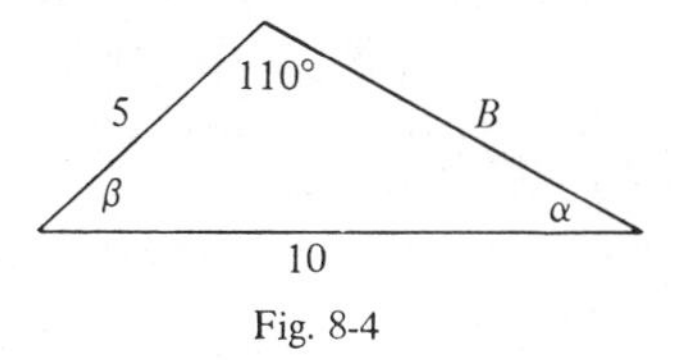

Fig. 8-4

Solution. The law of sines tells us that $5/\sin \alpha = B/\sin \beta = 10/\sin 110°$. In particular, $\sin \alpha = 5 \sin 110°/10 = \frac{1}{2} \sin 110° = \frac{1}{2} \sin 70° = 0.9397/2 = 0.46985$. Since α must be less than 90° (why?), we have $\alpha = 28°2'$. Hence $\beta = 180° - 110° - 28°2' = 41°58'$. Finally, $B = 10 \sin \beta/\sin 110°$ and so $\log B = 1 + \log \sin 41°58' - \log \sin 70° = 1 + 0.8252 - 1 - (0.9730 - 1) = 0.8512$. Hence $B = 7.10$.

The law of sines enables us to solve triangles if we are given one side and two angles (and hence all angles) or if we are given two sides and an angle opposite one of these sides. From the familiar "angle-side-angle" of geometry a triangle is completely determined if we know the angles and one side. However, it is not necessarily enough to know two sides and an opposite angle—the forbidden "angle-side-side". In Example 2 it *was* enough because we knew that the unknown angles were acute. The ambiguous case is illustrated in Fig. 8-5. Both triangles have $\alpha = 45°$, $A = 4$, and $B = 5$. However, they are quite distinct. To see how these two cases arise when solving such a triangle, apply the law of sines. We get $4/\sin 45° = 5/\sin \beta = C/\sin \gamma$. The first equation tells us that $\sin \beta = (5/4) \sin 45° = 0.8839$ and so $\beta = 62°7'$ *or* $\beta = 117°53'$. These values of β correspond to the two triangles in Fig. 8-5.

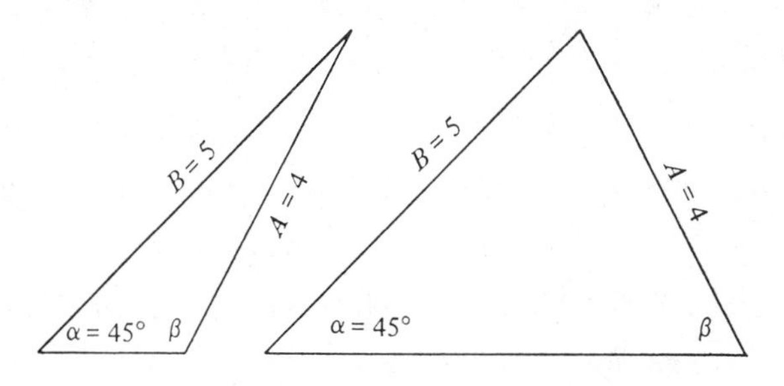

Fig. 8-5

We now turn to the geometric meaning of the number $k = A/\sin\alpha = B/\sin\beta = C/\sin\gamma$. Consider the circle which passes through the three vertices of the triangle (the circumscribed circle). Draw in the two radii from the center of the circle to the vertices of the side A and drop a perpendicular from the center to the side A (see Fig. 8-6). From geometry we know that the angle between the two radii is 2α, and hence the angle from the perpendicular to either radius is α. Thus the two pieces into which A is divided by the perpendicular both have length $r\sin\alpha$, so $A = 2r\sin\alpha$ which says that $A/\sin\alpha = 2r$, the diameter of the circumscribed circle. This is the geometric meaning of the number k; it is the diameter of the circumscribed circle.

If we are given two sides and the included angle of a triangle, the "side-angle-side" of geometry, we cannot simply use the law of sines to solve the triangle. In this situation we apply the law of cosines which is covered in the next section.

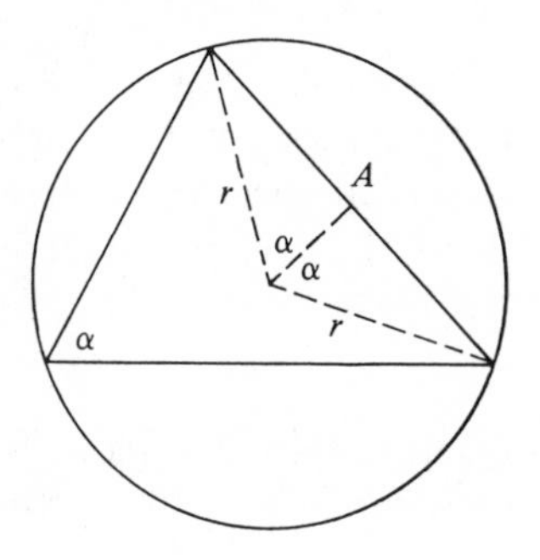

Fig. 8-6

Problems 8–1

Solve the following triangles. If the data given is insufficient to specify a unique triangle, solve all possible triangles that arise. If the data does not specify any triangle, say why.

1. $A = 3.21$, $\beta = 35°$, $\gamma = 27°10'$.

2. $C = 46.4$, $\beta = 80°40'$, $\gamma = 52°20'$.

3. $B = 871$, $\alpha = 46°32'$, $\gamma = 121°10'$.

4. $B = 2.14$, $\beta = 15°22'$, $\gamma = 51°6'$.

5. $A = 62.5$, $B = 90.3$, $\alpha = 31°10'$.

6. $A = 7.14$, $C = 10.2$, $\alpha = 28°40'$.

7. $A = 5.31$, $B = 85.2$, $\alpha = 47°30'$.

8. $B = 2.38$, $C = 15.1$, $\beta = 30°10'$.

9. $A = 25.4$, $C = 36.9$, $\gamma = 110°20'$.

10. $B = 37.2$, $C = 21.3$, $\beta = 98°35'$.

11. $B = 60.4$, $C = 75.1$, $\beta = 36°40'$.

12. $A = 51.7$, $C = 9.03$, $\alpha = 42°15'$.

13. $A = 15.1$, $B = 23.7$, $\beta = 142°10'$.

14. $B = 4.135$, $C = 6.124$, $\gamma = 56°52'$.

15. $B = 25.4$, $\alpha = 72°8'$, $\beta = 70°10'$.

16. $C = 113$, $\alpha = 8°10'$, $\beta = 9°20'$.

17. $A = 20.36$, $\beta = 19°12'$, $\gamma = 27°17'$.

18. $C = 312.2$, $\alpha = 135°18'$, $\beta = 70°12'$.

8–2 *The Law of Cosines*

The familiar Pythagorean theorem deals with the situation depicted in Fig. 8-7, where θ is a right angle. It states that $C^2 = A^2 + B^2$. If, on the other hand, θ is not a right angle, this formula is no longer valid. In this situation the question, "How big is C?" is answered by the *law of cosines.*

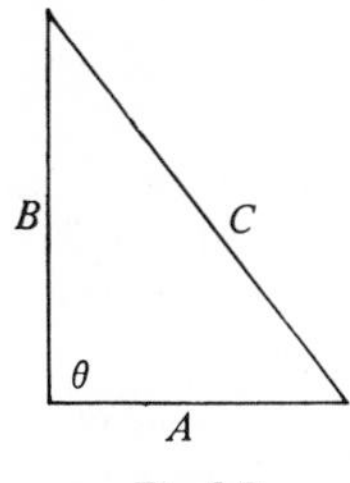

Fig. 8-7

Law of Cosines. *If A, B, and C are the lengths of the sides of a triangle and θ is the angle between A and B, then*

$$C^2 = A^2 + B^2 - 2AB\cos\theta.$$

Proof. Consider Fig. 8-8 and the triangle formed by C and the dashed line

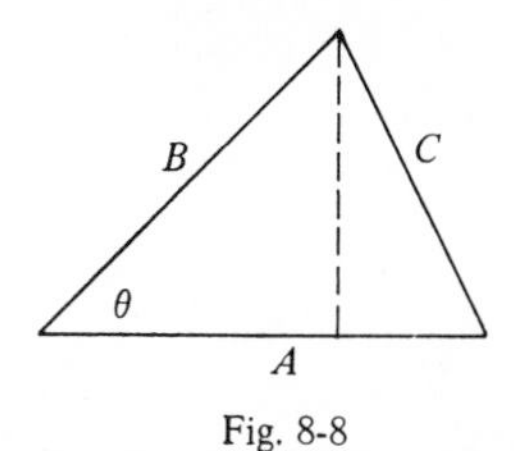

Fig. 8-8

perpendicular to A. The length of the dashed line is $B\sin\theta$. The length of the base of the triangle is $A - B\cos\theta$. Hence the Pythagorean theorem says that

$$(B\sin\theta)^2 + (A - B\cos\theta)^2 = C^2$$

and so

$$B^2\sin^2\theta + A^2 - 2AB\cos\theta + B^2\cos^2\theta = C^2,$$

or, since $\sin^2\theta + \cos^2\theta = 1$,

$$A^2 + B^2 - 2AB\cos\theta = C^2.$$

The student should go through the argument for Fig. 8-9 and Fig. 8-10. Note that for $\theta = 90°$ the law of cosines is simply the Pythagorean theorem.

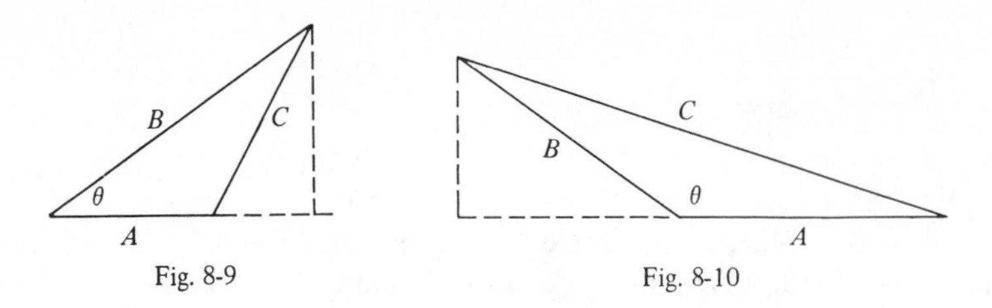

Fig. 8-9

Fig. 8-10

Example 1. Solve the triangle $A = 2.34$, $B = 3.57$, $\gamma = 24°10'$ (see Fig. 8-11).

Solution. The law of cosines says that $C^2 = (2.34)^2 + (3.57)^2 - 2(2.34)(3.57) \times \cos 24°10' = 5.4756 + 12.7449 - (16.7076) \cdot (0.9124) = 18.2205 - 15.24401424 = 2.97648576$. Since the value 0.9124 for $\cos 24°10'$ has only four significant digits, the value 15.24401424 is only significant to 15.24. Hence only 2.98 is significant in our computation of C^2. (This is an example of how you can lose significant digits when you subtract, one of the drawbacks of the law of cosines.) Now, taking logs, we have $2 \log C = \log 2.98 = 0.4742$. Thus $\log C = 0.2371$ and we get $C = 1.73$. By the law of sines, $C/\sin 24°10' = 3.57/\sin \beta$ so $\log \sin \beta = \log 3.57 + \log \sin 24°10' - \log C = 0.5527 + 0.6121 - 1 - 0.2371 = 0.9277 - 1$, and $\beta = 58°50'$ or $121°10'$. Since the first value would make $\alpha > 90°$ (why?) which it is not (why not?), we conclude that $\beta = 121°10'$; hence $\alpha = 180° - 24°10' - 121°10' = 34°40'$, and we have solved the triangle.

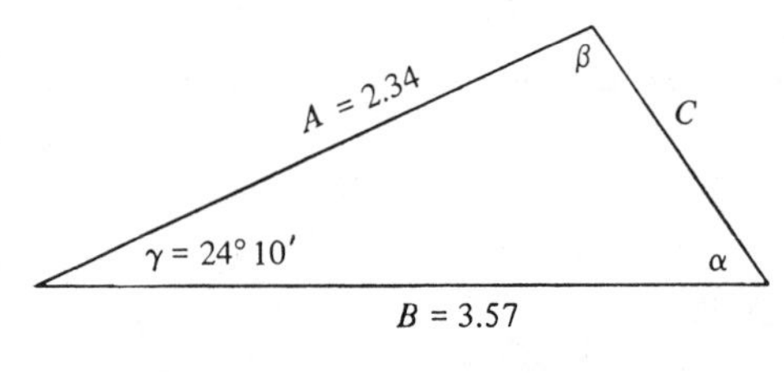

Fig. 8-11

Example 1 shows how the law of cosines can be used to solve the "side-angle-side" situation. The law of cosines can also be used to solve a triangle, if the three sides are given.

Example 2. Solve the triangle $A = 5.2$, $B = 3.1$, $C = 6.7$ (Fig. 8-12).

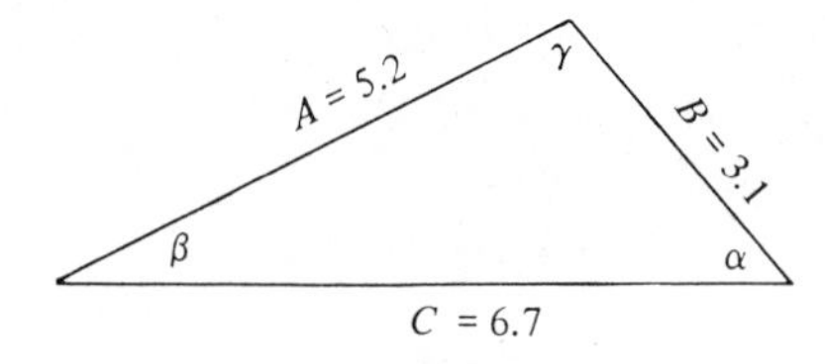

Fig. 8-12

Solution. The law of cosines tells us that

$$(6.7)^2 = (5.2)^2 + (3.1)^2 - 2(5.2)(3.1)\cos\gamma.$$

Hence

$$\cos\gamma = \frac{(5.2)^2 + (3.1)^2 - (6.7)^2}{2(5.2)(3.1)}$$

$$= \frac{27.04 + 9.61 - 44.89}{32.24} = -\frac{8.24}{32.24}.$$

Thus $\cos(180° - \gamma) = -\cos\gamma = 8.24/32.24$. Taking logs yields

$$\begin{aligned}\log\cos(180° - \gamma) &= \log 8.24 - \log 32.24 = 0.9159 - 1.5084\\ &= 0.9159 - 0.5084 - 1 = 0.4075 - 1,\end{aligned}$$

and so $180° - \gamma = 75°12'$. Thus $\gamma = 104°48'$.

To get the remaining angles we use the law of sines. We have $5.2/\sin\alpha = 3.1/\sin\beta = 6.7/\sin 104°48'$. Hence $\log\sin\alpha = \log 5.2 + \log\sin 104°48' - \log 6.7 = 0.7160 + 0.9854 - 1 - 0.8261 = 0.8753 - 1$, so that $\alpha = 48°37'$. Also, $\log\sin\beta = \log 3.1 + \log\sin 104°48' - \log 6.7 = 0.4914 + 0.9854 - 1 - 0.8261 = 0.6507 - 1$, so $\beta = 26°35'$. As a check we add: $\alpha + \beta + \gamma = 48°37' + 26°35' + 104°48' = 180°$, as it should.

It is important not to get bogged down by the specific letters used in the statement of the law of cosines, as in any mathematical formula. What the law of cosines says is that *the square of the length of a side of a triangle is equal to the sum of the squares of the lengths of the other two sides minus twice the product of the lengths of the other two sides with the cosine of the opposite angle.* It is simpler and more readable to assign letters to the various sides and angles and express the previous sentence by a compact formula: $C^2 = A^2 + B^2 - 2AB\cos\theta$. On the other hand, if we are given the two sides C and A and the angle β opposite the side B, the formula for the law of cosines would read $B^2 = A^2 + C^2 - 2AC\cos\beta$. This is still the same law; only the *names* of the sides have changed.

In Example 2 we could have used the law of cosines to compute α and β instead of the (easier) law of sines. The computation for α would come from the formula $A^2 = B^2 + C^2 - 2BC\cos\alpha$. We would get $(5.2)^2 = (3.1)^2 + (6.7)^2 - 2(3.1)(6.7)\cos\alpha$, or

$$\cos\alpha = \frac{(3.1)^2 + (6.7)^2 - (5.2)^2}{2(3.1)(6.7)}$$

$$= \frac{9.61 + 44.89 - 27.04}{41.54} = \frac{27.46}{41.54}.$$

Hence $\log\cos\alpha = \log 27.46 - \log 41.54 = 1.4387 - 1.6184 = 1.4387 - 0.6184 - 1 = 0.8203 - 1$ so $\alpha = 48°37'$, as before.

Problems 8–2

Solve the following triangles.

1. $A = 5.32$, $C = 3.04$, $\beta = 125°$.

2. $A = 42.2$, $B = 65.4$, $\gamma = 31°10'$.

3. $B = 51.1$, $C = 53.8$, $\alpha = 71°50'$.

4. $A = 11.4$, $C = 11.7$, $\beta = 27°15'$.

5. $B = 6.75$, $C = 1.06$, $\alpha = 129°40'$.

6. $A = 352$, $B = 175$, $\gamma = 1°$.

7. $A = 894$, $B = 806$, $C = 95$.

8. $A = 2.3$, $B = 113$, $C = 112$.

9. $A = 49.8$, $B = 73.6$, $C = 98.4$.

10. $A = 16.5$, $B = 25.5$, $C = 33.8$.

11. $A = 18.7$, $B = 25.3$, $C = 39.6$.

12. $A = 8.15$, $B = 6.83$, $C = 3.45$.

8–3 The Law of Tangents

The law of sines and the law of cosines are enough to solve any triangle; they are the most important relations, from a theoretical point of view, in a general triangle. We have seen, however, that indiscriminate use of the law of cosines sometimes results in a loss of precision. Let's look at another example of this.

Example 1. Solve the triangle where $A = 101$, $B = 100$, and $\gamma = 1°$, using the law of cosines (Fig. 8-13).

Solution. The law of cosines says that $C^2 = 100^2 + 101^2 - 2(100)(101)\cos 1° = 20{,}201 - 20{,}195.96 = 5.04$. Thus we would compute $2 \log C = 0.7024$, so $\log C = 0.3512$ and $C = 2.245$. We can see here the loss of precision introduced by the use of the law of cosines. The table gives cos 1° as 0.9998; hence its true value lies somewhere between 0.99975 and 0.99985. This means that the number 20,195.96 might be in error in its fifth digit—but this would cause an error in the *first* digit of 5.04 and hence possibly in the first digit of 2.245, the computed value of C. If we wish to get a fairly precise idea of what C is, we must choose another method of computation.

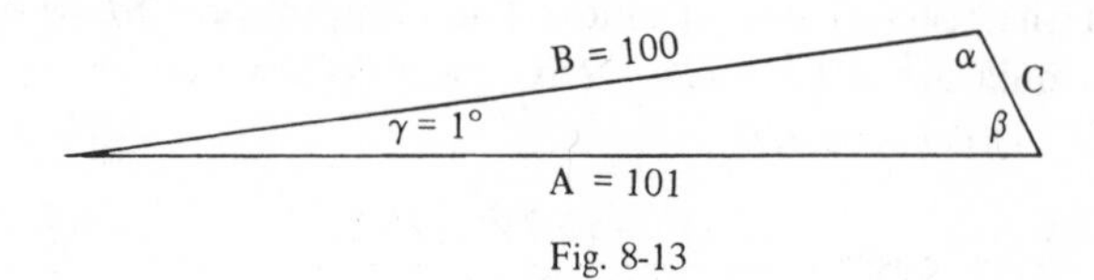

Fig. 8-13

One way to overcome the limitations of the law of cosines is by using the *law of tangents*. This identity is not as important as either the law of sines or the law of cosines and it appears a little cumbersome at first glance. However, it lends itself to computation much better than the law of cosines and may be used, in conjunction with the law of sines, instead of the law of cosines.

Law of Tangents. *If A and B are the lengths of two sides of a triangle, α the angle opposite A, and β the angle opposite B, then*

$$\frac{A-B}{A+B}=\frac{\tan \frac{1}{2}(\alpha-\beta)}{\tan \frac{1}{2}(\alpha+\beta)}.$$

Proof. By the law of sines we have $A/\sin \alpha = B/\sin \beta$. Hence $A/B = \sin \alpha/\sin \beta$. Adding 1 to both sides of this equation yields $(A+B)/B = (\sin \alpha + \sin \beta)/\sin \beta$; subtracting 1 from both sides gives $(A-B)/B = (\sin \alpha - \sin \beta)/\sin \beta$. Dividing these two equations we get $(A-B)/(A+B) = (\sin \alpha - \sin \beta)/(\sin \alpha + \sin \beta)$. From identity (25) and Exercise 1 in Section 5–4 we get

$$\frac{A-B}{A+B}=\frac{2 \cos \frac{1}{2}(\alpha+\beta) \sin \frac{1}{2}(\alpha-\beta)}{2 \sin \frac{1}{2}(\alpha+\beta) \cos \frac{1}{2}(\alpha-\beta)}=\frac{\tan \frac{1}{2}(\alpha-\beta)}{\tan \frac{1}{2}(\alpha+\beta)}.$$

Example 2. Solve the triangle where $A=101$, $B=100$, and $\gamma=1°$, using the law of tangents (Fig. 8-13).

Solution. The law of tangents says that $\tan \frac{1}{2}(\alpha-\beta)/\tan \frac{1}{2}(\alpha+\beta)=(A-B)/(A+B)=1/201$. But, since $\alpha+\beta+1°=180°$ we have $\frac{1}{2}(\alpha+\beta)=89°30'$ and so $\tan \frac{1}{2}(\alpha-\beta)=(\tan 89°30')/201$. Hence $\log \tan \frac{1}{2}(\alpha-\beta)=2.0591-2.3032=0.7559-1$ and so $\frac{1}{2}(\alpha-\beta)=29°41'$. But $\alpha=\frac{1}{2}(\alpha-\beta)+\frac{1}{2}(\alpha+\beta)=29°41' + 89°30'=119°11'$ and $\beta=\frac{1}{2}(\alpha+\beta)-\frac{1}{2}(\alpha-\beta)=89°30'-29°41'=59°49'$. Finally, by the law of sines, $100/\sin 59°49' = C/\sin 1°$, so $\log C = \log \sin 1° + 2 - \log \sin 59°49' = 0.2419-(0.9367-1)=0.3052$. Thus $C=2.019$ (compare with the result using the law of cosines in Example 1).

Problems 8–3

Solve the triangles in 1—8, using the law of tangents.

1. $A=143.7, B=144.9, \gamma=2°15'$.

2. $A=407, B=513, \gamma=66°34'$.

3. $B=46.34, C=75.19, \alpha=73°27'$.

4. $A=19.78, B=20.54, \gamma=1°30'$.

5. $B=72.14, C=53.46, \alpha=42°18'$.

6. $B=18.62, C=35.61, \alpha=52°18'$.

7. $A=463, B=628, \gamma=57°40'$.

8. $A=6.24, B=6.25, \gamma=35'$.

8–4 Semiperimeter Formulas

In a triangle whose sides have lengths A, B, and C we define the *semiperimeter* S to be $\frac{1}{2}(A+B+C)$, that is, one half the length of the perimeter. This quantity arises naturally during the course of many computations involving general triangles. One application of the semiperimeter is the *second law of tangents.*

Second Law of Tangents. *If the lengths of the sides of a triangle are A, B, and C, γ is the angle opposite C, and $S = \frac{1}{2}(A + B + C)$ is the semiperimeter, then*

$$\tan \tfrac{1}{2}\gamma = \sqrt{\frac{(S - A)(S - B)}{S(S - C)}}.$$

Proof. From the law of cosines we have $\cos \gamma = \dfrac{A^2 + B^2 - C^2}{2AB}$. Hence

$$1 + \cos \gamma = 1 + \frac{A^2 + B^2 - C^2}{2AB} = \frac{2AB + A^2 + B^2 - C^2}{2AB}$$

$$= \frac{(A + B)^2 - C^2}{2AB} = \frac{(A + B + C)(A + B - C)}{2AB}.$$

Thus

$$\tfrac{1}{2}(1 + \cos \gamma) = \frac{\frac{1}{2}(A + B + C)\frac{1}{2}(A + B - C)}{AB} = \frac{S(S - C)}{AB}.$$

Similarly, $\frac{1}{2}(1 - \cos \gamma) = \dfrac{(S - A)(S - B)}{AB}$. Thus, from the half angle formulas (Section 5–3, equations (23)), we have

$$\sin \tfrac{1}{2}\gamma = \sqrt{\frac{(S - A)(S - B)}{AB}}$$

and

$$\cos \tfrac{1}{2}\gamma = \sqrt{\frac{S(S - C)}{AB}}$$

and thus

$$\tan \tfrac{1}{2}\gamma = \sqrt{\frac{(S - A)(S - B)}{S(S - C)}}.$$

The second law of tangents may be used instead of the law of cosines to solve a triangle where three sides are given; it is somewhat better suited to computation.

Example 1. Solve the triangle where $A = 10.52$, $B = 12.31$, and $C = 6.47$, using the second law of tangents.

Solution. $S = \frac{1}{2}(10.52 + 12.31 + 6.47) = 14.65$. Hence $S - A = 4.13$, $S - B = 2.34$, and $S - C = 8.18$. Taking logs we have $\log S = 1.1658$, $\log (S - A) = 0.6160$, $\log (S - B) = 0.3692$, and $\log (S - C) = 0.9128$. The law of tangents says that $\log \tan \frac{1}{2}\gamma = \frac{1}{2}[\log (S - A) + \log (S - B) - \log S - \log (S - C)] = \frac{1}{2}(0.6160 + 0.3692 - 1.1658 - 0.9128) = \frac{1}{2}(0.9066 - 2) = 0.4533 - 1$. Hence $\frac{1}{2}\gamma = 15°51'$, and $\gamma = 31°42'$. To find α and β, replace A and B by the appropriate adjacent sides, and replace C by the opposite side. In this way we find $\log \tan \frac{1}{2}\alpha = \frac{1}{2}(\log (S - B) + \log (S - C) - \log S - \log (S - A)) = \frac{1}{2}(0.3692 + 0.9128 - 1.1658 - 0.6160) = \frac{1}{2}(1.5002 - 2) = 0.7501 - 1$. Hence $\frac{1}{2}\alpha = 29°21'$ so $\alpha = 58°42'$. Similarly,

$$\begin{aligned}\log \tan \tfrac{1}{2}\beta &= \tfrac{1}{2}[\log (S - A) + \log (S - C) - \log S - \log (S - B)]\\ &= \tfrac{1}{2}(0.6160 + 0.9128 - 1.1658 - 0.3692)\\ &= \tfrac{1}{2}(1.9938 - 2) = 0.9969 - 1.\end{aligned}$$

Hence $\frac{1}{2}\beta = 44°48'$ so $\beta = 89°36'$. As a check we note that $\alpha + \beta + \gamma = 58°42' + 89°36' + 31°42' = 180°$.

There are two circles associated with every triangle: the *circumscribed circle* and the *inscribed circle*. The circumscribed circle is the circle which passes through the vertices of the triangle; we have seen in Section 8-1 that the diameter of the circumscribed circle is equal to the ratio of any side to the sine of the opposite angle. The inscribed circle is constructed around the point where the bisectors of the three angles of the triangle meet, its radius being the length of the perpendicular dropped from that point to any side (Fig. 8-14). We can use the second law of tangents to compute the radius of the inscribed circle.

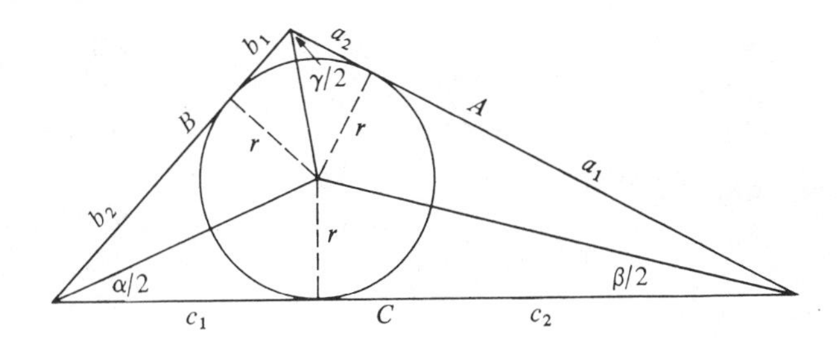

Fig. 8-14

Theorem 1. *If the lengths of the sides of a triangle are A, B, and C, then the radius r of the inscribed circle is given by*

$$r = \sqrt{\frac{(S - A)(S - B)(S - C)}{S}},$$

where $S = \frac{1}{2}(A + B + C)$.

Proof. Consider Fig. 8-14. The perimeter of the triangle is given by $2S = A + B + C = a_1 + a_2 + b_1 + b_2 + c_1 + c_2$. By elementary geometry we have $a_2 = b_1$, $b_2 = c_1$, and $c_2 = a_1$. Hence $2S = a_1 + b_1 + b_1 + c_1 + c_1 + a_1 = 2(a_1 + b_1 + c_1)$, and so $S = a_1 + b_1 + c_1 = a_1 + a_2 + c_1 = A + c_1$. Thus $c_1 = S - A$. But $r/c_1 = \tan \frac{1}{2}\alpha = \sqrt{(S - B)(S - C)/S(S - A)}$, and thus $r = (S - A)\sqrt{(S - B)(S - C)/S(S - A)} = \sqrt{(S - A)(S - B)(S - C)/S}$.

Example 2. Find the radius of the inscribed circle of the triangle in Example 1.

Solution. We have

$$\begin{aligned}\log r &= \tfrac{1}{2}[\log(S-A) + \log(S-B) + \log(S-C) - \log S] \\ &= \tfrac{1}{2}(0.6160 + 0.3692 + 0.9128 - 1.1658) = \tfrac{1}{2}(0.7322) = 0.3661,\end{aligned}$$

so $r = 2.323$.

Consider the triangle in Fig. 8-14. The angle bisectors split it up into three smaller triangles; the areas of these three triangles are given by $\frac{1}{2}rA$, $\frac{1}{2}rB$, and $\frac{1}{2}rC$. Thus the area of the whole triangle is $\frac{1}{2}rA + \frac{1}{2}rB + \frac{1}{2}rC = r\frac{1}{2}(A + B + C) = rS$. Using the expression in Theorem 1 for r we get the following.

Area Formula. If the lengths of the sides of a triangle are A, B, and C, then the area of the triangle is given by the expression

$$\sqrt{S(S-A)(S-B)(S-C)},$$

where $S = \frac{1}{2}(A + B + C)$.

Example 3. Find the area of the triangle in Example 1.

Solution. The log of the area is given by

$$\begin{aligned}&\tfrac{1}{2}[\log S + \log(S-A) + \log(S-B) + \log(S-C)] \\ &\quad = \tfrac{1}{2}(1.1658 + 0.6160 + 0.3692 + 0.9128) = \tfrac{1}{2}(3.0638) = 1.5319;\end{aligned}$$

thus the area is 34.03.

Problems 8–4

1. Show that $\tan\frac{1}{2}\alpha = r/(S-A)$, $\tan\frac{1}{2}\beta = r/(S-B)$, and $\tan\frac{1}{2}\gamma = r/(S-C)$. (In using the second law of tangents to solve a triangle completely it is a little easier first to compute $\log r$, even though this quantity is not desired, and then employ the preceding equations.)
2. Solve the triangle where $A = 72.1$, $B = 35.8$, and $C = 100.2$, using the second law of tangents. Check by adding up the computed values of the angles.
3. Use the second law of tangents to find β if $A = 21.3$, $B = 2.7$, and $C = 20.8$.
4. Compute β by the second law of tangents and then by the law of cosines if $A = 18.1$, $B = 1.2$, and $C = 17.9$.
5. Find the area of the triangle where $A = 7.8$, $B = 8.5$, and $C = 9.2$.
6. Find the area of the triangle where $A = 2.5$, $B = 3.1$, and $C = 2.9$.
7. Show that the area of a triangle is given by $\frac{1}{2}AB\sin\gamma$.
8. Find the radii of the inscribed and circumscribed circles of the triangle with sides $A = 10.4$, $B = 12.3$, and $C = 11.7$.

9 *Inverse Trigonometric Functions and Trigonometric Equations*

9–1 The Inverse Sine and Cosine Functions

The following question arises frequently when working with the trigonometric functions: for which angles x is $\sin x = y$? This is similar to the question of whether the sine function has an inverse. Recall that the inverse of a function f gives the solution for x in the equation $f(x) = y$: if g is the inverse of f, then $x = g(f(x)) = g(y)$. In the case of the sine function, however, if there is one such x there are infinitely many, since $\sin x = \sin (x + 2\pi) = \sin (x + 4\pi) = \sin (x + 6\pi) = \dots$.

The general topic of inverse functions was covered in Chapter 7. It was pointed out there that a function has an inverse if and only if it is a one-to-one function. A glance at the graph of the sine function tells us that it does not have this property. Indeed, the fact that if there is one x with $\sin x = y$ then there are many is a reflection of the fact that the function sin does not have an inverse. Nevertheless we do frequently want to find one solution for x in $\sin x = y$, and as with several functions in Chapter 7, we solve the dilemma by restricting the domain of the sine function sufficiently so that there will be at most one such x in this domain.

To help choose the restricted domain we look back at the graph of the sine function in Fig. 9-1. The largest increasing, or decreasing, portions of the graph occur for the intervals between odd multiples of $\pi/2$: between $-3\pi/2$ and $-\pi/2$, between $-\pi/2$ and $\pi/2$, between $\pi/2$ and $3\pi/2$, etc. A reasonable choice would be one of these intervals. Also notice that the entire graph could be reconstructed from the knowledge of sine on any one of these intervals, using symmetry and periodicity; therefore, no great loss is incurred

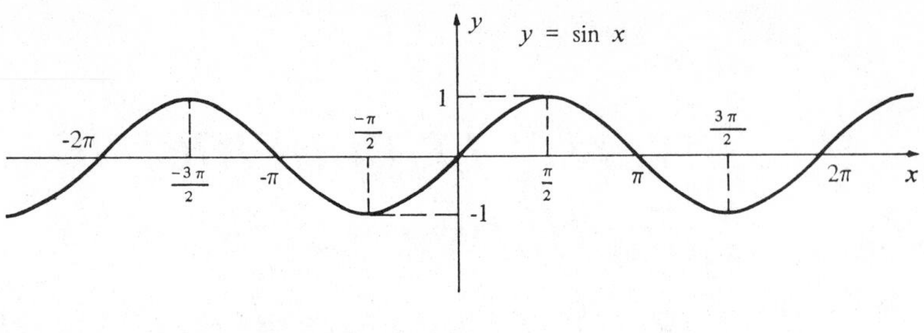

Fig. 9-1

by restriction to one of these intervals. Since nothing else appears to motivate the choice of one of these intervals over another, the interval with 0 in it is chosen, namely $-\pi/2 \leq x \leq \pi/2$.

The graph of $y = \sin x$ for this interval $-\pi/2 \leq x \leq \pi/2$ is depicted in Fig. 9-2. This is the graph of a strictly increasing, and hence one-to-one, function. Therefore, this function has an inverse. We denote this inverse by arcsin x. (It is also commonly denoted by $\sin^{-1} x$.) This inverse function is generally referred to as the "arc sine of x," the "inverse sine of x," or the "angle whose sine is x."

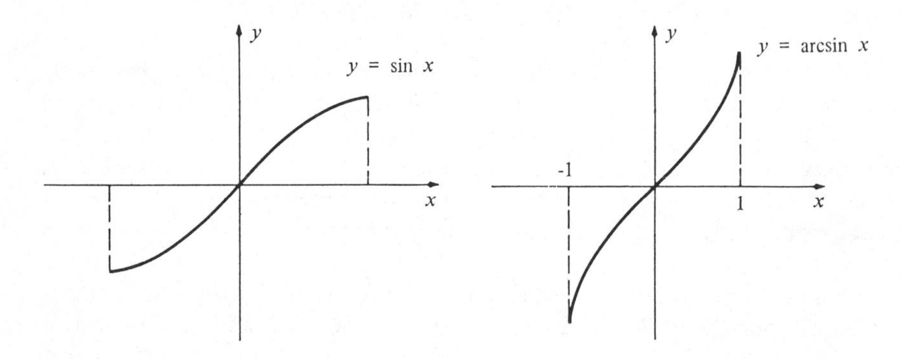

Fig. 9-2

Since the function $y = \sin x$ has domain $-\pi/2 \leq x \leq \pi/2$ and image $-1 \leq y \leq 1$, the inverse function $y = \arcsin x$ has domain $-1 \leq x \leq 1$ and image $-\pi/2 \leq y \leq \pi/2$. The graph of $y = \arcsin x$ is shown in Fig. 9-2. It is obtained from the graph of $y = \sin x$, $-\pi/2 \leq x \leq \pi/2$, by a reflection about the line $y = x$.

It is interesting to compare the graph of the equation $x = \sin y$ with the graph of the function $y = \arcsin x$. This is done in Fig. 9-3. The values of y singled out by the function $y = \arcsin x$ are usually called the *principal values* of the equation $x = \sin y$. Although the equation $x = \sin y$ does not describe a function, the *two* conditions $x = \sin y$ and $-\pi/2 \leq y \leq \pi/2$ do

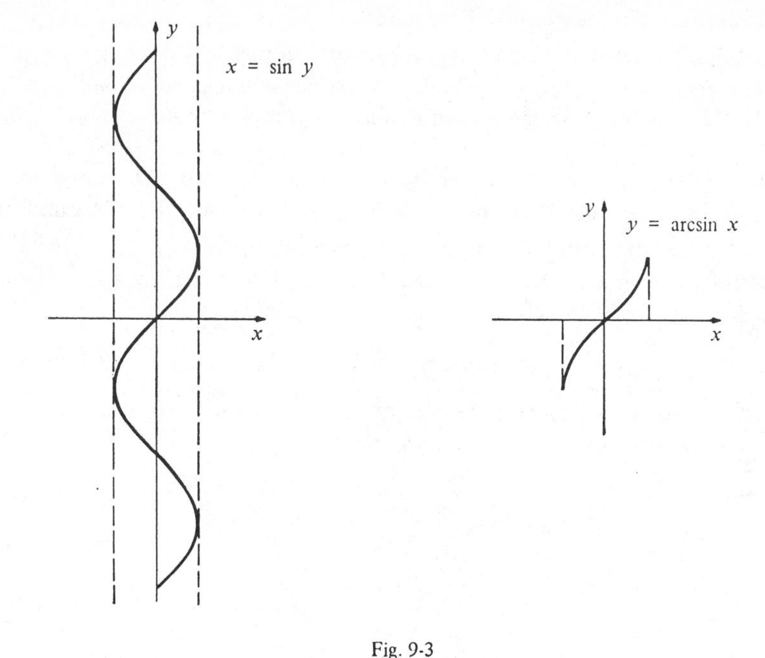

Fig. 9-3

determine y as a function of x. In other words, the function $y = \arcsin x$, for $|x| \leq 1$, is uniquely determined by the following two properties.

$$\sin(\arcsin x) = x,$$
$$-\frac{\pi}{2} \leq \arcsin x \leq \frac{\pi}{2}. \tag{1}$$

As with the trigonometric functions, it is common to use degrees when working with the inverse trigonometric functions. For most of the examples and problems we consider the inverse trigonometric functions to take their values in degrees rather than radians or real numbers. This gives us the range $-90° \leq \arcsin x \leq 90°$. In order to compute the values of the function $y = \arcsin x$ we use the trigonometric tables and the interpolation techniques introduced in Chapter 4.

Example 1. Find the value of arcsin 1/3.

Solution. We find in the table that $\sin 19°20' = 0.3311$ and $\sin 19°30' = 0.3338$. Thus the angle, measured in degrees, which lies between $-90°$ and $90°$ and has sine equal to 1/3, lies between $19°20'$ and $19°30'$. This change of $10'$ results in a change of 0.0027 in the sine, or a change of about 0.00027 per minute. Thus 0.3333 is the sin of $19°28'$, to the nearest minute, i.e., $\arcsin 1/3 = 19°28'$.

Example 2. Find the value of arcsin 0.5962.

Solution. We find in the table that $\sin 36°30' = 0.5948$ and $\sin 36°40' = 0.5972$. This represents a change of about 0.00024 per minute, and by interpolation $0.5962 = \sin 36°36'$ to the nearest minute. Thus $\arcsin 0.5962 = 36°36'$.

If $x = \arcsin \alpha$, we know $\sin x = \alpha$. What can we determine about $\cos x$, $\tan x$, etc.? Knowing not only that $\sin x = \alpha$ but also the quadrant in which x lies, we can say quite a bit. In general, $\cos x = \pm\sqrt{1 - \sin^2 x}$. If $x = \arcsin \alpha$, we know also that x lies in the first or fourth quadrant (since $-\pi/2 \leq x \leq \pi/2$); thus $\cos x$ is positive and we have

$$\cos(\arcsin \alpha) = \sqrt{1 - \alpha^2}. \tag{2}$$

Combining Equation (2) with the identities $\tan x = \sin x/\cos x$, and $\cot x = \cos x/\sin x$ yields, for $x = \arcsin \alpha$, the identities

$$\begin{aligned} \tan(\arcsin \alpha) &= \frac{\alpha}{\sqrt{1 - \alpha^2}} \quad \text{if } \alpha \neq \pm 1, \\ \cot(\arcsin \alpha) &= \frac{\sqrt{1 - \alpha^2}}{\alpha} \quad \text{if } \alpha \neq 0. \end{aligned} \tag{3}$$

From the relations between the secant and cosecant functions and the cosine and sine functions, we obtain the identities

$$\begin{aligned} \sec(\arcsin \alpha) &= \frac{1}{\sqrt{1 - \alpha^2}} \quad \text{if } \alpha \neq \pm 1, \\ \csc(\arcsin \alpha) &= \frac{1}{\alpha} \quad \text{if } \alpha \neq 0. \end{aligned} \tag{4}$$

It is also of interest to consider an inverse function for the cosine function. Again, the cosine function does not have an inverse, but restricting the domain sufficiently gives a function which does have an inverse. Looking at the graph of the cosine function (Fig. 9-4), we see that on any interval between consecutive multiples of π, such as π to 2π, 2π to 3π, etc., the cosine is either increasing or decreasing, and hence has an inverse. Also the entire graph of

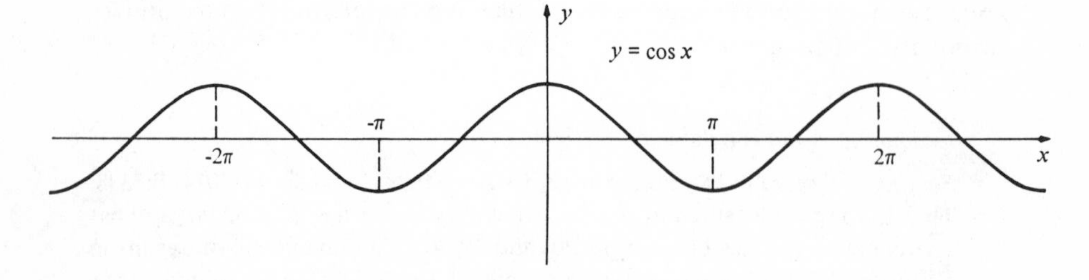

Fig. 9-4

the cosine function could be reconstructed from its graph on any of these intervals, using the symmetry and periodicity of the graph.

The natural choice is the interval from 0 to π. The inverse cosine function, denoted by $\arccos x$ (or $\cos^{-1} x$), then has domain $-1 \leq x \leq 1$ and range $0 \leq y \leq \pi$. Its graph appears in Fig. 9-5. The graph is obtained from a reflection of the graph $y = \cos x$, for $0 \leq x \leq \pi$, about the line $y = x$.

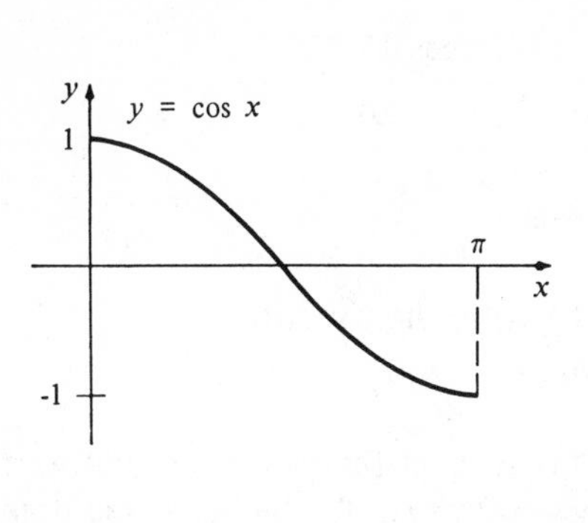

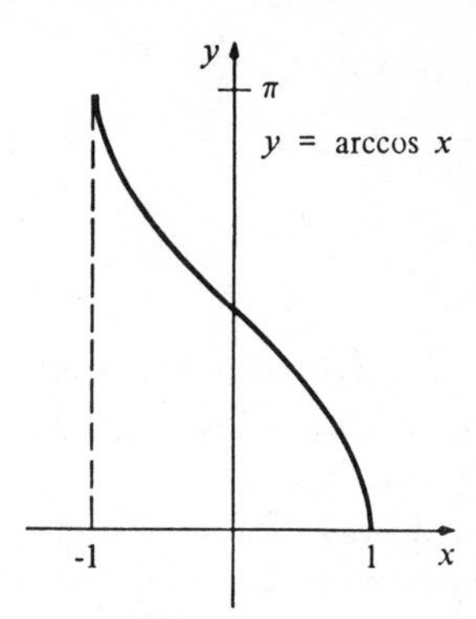

Fig. 9-5

The values of the function $\arccos x$ are determined by the following two properties.

$$\begin{aligned} &\cos(\arccos x) = x, \\ &0 \leq \arccos x \leq \pi. \end{aligned} \tag{5}$$

Example 3. Find the value of arccos 0.3652.

Solution. In the table we find $\cos 68°30' = 0.3665$ and $\cos 68°40' = 0.3638$. Thus $0.3652 = \cos 68°35'$ to the nearest minute, or $\arccos 0.3652 = 68°35'$.

Example 4. Prove $\arcsin x + \arccos x = \pi/2$ for all x with $|x| \leq 1$.

Solution. Using the identity $\cos \alpha = \sin(\pi/2 - \alpha)$, we obtain

$$\sin\left(\frac{\pi}{2} - \arccos x\right) = \cos(\arccos x) = x = \sin(\arcsin x).$$

Now $0 \leq \arccos x \leq \pi$ implies $\pi/2 \geq \pi/2 - \arccos x \geq -\pi/2$. Since $\arcsin x$ and $\pi/2 - \arccos x$ both lie in the interval between $-\pi/2$ and $\pi/2$, $\sin(\arcsin x) = \sin(\pi/2 - \arccos x)$ implies that $\arcsin x = \pi/2 - \arccos x$.

Problems 9–1

1. Sketch the graph of the equation $x = \cos y$.

Establish identities for the expressions in 2—6 in terms of t.

2. $\sin(\arccos t)$.

3. $\tan(\arccos t)$.

4. cot (arccos t). **5.** sec (arccos t).

6. csc (arccos t).

Evaluate the expressions in 7—14 (in degrees and minutes).

7. arcsin 0.2193. **8.** arcsin 0.9876.

9. arcsin -0.4672. **10.** arcsin 0.0013.

11. arccos 0.3197. **12.** arccos 0.7777.

13. arccos -0.6453. **14.** arccos 0.0097.

9–2 The Inverse Tangent, Cotangent, Secant, and Cosecant Functions

From consideration of the graph of the tangent function (Fig. 9-6) we find it natural to choose the interval from $-\pi/2$ to $\pi/2$ for the restricted domain to obtain an inverse. By reflecting this portion of the graph about the line $y = x$ we obtain the graph of the inverse function (Fig. 9-7). This function is denoted by arctan x (the arc tangent of x) or $\tan^{-1} x$ (the inverse tangent of x). The function arctan x has domain the set of all real numbers and range $-\pi/2 < y < \pi/2$. It is uniquely determined by the following two properties.

$$\tan(\arctan x) = x,$$
$$-\frac{\pi}{2} < \arctan x < \frac{\pi}{2}. \tag{6}$$

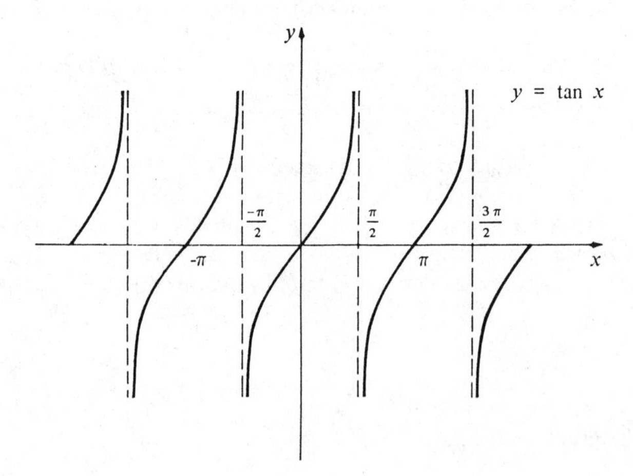

Fig. 9-6

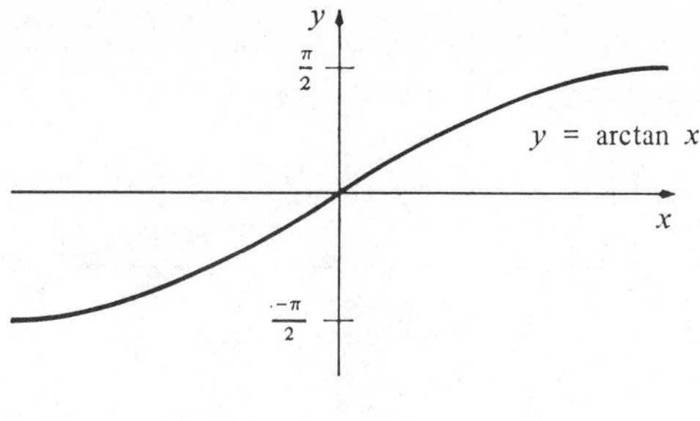

Fig. 9-7

For the cotangent function, depicted in Fig. 9-8, we choose the restricted domain $0 < x < \pi$. The inverse function $\operatorname{arccot} x$ is then determined by the two conditions

$$\begin{aligned} 0 < \operatorname{arccot} x < \pi, \\ \cot(\operatorname{arccot} x) = x. \end{aligned} \tag{7}$$

The domain of the function $\operatorname{arccot} x$ is the set of all real numbers. The graph is depicted in Fig. 9-9.

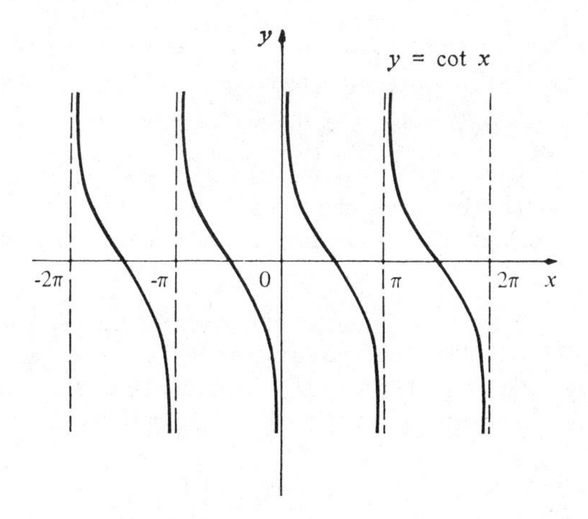

Fig. 9-8

Example 1. Show that $\arctan x + \operatorname{arccot} x = \pi/2$ for any number x.

Solution. $\tan(\pi/2 - \operatorname{arccot} x) = \cot(\operatorname{arccot} x) = x = \tan(\arctan x)$, using the identity $\tan(\pi/2 - \theta) = \cot\theta$. Since $0 < \operatorname{arccot} x < \pi$, we have $-\pi/2 < \pi/2 - \operatorname{arccot} x < \pi/2$. Thus $\pi/2 - \operatorname{arccot} x$ satisfies the two conditions of (3), and we have $\pi/2 - \operatorname{arccot} x = \arctan x$.

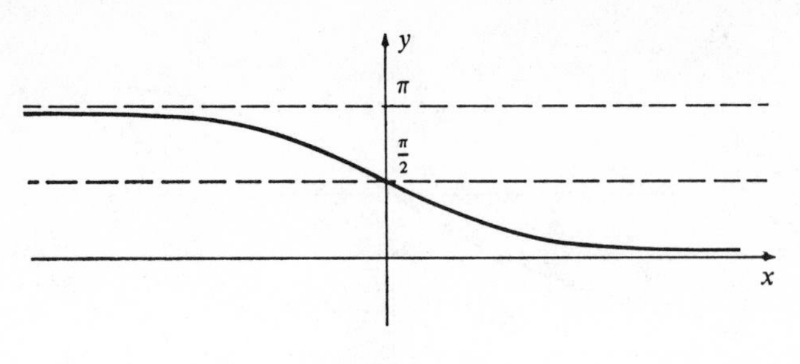

Fig. 9-9

Example 2. Use right triangle trigonometry to verify that $\arctan x = \arcsin x/\sqrt{1+x^2}$.

Solution. Let $\theta = \arctan x$ and consider the right triangle depicted in Fig. 9-10.

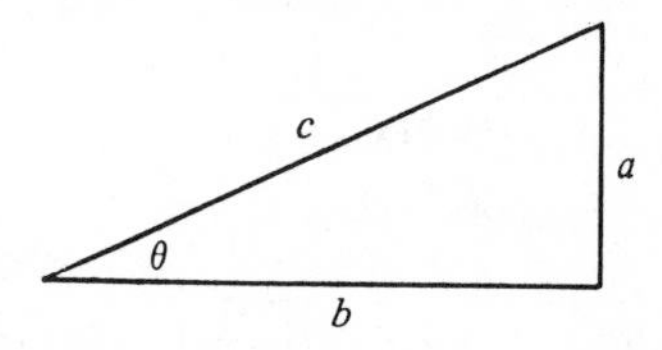

Fig. 9-10

The tangent of θ is a/b, so $x = a/b$. Thus $c = \sqrt{a^2+b^2} = \sqrt{b^2x^2+b^2} = b\sqrt{x^2+1}$. The sine of θ is $a/c = bx/b\sqrt{x^2+1} = x/\sqrt{x^2+1}$. Then $\sin\theta = x/\sqrt{x^2+1}$, and $-\pi/2 < \theta < \pi/2$, imply $\theta = \arcsin x/\sqrt{x^2+1}$.

Example 3. In calculus it is shown that the area bounded by the curve $y = 1/(1+x^2)$, the x axis and the vertical lines $x = a$ and $x = b$ with $a < b$, is given by the formula $\arctan b - \arctan a$. (See Fig. 9-11.) What is the area when $a = 1, b = 2$?

Solution. The corresponding number of degrees is $\arctan 2 - \arctan 1 = 63°26' - 45° = 18°26'$. To obtain the area we need to find the radian measure of this angle. Now $18°26' = 18.43°$ so the radian measure is $(18.43) \cdot (0.01745) = 0.3216$. (The reader can convince himself this answer is at least reasonable by

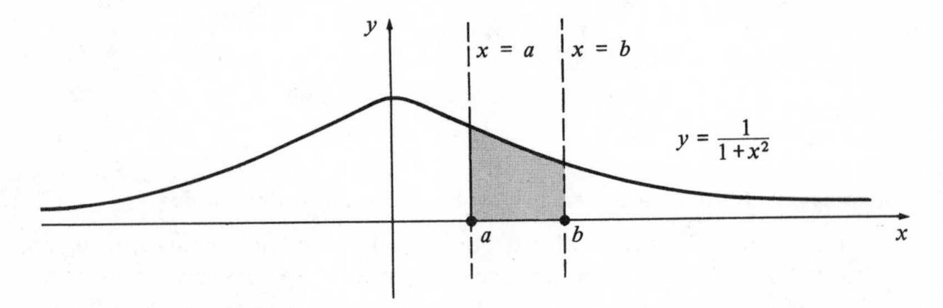

Fig. 9-11

computing the areas of appropriate rectangles. For example, in Fig. 9-12 the area of the smaller rectangle is 1/5 and the area of the larger rectangle is 1/2, so the area bounded by the curve is between 1/5 and 1/2.)

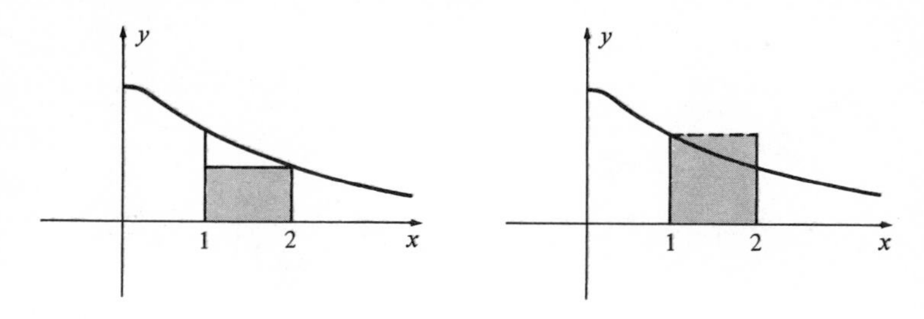

Fig. 9-12

In order to consider inverse functions for the secant and cosecant functions we again need to consider restricted domains, as evidenced by their graphs in Fig. 9-13. In these cases, however, there is not complete uniformity among authors in the choice of domain. We take $0 \leq x \leq \pi$ for the restriction of the domain for the secant function and $-\pi/2 \leq x \leq \pi/2$ for the restriction of the domain of the cosecant function. Then the inverse functions are determined by the following conditions.

$$\sec(\operatorname{arcsec} x) = x, \quad 0 \leq \operatorname{arcsec} x \leq \pi. \tag{8}$$

$$\csc(\operatorname{arccsc} x) = x, \quad -\pi/2 \leq \operatorname{arccsc} x \leq \pi/2. \tag{9}$$

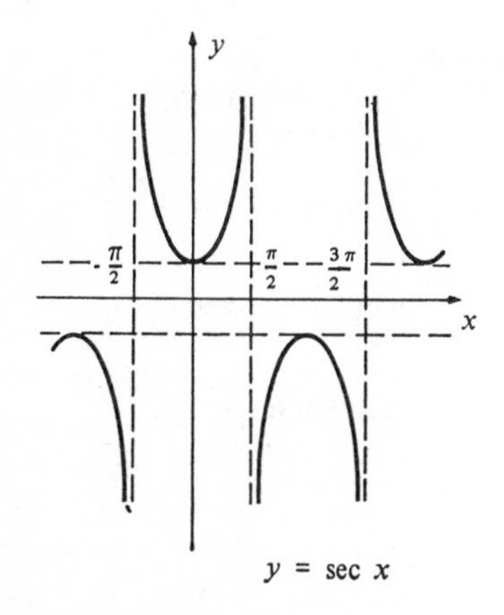

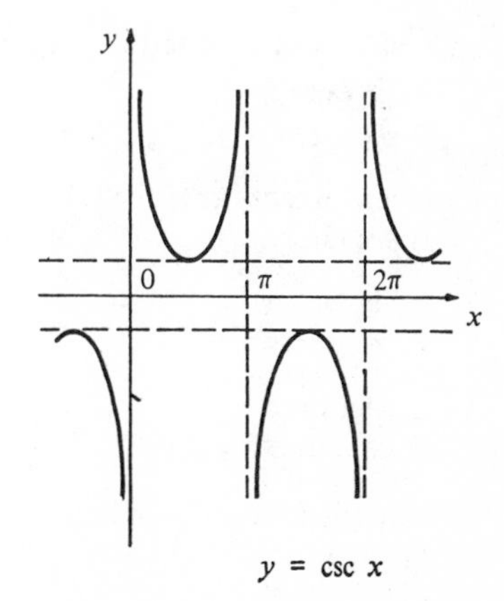

Fig. 9-13

The graphs of these functions are depicted in Fig. 9-14. This choice of range for these inverse functions is motivated by Example 4. The function arcsec x has domain $|x| \geq 1$ and range $0 \leq y \leq \pi$, $y \neq \pi/2$. The function arccsc x has domain $|x| \geq 1$ and range $-\pi/2 \leq y \leq \pi/2$, $y \neq 0$.

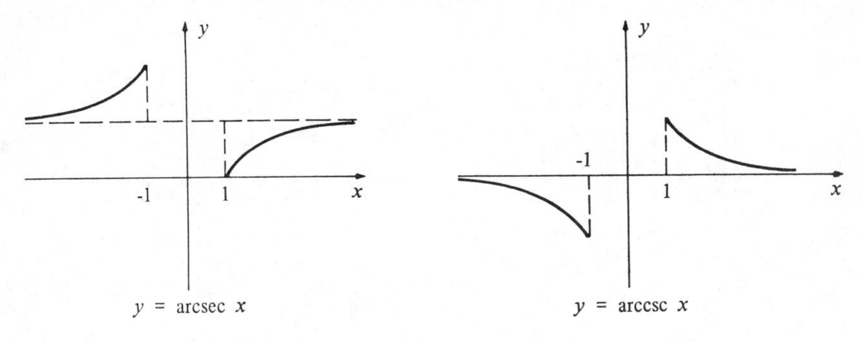

Fig. 9-14

Example 4. Verify that arcsec x + arccsc $x = \pi/2$ for $|x| \geq 1$.

Solution. $\sec(\pi/2 - \text{arccsc}\, x) = \csc(\text{arccsc}\, x) = x$. With $-\pi/2 \leq \text{arccsc}\, x \leq \pi/2$, we have $0 \leq \pi/2 - \text{arccsc}\, x \leq \pi$, so $\pi/2 - \text{arccsc}\, x = \text{arcsec}\, x$.

Problems 9–2

1. Sketch the graph of the equation $x = \tan y$.
2. Sketch the graph of the equation $x = \cot y$.
3. Sketch the graph of the equation $x = \csc y$.
4. Sketch the graph of the equation $x = \sec y$.

Establish identities in terms of t for the expressions in 5—8.

5. a) sin (arctan t), b) cos (arctan t), c) cot (arctan t), d) sec (arctan t), e) csc (arctan t).
6. a) sin (arccot t), b) cos (arccot t), c) tan (arccot t), d) sec (arccot t), e) csc (arccot t).
7. a) sin (arcsec t), b) cos (arcsec t), c) tan (arcsec t), d) cot (arcsec t), e) csc (arcsec t).
8. a) sin (arccsc t), b) cos (arccsc t), c) tan (arccsc t), d) cot (arccsc t), e) sec (arccsc t).

Evaluate the following (in degrees and minutes).

9. arctan 8.
10. arccot 38.
11. arcsec 22.
12. arccsc $\sqrt{7}$.

13. arccot 0.514.

14. arctan 0.971.

15. arctan −9.555.

16. arctan −16.67.

17. arccot −0.317.

18. arccot −986.4.

19. arctan 6.222 + arcsin 0.2256.

20. arccot 3.927 + arccos 0.9362.

9–3 Trigonometric Equations

The equation $\sin x = y$ is a special example of a trigonometric equation. It has solutions if $|y| \le 1$, and it has no solutions if $|y| > 1$. In Section 9–1 we investigated means of finding one solution, in case $|y| \le 1$, namely $x = \arcsin y$. How does one describe the complete set of solutions? From the identities, $\sin x = \sin (x + 2\pi n)$, and $\sin x = \sin (\pi - x)$, we see that if x is a solution then so are $x + 2\pi n$ and $\pi - x + 2\pi n$, for $n = 0, \pm 1, \pm 2, \ldots$, that is, x plus *even* multiples of π or $-x$ plus *odd* multiples of π. This can be described in one expression: $(-1)^n x + \pi n$, $n = 0, \pm 1, \pm 2, \ldots$, since $(-1)^n$ is 1 if n is even, and -1 if n is odd. This gives at most two solutions in each interval of length 2π, and an examination of the graph of $y = \sin x$ in Fig. 9-15 will

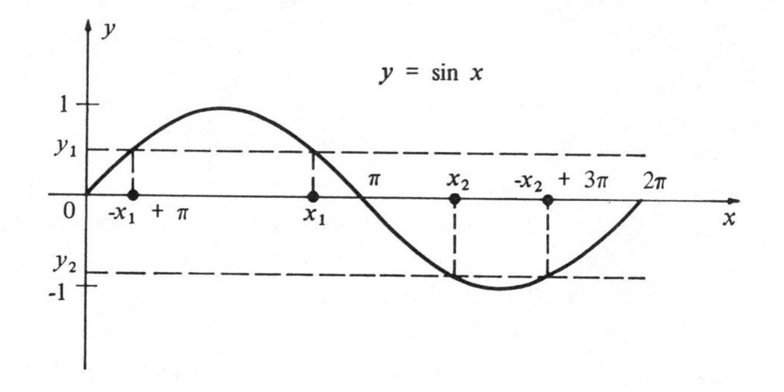

Fig. 9-15

convince you that these are all of the solutions. Thus a complete set of solutions for $\sin x = y$, with $|y| \le 1$, is given by

$$x = (-1)^n \arcsin y + \pi n, \quad n = 0, \pm 1, \pm 2, \ldots . \tag{10}$$

For the equation $\cos x = y$ the identities $\cos x = \cos (x + 2\pi n)$ and $\cos x = \cos (-x)$ give solutions

$$x = \pm \arccos y + 2\pi n, \quad n = 0, \pm 1, \pm 2, \ldots, \tag{11}$$

for $|y| \le 1$, and again an examination of the graph of $y = \cos x$ will convince you this is a complete set of solutions.

Consider the equation $\tan x = y$. This function is periodic of period π and one-to-one between any two odd multiples of $\pi/2$. Thus a complete set of solutions to $\tan x = y$ is given by

$$x = \arctan y + \pi n, \quad n = 0, \pm 1, \pm 2, \ldots. \tag{12}$$

There are solutions for every value of y. You will be asked to find the complete sets of solutions for the equations $\cot x = y$, $\sec x = y$, and $\csc x = y$ in the problems at the end of this section.

We now look at more complicated equations $f(x) = y$ involving the trigonometric functions. Many of these equations can be solved according to the following steps.

1. Express $f(x) - y$ in terms of a single trigonometric function, or express it as a product of factors, each involving at most one trigonometric function.
2. Set each of these factors equal to 0 and, using algebraic methods, solve for the trigonometric function.
3. Use the inverse trigonometric functions to find the solutions.

These steps are illustrated in the following examples.

Example 1. Solve $3 \sin^2 x + 4 \sin x + 6 = 5$.

Solution. The expression $3 \sin^2 x + 4 \sin x + 1$ involves only one trigonometric function so nothing needs to be done for step 1. For step 2, $3 \sin^2 x + 4 \sin x + 1 = 0$ can be solved for $\sin x$ by means of the quadratic formula; namely,

$$\sin x = \frac{-4 \pm \sqrt{16 - 12}}{6} = -\frac{2}{3} \pm \frac{1}{3}.$$

Both values, -1 and $-1/3$, lie in the image of $\sin x$ and hence in the domain of $\arcsin x$. Thus solutions are given by $x = \arcsin(-1)$ and $x = \arcsin(-1/3)$. A complete set of solutions is given by

$$x = (-1)^n \arcsin(-1) + \pi n \quad \text{and} \quad x = (-1)^n \arcsin\left(-\frac{1}{3}\right) + \pi n,$$

$$n = 0, \pm 1, \pm 2, \ldots.$$

One may find approximate numerical solutions by using the methods of the last sections, obtaining $\arcsin(-1) = -90°$ and $\arcsin(-1/3) = -19°28'$. (See Example 1 of Section 9–1.)

Example 2. Solve $\tan 2\alpha + \cot 2\alpha = 5$.

Solution. We use the relation between tangent and cotangent to write $\tan 2\alpha + \cot 2\alpha - 5 = \tan 2\alpha + 1/\tan 2\alpha - 5$. Both sides are undefined when $\tan 2\alpha = 0$, so we may assume $\tan 2\alpha \neq 0$. In this case, $\tan 2\alpha + 1/\tan 2\alpha - 5 = 0$ exactly when $[\tan 2\alpha + 1/\tan 2\alpha - 5] \tan 2\alpha = 0$. Multiplying through we obtain the equation

$$\tan^2 2\alpha - 5 \tan 2\alpha + 1 = 0,$$

which can be solved for $\tan 2\alpha$ by means of the quadratic formula. This gives solutions

$$\tan 2\alpha = \frac{5 \pm \sqrt{25 - 4}}{2} = \frac{5 \pm \sqrt{21}}{2}.$$

A complete set of solutions is now given by

$$\alpha = \frac{1}{2}\left[\arctan\left(\frac{5 \pm \sqrt{21}}{2}\right) + \pi n\right], \quad n = 0, \pm 1, \pm 2, \ldots.$$

Example 3. Solve $5 \sin \beta = \sin \beta/2$.

Solution. We use the identity $\sin \beta = 2 \sin \beta/2 \cos \beta/2$ to get $5 \sin \beta - \sin \beta/2 = 10 \sin \beta/2 \cos \beta/2 - \sin \beta/2 = \sin \beta/2\,(10 \cos \beta/2 - 1)$. Setting each of these factors equal to 0, we get solutions $\beta = 2((-1)^n \arcsin 0 + \pi n) = 2\pi n$ and $\beta = 2[\pm\arccos 1/10 + 2\pi n]$, $n = 0, \pm 1, \pm 2, \ldots$.

Example 4. Solve $\sin 2\alpha \cos \alpha = \sin 3\alpha$.

Solution. We express this in terms of $\sin \alpha$:

$$\begin{aligned}
\sin 2\alpha \cos \alpha - \sin 3\alpha &= (2 \sin \alpha \cos \alpha) \cos \alpha - (3 \sin \alpha - 4 \sin^3 \alpha) \\
&= 2 \sin \alpha \cos^2 \alpha - 3 \sin \alpha + 4 \sin^3 \alpha \\
&= 2 \sin \alpha\,(1 - \sin^2 \alpha) - 3 \sin \alpha + 4 \sin^3 \alpha \\
&= \sin \alpha\,(2 - 2 \sin^2 \alpha - 3 + 4 \sin^2 \alpha) \\
&= \sin \alpha\,(2 \sin^2 \alpha - 1).
\end{aligned}$$

Setting each factor equal to 0, we obtain the equations $\sin \alpha = 0$ and $\sin^2 \alpha = 1/2$; i.e., $\sin \alpha = 0$ and $\sin \alpha = \pm 1/\sqrt{2}$. Thus a complete set of solutions is given by

$$\alpha = \pi n \quad \text{and} \quad \alpha = (-1)^n \arcsin\left(\frac{\pm 1}{\sqrt{2}}\right) + \pi n, \quad n = 0, \pm 1, \pm 2, \ldots.$$

Example 5. Solve $2 \sin \alpha + 5 \cos \alpha = 5$.

Solution. We can express this in terms of the sine function alone by means of the identity $\cos^2 \alpha + \sin^2 \alpha = 1$. To apply this identity we need to transform the equation to one involving sine and the *square* of cosine. This is effected by writing the equation as $5 \cos \alpha = 5 - 2 \sin \alpha$ and squaring both sides. This gives us

$$25 \cos^2 \alpha = 25 - 10 \sin \alpha + 4 \sin^2 \alpha.$$

Substituting $1 - \sin^2 \alpha$ for $\cos^2 \alpha$ and collecting terms yields

$$29 \sin^2 \alpha - 20 \sin \alpha = 0.$$

(This new equation may have more solutions than the original equation; thus the solutions must be checked in the original equation.) Since this equation says that $(\sin \alpha)(29 \sin \alpha - 20) = 0$, solutions are given by

$$\sin \alpha = 0, \quad \text{or} \quad \sin \alpha = \frac{20}{29};$$

i.e., $\alpha = \pi n$, $\alpha = \arcsin \frac{20}{29} + 2\pi n$, and $\alpha = -\arcsin \frac{20}{29} + (2n+1)\pi$, $n = 0, \pm 1, \pm 2, \ldots$. It is necessary to check which of these solutions satisfy the original equation. First,

$$2 \sin \pi n + 5 \cos \pi n = \begin{cases} 5 & \text{if } n \text{ is even,} \\ -5 & \text{if } n \text{ is odd.} \end{cases}$$

Thus $\alpha = 2\pi n$, $n = 0, \pm 1, \pm 2, \ldots$, are solutions. Second,

$$2 \sin \left(\arcsin \frac{20}{29} + 2\pi n\right) + 5 \cos \left(\arcsin \frac{20}{29} + 2\pi n\right)$$
$$= 2\left(\frac{20}{29}\right) + 5\sqrt{1 - \left(\frac{20}{29}\right)^2} = 5,$$

and $\alpha = \arcsin \frac{20}{29} + 2\pi n$, $n = 0, \pm 1, \pm 2, \ldots$, are solutions. Finally,

$$2 \sin \left(-\arcsin \frac{20}{29} + (2n+1)\pi\right) + 5 \cos \left(-\arcsin \frac{20}{29} + (2n+1)\pi\right)$$
$$= 2 \sin \left(\arcsin \frac{20}{29}\right) - 5 \cos \left(\arcsin \frac{20}{29}\right) = 2\left(\frac{20}{29}\right) - 5\left(\frac{21}{29}\right) = -\frac{65}{29} \neq 5.$$

Thus there are no additional solutions.

Problems 9–3

Solve the following trigonometric equations.

1. $\sin t = \cot t$.

2. $y = \cot x$.

3. $\sin \beta = 2 \cos \beta \sin \beta$.

4. $y = \sec x$.

5. $y = \csc x$.

6. $8 \tan x - 13 + 5 \tan^2 x = 3$.

7. $\sin x = 2 \cos x$.

8. $\sin 5x = 5 \cos 5x$.

9. $4 \sin t = 3 \cos^2 t + 3$.

10. $5 \sin^2 t - 4 \cos^2 t = 0$.

11. $5 \sec \theta \tan \theta = \sec^2 \theta$.

12. $\sec^2 t = 2 - \tan^2 t$.

13. $4 \sec x \tan x - \tan^2 x = 2$.

14. $4 \cot y \cos^2 y - 4 \cos^2 y = 2 \cot y - 2$.

15. $8 \sec y = \cot y + \tan y$.

16. $14 \sin y - 11 \csc y = 0$.

17. $5 \sin x - 4 \sin 2x = 0$.

18. $3 \sec t \tan t = 4 \sin t$.

19. $\sqrt{2} \sin \theta + 5 \cos 2\theta = 4$.

20. $3 \tan^2 t - 8 \tan t = 16$.

21. $4 \cot t + 2 = \cot^2 t$.

22. $\tan^2 x - \cot^2 x = 1$.

23. $\cos^2 5t - \sin^2 5t = 0.59$.

24. $\sin^2 x - \cos^2 x = 1/8$.

9-4 Simple Harmonic Motion

When an object, supported by a steel spring, is pulled down from its rest position and then released, it oscillates up and down as indicated in Fig. 9-16. The motion that the object undergoes is called *simple harmonic motion*. This type of motion is a consequence of the fact that the force exerted by the spring on the object, which always tends to bring it back to the rest position, is proportional to the distance of the object from the rest position (Hooke's Law).

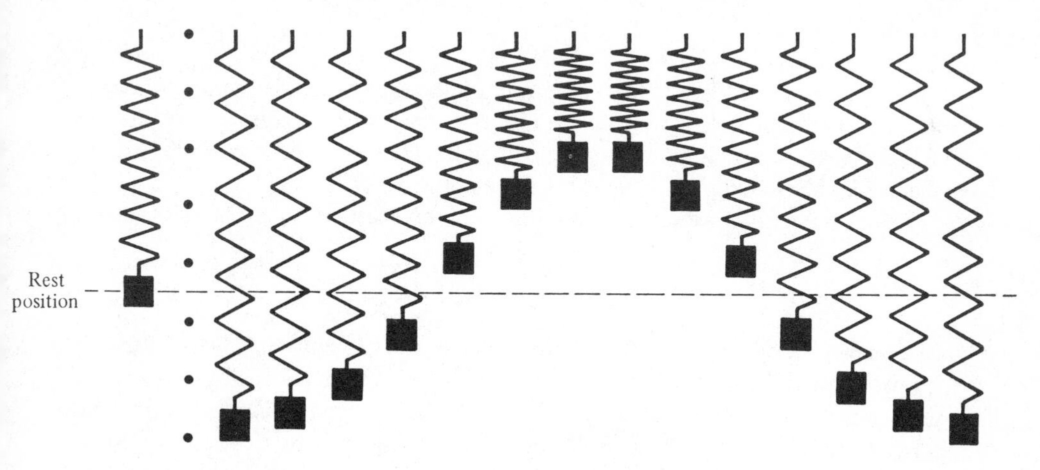

Fig. 9-16

To describe simple harmonic motion by figuring out the motion of an object supported by a spring requires a knowledge of physics and calculus. A simple method is to consider the shadow cast by an object which is moving at a constant speed around a circle. Admittedly it is not apparent that these two motions are the same, but they are, and this fact is one of the beautiful insights of mathematical physics. Consider the situation illustrated in Fig. 9-17, where the sun's rays are coming in from the left and the object in the middle is traveling at a constant speed counterclockwise around the circle and casting a shadow on the wall at the right.

The position of the object on the circle is given by the angle the line drawn from the object to the center of the circle makes with a horizontal line. This angle is labeled α in the figure. Since we know that the object is traveling around the circle at a constant speed, its motion is specified by two quantities: where it started and how fast it is going. Suppose t is the time, in seconds, since the motion started. Then at the start, when $t = 0$, α will have some value, say θ. If v is the speed of the object in feet per second, then after t seconds the object will have traveled vt feet around the circle. This will

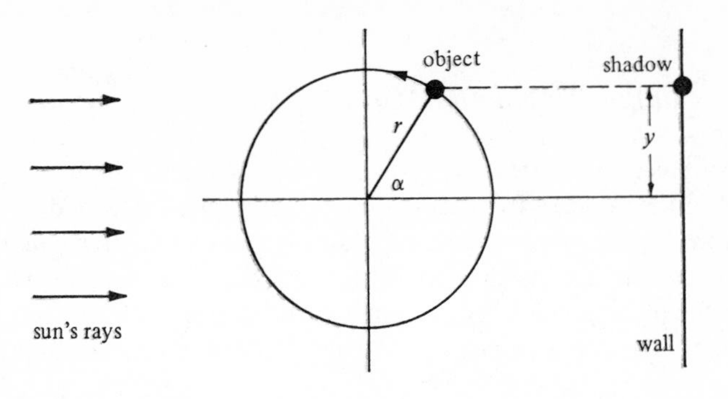

Fig. 9-17

increase α (measured in radians) by an amount vt/r, where r is the radius of the circle. Thus $\alpha = \theta + (v/r)t$. The number v/r is called the *angular velocity* of the object and is commonly denoted by ω. Hence we have $\alpha = \theta + \omega t$, where θ is the starting angle and ω is the angular velocity.

Now we wish to describe the motion of the shadow. It is readily seen that $y = r \sin \alpha$; i.e.,

$$y = r \sin (\omega t + \theta). \tag{13}$$

This is the general equation describing simple harmonic motion. The number r is called the *amplitude* of the motion; for the object on the spring it is the maximum distance the object gets away from the rest position—for the shadow it is the distance from the middle of the shadow's path to either extreme point. The number $\omega/2\pi$ is referred to as the *frequency* of the motion; indeed, since the angle α increases by ω every second, the shadow (or the spring) bobs up and down $\omega/2\pi$ times each second. The number θ represents a *phase shift* (see Section 3–4); it simply describes where things are at $t = 0$. For example, the two motions described by $3 \sin (2t + \pi/2)$ and $3 \sin (2t + \pi)$ may be considered as the same motion started at different times. They are "out of phase."

Consider the result of adding two simple harmonic motions with the same frequency. This is described by an expression of the form

$$A \sin (\omega t + a) + B \sin (\omega t + b). \tag{14}$$

Does this again describe simple harmonic motion, i.e. can we find C and θ for which

$$A \sin (\omega t + a) + B \sin (\omega t + b) = C \sin (\omega t + \theta)? \tag{15}$$

Applying the addition formula to both sides of this equation, we get

$$(A \cos a + B \cos b) \sin \omega t + (A \sin a + B \sin b) \cos \omega t$$
$$= (C \cos \theta) \sin \omega t + (C \sin \theta) \cos \omega t. \tag{16}$$

If we can find C and θ such that

$$C\cos\theta = A\cos a + B\cos b \quad \text{and} \qquad C\sin\theta = A\sin a + B\sin b, \tag{17}$$

we will have solved (16) and hence (15). It is indeed the case, if u and v are any real numbers, that we can find a nonnegative real number C and an angle θ such that $C\cos\theta = u$ and $C\sin\theta = v$. To see this let $C = \sqrt{u^2 + v^2}$. If $C = 0$ then $u = 0$ and $v = 0$ and we may choose θ to be anything. If $C \neq 0$ then we must solve the pair of equations

$$\cos\theta = \frac{u}{\sqrt{u^2+v^2}} = x \qquad \sin\theta = \frac{v}{\sqrt{u^2+v^2}} = y. \tag{18}$$

But (x, y) is a point on the unit circle and hence is $P(\theta) = (\cos\theta, \sin\theta)$ for some angle θ. Formulas for C and θ are given in the following theorem.

Theorem 1. *The sum of two simple harmonic motions with the same frequency is again simple harmonic motion, i.e., given real numbers A and B and angles a and b there is a number C and an angle θ for which $A\sin(\omega t + a) + B\sin(\omega t + b) = C\sin(\omega t + \theta)$. If $u = A\cos a + B\cos b$ and $v = A\sin a + B\sin b$, then a solution is given by*

$$C = \sqrt{u^2 + v^2}$$

and

$$\theta = \begin{cases} \arctan(v/u) & \text{if } u > 0 \\ \arctan(v/u) + 180^\circ & \text{if } u < 0 \\ 90^\circ & \text{if } u = 0 \text{ and } v \geq 0 \\ -90^\circ & \text{if } u = 0 \text{ and } v < 0. \end{cases}$$

Proof. We have already observed that $C = \sqrt{u^2 + v^2}$, and that a solution will be given by a solution of the pair of equations $C\cos\theta = u$ and $C\sin\theta = v$. If $u = 0$, then $C = \sqrt{u^2 + v^2} = \sqrt{v^2} = |v|$, and we require that $\cos\theta = 0$ and $\sin\theta = \frac{v}{|v|}$. Thus we choose $\theta = 90^\circ$ if $v \geq 0$ and $\theta = -90^\circ$ if $v < 0$. If $u \neq 0$, we divide the two equations and get $\tan\theta = v/u$. Hence $\theta = \arctan(v/u)$ if (u, v) lies in the first or fourth quadrant, i.e., if $u > 0$, and $\theta = \arctan(v/u) + 180^\circ$ if (u, v) lies in the second or third quadrant, i.e. if $u < 0$.

Example 1. Solve the equation $4\sin 2t + 5\cos 2t = C\sin(\omega t + \theta)$ for C, ω, and θ.

Solution. In the notation of the theorem, $a = b = 0$, $u = A = 4$ and $v = B = 5$. Thus a solution is given by $\omega = 2$, $C = \sqrt{4^2 + 5^2} = \sqrt{41}$, and $\theta = \arctan 0.8 = 38^\circ 40'$.

Example 2. Solve the equation $3 \sin (4t - 72°31') + 9 \sin (4t + 204°35') = C \sin (\omega t + \theta)$, for C, ω, and θ.

Solution. $v = 3 \sin -72°31' + 9 \sin 204°35'$

$$= 3(-0.9538) + 9(-0.4160) = -6.6054$$

and

$$u = 3 \cos -72°31' + 9 \cos 204°35'$$
$$= 3(0.3004) + 9(-0.9094) = -7.2834.$$

Thus $C = \sqrt{(6.6054)^2 + (7.2834)^2} = 9.83$, $\omega = 4$, and $\theta = \arctan (-6.6054)/(-7.2834) + 180° = \arctan 0.9069 + 180° = 42°12' + 180° = 222°12'$.

Example 3. Solve the equation $\sin (3x + 13°) + 2 \cos (3x + 73°) = C \sin (3x + \theta)$ for C and θ.

Solution. Using the identity $\cos (3x + 73°) = \sin (3x + 163°)$, we can apply Theorem 1, with $A = 1$, $B = 2$, $a = 13°$, and $b = 163°$. This gives

$$v = \sin 13° + 2 \sin 163°$$
$$= 0.2250 + 2(0.2924) = 0.8098,$$

and

$$u = \cos 13° + 2 \cos 163°$$
$$= 0.9744 + 2(-0.9563) = -0.9382.$$

Thus $C = \sqrt{(0.8098)^2 + (0.9382)^2} = 1.24$, and

$$\theta = \arctan (0.8098)/(-0.9382) + 180°$$
$$= \arctan -0.8625 + 180° = -40°47' + 180°$$
$$= 139°13'.$$

For an example of the result of adding two motions of different frequencies refer to Example 8 and Fig. 3-32 of section 3-4. In general, the result is not simple harmonic motion.

Problems 9–4

Solve the equations in 1—6 for C and θ. Find approximate values for C and θ.

1. $16 \sin (5t + 2°) + 4 \sin (5t + 17°) = C \sin (5t + \theta)$.

2. $\frac{1}{2} \sin \left(\frac{x}{2} + 23°\right) + \frac{1}{3} \sin \left(\frac{x}{2} + 32°\right) = C \sin \left(\frac{x}{2} + \theta\right)$.

3. $7 \sin (t + 5°) - 2 \cos (t - 75°) = C \sin (t + \theta)$.

4. $6 \cos (22x + 39°) + 18 \sin (22x - 14°) = C \sin (x + \theta)$.

5. $11 \cos (x + 22°) + 11 \cos (x + 5°) = C \sin (x + \theta)$.

6. $\sqrt{2} \sin (4t + 5°) + \sqrt{3} \cos (4t - 5°) = C \sin (4t + \theta)$.

In 7—10 a particle is moving at constant speed counterclockwise around a circle. Its shadow is projected on a wall as in Fig. 9-17. Find the equation $y = A \sin(\omega t + \theta)$, in each case, which describes the motion of the shadow. For each problem, A should represent the amplitude in *feet*, ω the angular velocity, with velocity measured in *radians per second*, and θ the starting angle in *radians*.

7. A particle starts at the lowest point on a circle of radius 2 feet, and makes 240 revolutions per minute.

8. A particle starts at the highest point on a circle of radius 5 feet, and makes 15 revolutions per second.

9. A particle starts at the far left point on a circle of radius 10 feet, and moves at a constant speed of 10 feet per second.

10. A particle starts at the far right position on a circle of radius 3 inches, and moves at a constant speed of 1000 feet per second.

Appendices

Table I. LOGARITHMS OF NUMBERS

N	0	1	2	3	4	5	6	7	8	9
1.0	.0000	.0043	.0086	.0128	.0170	.0212	.0253	.0294	.0334	.0374
1.1	.0414	.0453	.0492	.0531	.0569	.0607	.0645	.0682	.0719	.0755
1.2	.0792	.0828	.0864	.0899	.0934	.0969	.1004	.1038	.1072	.1106
1.3	.1139	.1173	.1206	.1239	.1271	.1303	.1335	.1367	.1399	.1430
1.4	.1461	.1492	.1523	.1553	.1584	.1614	.1644	.1673	.1703	.1732
1.5	.1761	.1790	.1818	.1847	.1875	.1903	.1931	.1959	.1987	.2014
1.6	.2041	.2068	.2095	.2122	.2148	.2175	.2201	.2227	.2253	.2279
1.7	.2304	.2330	.2355	.2380	.2405	.2430	.2455	.2480	.2504	.2529
1.8	.2553	.2577	.2601	.2625	.2648	.2672	.2695	.2718	.2742	.2765
1.9	.2788	.2810	.2833	.2856	.2878	.2900	.2923	.2945	.2967	.2989
2.0	.3010	.3032	.3054	.3075	.3096	.3118	.3139	.3160	.3181	.3201
2.1	.3222	.3243	.3263	.3284	.3304	.3324	.3345	.3365	.3385	.3404
2.2	.3424	.3444	.3464	.3483	.3502	.3522	.3541	.3560	.3579	.3598
2.3	.3617	.3636	.3655	.3674	.3692	.3711	.3729	.3747	.3766	.3784
2.4	.3802	.3820	.3838	.3856	.3874	.3892	.3909	.3927	.3945	.3962
2.5	.3979	.3997	.4014	.4031	.4048	.4065	.4082	.4099	.4116	.4133
2.6	.4150	.4166	.4183	.4200	.4216	.4232	.4249	.4265	.4281	.4298
2.7	.4314	.4330	.4346	.4362	.4378	.4393	.4409	.4425	.4440	.4456
2.8	.4472	.4487	.4502	.4518	.4533	.4548	.4564	.4579	.4594	.4609
2.9	.4624	.4639	.4654	.4669	.4683	.4698	.4713	.4728	.4742	.4757
3.0	.4771	.4786	.4800	.4814	.4829	.4843	.4857	.4871	.4886	.4900
3.1	.4914	.4928	.4942	.4955	.4969	.4983	.4997	.5011	.5024	.5038
3.2	.5051	.5065	.5079	.5092	.5105	.5119	.5132	.5145	.5159	.5172
3.3	.5185	.5198	.5211	.5224	.5237	.5250	.5263	.5276	.5289	.5302
3.4	.5315	.5328	.5340	.5353	.5366	.5378	.5391	.5403	.5416	.5428
3.5	.5441	.5453	.5465	.5478	.5490	.5502	.5514	.5527	.5539	.5551
3.6	.5563	.5575	.5587	.5599	.5611	.5623	.5635	.5647	.5658	.5670
3.7	.5682	.5694	.5705	.5717	.5729	.5740	.5752	.5763	.5775	.5786
3.8	.5798	.5809	.5821	.5832	.5843	.5855	.5866	.5877	.5888	.5899
3.9	.5911	.5922	.5933	.5944	.5955	.5966	.5977	.5988	.5999	.6010
4.0	.6021	.6031	.6042	.6053	.6064	.6075	.6085	.6096	.6107	.6117
4.1	.6128	.6138	.6149	.6160	.6170	.6180	.6191	.6201	.6212	.6222
4.2	.6232	.6243	.6253	.6263	.6274	.6284	.6294	.6304	.6314	.6325
4.3	.6335	.6345	.6355	.6365	.6375	.6385	.6395	.6405	.6415	.6425
4.4	.6435	.6444	.6454	.6464	.6474	.6484	.6493	.6503	.6513	.6522
4.5	.6532	.6542	.6551	.6561	.6571	.6580	.6590	.6599	.6609	.6618
4.6	.6628	.6637	.6646	.6656	.6665	.6675	.6684	.6693	.6702	.6712
4.7	.6721	.6730	.6739	.6749	.6758	.6767	.6776	.6785	.6794	.6803
4.8	.6812	.6821	.6830	.6839	.6848	.6857	.6866	.6875	.6884	.6893
4.9	.6902	.6911	.6920	.6928	.6937	.6946	.6955	.6964	.6972	.6981
5.0	.6990	.6998	.7007	.7016	.7024	.7033	.7042	.7050	.7059	.7067
5.1	.7076	.7084	.7093	.7101	.7110	.7118	.7126	.7135	.7143	.7152
5.2	.7160	.7168	.7177	.7185	.7193	.7202	.7210	.7218	.7226	.7235
5.3	.7243	.7251	.7259	.7267	.7275	.7284	.7292	.7300	.7308	.7316
5.4	.7324	.7332	.7340	.7348	.7356	.7364	.7372	.7380	.7388	.7396
N	0	1	2	3	4	5	6	7	8	9

Table I. LOGARITHMS OF NUMBERS (CONT.)

N	0	1	2	3	4	5	6	7	8	9
5.5	.7404	.7412	.7419	.7427	.7435	.7443	.7451	.7459	.7466	.7474
5.6	.7482	.7490	.7497	.7505	.7513	.7520	.7528	.7536	.7543	.7551
5.7	.7559	.7566	.7574	.7582	.7589	.7597	.7604	.7612	.7619	.7627
5.8	.7634	.7642	.7649	.7657	.7664	.7672	.7679	.7686	.7694	.7701
5.9	.7709	.7716	.7723	.7731	.7738	.7745	.7752	.7760	.7767	.7774
6.0	.7782	.7789	.7796	.7803	.7810	.7818	.7825	.7832	.7839	.7846
6.1	.7853	.7860	.7868	.7875	.7882	.7889	.7896	.7903	.7910	.7917
6.2	.7924	.7931	.7938	.7945	.7952	.7959	.7966	.7973	.7980	.7987
6.3	.7993	.8000	.8007	.8014	.8021	.8028	.8035	.8041	.8048	.8055
6.4	.8062	.8069	.8075	.8082	.8089	.8096	.8102	.8109	.8116	.8122
6.5	.8129	.8136	.8142	.8149	.8156	.8162	.8169	.8176	.8182	.8189
6.6	.8195	.8202	.8209	.8215	.8222	.8228	.8235	.8241	.8248	.8254
6.7	.8261	.8267	.8274	.8280	.8287	.8293	.8299	.8306	.8312	.8319
6.8	.8325	.8331	.8338	.8344	.8351	.8357	.8363	.8370	.8376	.8382
6.9	.8388	.8395	.8401	.8407	.8414	.8420	.8426	.8432	.8439	.8445
7.0	.8451	.8457	.8463	.8470	.8476	.8482	.8488	.8494	.8500	.8506
7.1	.8513	.8519	.8525	.8531	.8537	.8543	.8549	.8555	.8561	.8567
7.2	.8573	.8579	.8585	.8591	.8597	.8603	.8609	.8615	.8621	.8627
7.3	.8633	.8639	.8645	.8651	.8657	.8663	.8669	.8675	.8681	.8686
7.4	.8692	.8698	.8704	.8710	.8716	.8722	.8727	.8733	.8739	.8745
7.5	.8751	.8756	.8762	.8768	.8774	.8779	.8785	.8791	.8797	.8802
7.6	.8808	.8814	.8820	.8825	.8831	.8837	.8842	.8848	.8854	.8859
7.7	.8865	.8871	.8876	.8882	.8887	.8893	.8899	.8904	.8910	.8915
7.8	.8921	.8927	.8932	.8938	.8943	.8949	.8954	.8960	.8965	.8971
7.9	.8976	.8982	.8987	.8993	.8998	.9004	.9009	.9015	.9020	.9025
8.0	.9031	.9036	.9042	.9047	.9053	.9058	.9063	.9069	.9074	.9079
8.1	.9085	.9090	.9096	.9101	.9106	.9112	.9117	.9122	.9128	.9133
8.2	.9138	.9143	.9149	.9154	.9159	.9165	.9170	.9175	.9180	.9186
8.3	.9191	.9196	.9201	.9206	.9212	.9217	.9222	.9227	.9232	.9238
8.4	.9243	.9248	.9253	.9258	.9263	.9269	.9274	.9279	.9284	.9289
8.5	.9294	.9299	.9304	.9309	.9315	.9320	.9325	.9330	.9335	.9340
8.6	.9345	.9350	.9355	.9360	.9365	.9370	.9375	.9380	.9385	.9390
8.7	.9395	.9400	.9405	.9410	.9415	.9420	.9425	.9430	.9435	.9440
8.8	.9445	.9450	.9455	.9460	.9465	.9469	.9474	.9479	.9484	.9489
8.9	.9494	.9499	.9504	.9509	.9513	.9518	.9523	.9528	.9533	.9538
9.0	.9542	.9547	.9552	.9557	.9562	.9566	.9571	.9576	.9581	.9586
9.1	.9590	.9595	.9600	.9605	.9609	.9614	.9619	.9624	.9628	.9633
9.2	.9638	.9643	.9647	.9652	.9657	.9661	.9666	.9671	.9675	.9680
9.3	.9685	.9689	.9694	.9699	.9703	.9708	.9713	.9717	.9722	.9727
9.4	.9731	.9736	.9741	.9745	.9750	.9754	.9759	.9763	.9768	.9773
9.5	.9777	.9782	.9786	.9791	.9795	.9800	.9805	.9809	.9814	.9818
9.6	.9823	.9827	.9832	.9836	.9841	.9845	.9850	.9854	.9859	.9863
9.7	.9868	.9872	.9877	.9881	.9886	.9890	.9894	.9899	.9903	.9908
9.8	.9912	.9917	.9921	.9926	.9930	.9934	.9939	.9943	.9948	.9952
9.9	.9956	.9961	.9965	.9969	.9974	.9978	.9983	.9987	.9991	.9996
N	0	1	2	3	4	5	6	7	8	9

Table II. VALUES OF TRIGONOMETRIC FUNCTIONS

Angle	Sin	Cos	Tan	Cot	Sec	Csc	Coangle
0°00′	.0000	1.0000	.0000	—	1.000	—	**90°00′**
10	.0029	1.0000	.0029	343.8	1.000	343.8	50
20	.0058	1.0000	.0058	171.9	1.000	171.9	40
30	.0087	1.0000	.0087	114.6	1.000	114.6	30
40	.0116	.9999	.0116	85.94	1.000	85.95	20
50	.0145	.9999	.0145	68.75	1.000	68.76	10
1°00′	.0175	.9998	.0175	57.29	1.000	57.30	**89°00′**
10	.0204	.9998	.0204	49.10	1.000	49.11	50
20	.0233	.9997	.0233	42.96	1.000	42.98	40
30	.0262	.9997	.0262	38.19	1.000	38.20	30
40	.0291	.9996	.0291	34.37	1.000	34.38	20
50	.0320	.9995	.0320	31.24	1.001	31.26	10
2°00′	.0349	.9994	.0349	28.64	1.001	28.65	**88°00′**
10	.0378	.9993	.0378	26.43	1.001	26.45	50
20	.0407	.9992	.0407	24.54	1.001	24.56	40
30	.0436	.9990	.0437	22.90	1.001	22.93	30
40	.0465	.9989	.0466	21.47	1.001	21.49	20
50	.0494	.9988	.0495	20.21	1.001	20.23	10
3°00′	.0523	.9986	.0524	19.08	1.001	19.11	**87°00′**
10	.0552	.9985	.0553	18.07	1.002	18.10	50
20	.0581	.9983	.0582	17.17	1.002	17.20	40
30	.0610	.9981	.0612	16.35	1.002	16.38	30
40	.0640	.9980	.0641	15.60	1.002	15.64	20
50	.0669	.9978	.0670	14.92	1.002	14.96	10
4°00′	.0698	.9976	.0699	14.30	1.002	14.34	**86°00′**
10	.0727	.9974	.0729	13.73	1.003	13.76	50
20	.0756	.9971	.0758	13.20	1.003	13.23	40
30	.0785	.9969	.0787	12.71	1.003	12.75	30
40	.0814	.9967	.0816	12.25	1.003	12.29	20
50	.0843	.9964	.0846	11.83	1.004	11.87	10
5°00′	.0872	.9962	.0875	11.43	1.004	11.47	**85°00′**
10	.0901	.9959	.0904	11.06	1.004	11.10	50
20	.0929	.9957	.0934	10.71	1.004	10.76	40
30	.0958	.9954	.0963	10.39	1.005	10.43	30
40	.0987	.9951	.0992	10.08	1.005	10.13	20
50	.1016	.9948	.1022	9.788	1.005	9.839	10
6°00′	.1045	.9945	.1051	9.514	1.006	9.567	**84°00′**
10	.1074	.9942	.1080	9.255	1.006	9.309	50
20	.1103	.9939	.1110	9.010	1.006	9.065	40
30	.1132	.9936	.1139	8.777	1.006	8.834	30
40	.1161	.9932	.1169	8.556	1.007	8.614	20
50	.1190	.9929	.1198	8.345	1.007	8.405	10
7°00′	.1219	.9925	.1228	8.144	1.008	8.206	**83°00′**
10	.1248	.9922	.1257	7.953	1.008	8.016	50
20	.1276	.9918	.1287	7.770	1.008	7.834	40
30	.1305	.9914	.1317	7.596	1.009	7.661	30
40	.1334	.9911	.1346	7.429	1.009	7.496	20
50	.1363	.9907	.1376	7.269	1.009	7.337	10
8°00′	.1392	.9903	.1405	7.115	1.010	7.185	**82°00′**
10	.1421	.9899	.1435	6.968	1.010	7.040	50
20	.1449	.9894	.1465	6.827	1.011	6.900	40
30	.1478	.9890	.1495	6.691	1.011	6.765	30
40	.1507	.9886	.1524	6.561	1.012	6.636	20
50	.1536	.9881	.1554	6.435	1.012	6.512	10
9°00′	.1564	.9877	.1584	6.314	1.012	6.392	**81°00′**
Coangle	Cos	Sin	Cot	Tan	Csc	Sec	Angle

Table II. VALUES OF TRIGONOMETRIC FUNCTIONS (CONT.)

Angle	Sin	Cos	Tan	Cot	Sec	Csc	Coangle
9°00′	.1564	.9877	.1584	6.314	1.012	6.392	**81°00′**
10	.1593	.9872	.1614	6.197	1.013	6.277	50
20	.1622	.9868	.1644	6.084	1.013	6.166	40
30	.1650	.9863	.1673	5.976	1.014	6.059	30
40	.1679	.9858	.1703	5.871	1.014	5.955	20
50	.1708	.9853	.1733	5.769	1.015	5.855	10
10°00′	.1736	.9848	.1763	5.671	1.015	5.759	**80°00′**
10	.1765	.9843	.1793	5.576	1.016	5.665	50
20	.1794	.9838	.1823	5.485	1.016	5.575	40
30	.1822	.9833	.1853	5.396	1.017	5.487	30
40	.1851	.9827	.1883	5.309	1.018	5.403	20
50	.1880	.9822	.1914	5.226	1.018	5.320	10
11°00′	.1908	.9816	.1944	5.145	1.019	5.241	**79°00′**
10	.1937	.9811	.1974	5.066	1.019	5.164	50
20	.1965	.9805	.2004	4.989	1.020	5.089	40
30	.1994	.9799	.2035	4.915	1.020	5.016	30
40	.2022	.9793	.2065	4.843	1.021	4.945	20
50	.2051	.9787	.2095	4.773	1.022	4.876	10
12°00′	.2079	.9781	.2126	4.705	1.022	4.810	**78°00′**
10	.2108	.9775	.2156	4.638	1.023	4.745	50
20	.2136	.9769	.2186	4.574	1.024	4.682	40
30	.2164	.9763	.2217	4.511	1.024	4.620	30
40	.2193	.9757	.2247	4.449	1.025	4.560	20
50	.2221	.9750	.2278	4.390	1.026	4.502	10
13°00′	.2250	.9744	.2309	4.331	1.026	4.445	**77°00′**
10	.2278	.9737	.2339	4.275	1.027	4.390	50
20	.2306	.9730	.2370	4.219	1.028	4.336	40
30	.2334	.9724	.2401	4.165	1.028	4.284	30
40	.2363	.9717	.2432	4.113	1.029	4.232	20
50	.2391	.9710	.2462	4.061	1.030	4.182	10
14°00′	.2419	.9703	.2493	4.011	1.031	4.134	**76°00′**
10	.2447	.9696	.2524	3.962	1.031	4.086	50
20	.2476	.9689	.2555	3.914	1.032	4.039	40
30	.2504	.9681	.2586	3.867	1.033	3.994	30
40	.2532	.9674	.2617	3.821	1.034	3.950	20
50	.2560	.9667	.2648	3.776	1.034	3.906	10
15°00′	.2588	.9659	.2679	3.732	1.035	3.864	**75°00′**
10	.2616	.9652	.2711	3.689	1.036	3.822	50
20	.2644	.9644	.2742	3.647	1.037	3.782	40
30	.2672	.9636	.2773	3.606	1.038	3.742	30
40	.2700	.9628	.2805	3.566	1.039	3.703	20
50	.2728	.9621	.2836	3.526	1.039	3.665	10
16°00′	.2756	.9613	.2867	3.487	1.040	3.628	**74°00′**
10	.2784	.9605	.2899	3.450	1.041	3.592	50
20	.2812	.9596	.2931	3.412	1.042	3.556	40
30	.2840	.9588	.2962	3.376	1.043	3.521	30
40	.2868	.9580	.2994	3.340	1.044	3.487	20
50	.2896	.9572	.3026	3.305	1.045	3.453	10
17°00′	.2924	.9563	.3057	3.271	1.046	3.420	**73°00′**
10	.2952	.9555	.3089	3.237	1.047	3.388	50
20	.2979	.9546	.3121	3.204	1.048	3.356	40
30	.3007	.9537	.3153	3.172	1.049	3.326	30
40	.3035	.9528	.3185	3.140	1.049	3.295	20
50	.3062	.9520	.3217	3.108	1.050	3.265	10
18°00′	.3090	.9511	.3249	3.078	1.051	3.236	**72°00′**
Coangle	Cos	Sin	Cot	Tan	Csc	Sec	Angle

Table II. VALUES OF TRIGONOMETRIC FUNCTIONS (CONT.)

Angle	Sin	Cos	Tan	Cot	Sec	Csc	Coangle
18°00′	.3090	.9511	.3249	3.078	1.051	3.236	**72°00′**
10	.3118	.9502	.3281	3.047	1.052	3.207	50
20	.3145	.9492	.3314	3.018	1.053	3.179	40
30	.3173	.9483	.3346	2.989	1.054	3.152	30
40	.3201	.9474	.3378	2.960	1.056	3.124	20
50	.3228	.9465	.3411	2.932	1.057	3.098	10
19°00′	.3256	.9455	.3443	2.904	1.058	3.072	**71°00′**
10	.3283	.9446	.3476	2.877	1.059	3.046	50
20	.3311	.9436	.3508	2.850	1.060	3.021	40
30	.3338	.9426	.3541	2.824	1.061	2.996	30
40	.3365	.9417	.3574	2.798	1.062	2.971	20
50	.3393	.9407	.3607	2.773	1.063	2.947	10
20°00′	.3420	.9397	.3640	2.747	1.064	2.924	**70°00′**
10	.3448	.9387	.3673	2.723	1.065	2.901	50
20	.3475	.9377	.3706	2.699	1.066	2.878	40
30	.3502	.9367	.3739	2.675	1.068	2.855	30
40	.3529	.9356	.3772	2.651	1.069	2.833	20
50	.3557	.9346	.3805	2.628	1.070	2.812	10
21°00′	.3584	.9336	.3839	2.605	1.071	2.790	**69°00′**
10	.3611	.9325	.3872	2.583	1.072	2.769	50
20	.3638	.9315	.3906	2.560	1.074	2.749	40
30	.3665	.9304	.3939	2.539	1.075	2.729	30
40	.3692	.9293	.3973	2.517	1.076	2.709	20
50	.3719	.9283	.4006	2.496	1.077	2.689	10
22°00′	.3746	.9272	.4040	2.475	1.079	2.669	**68°00′**
10	.3773	.9261	.4074	2.455	1.080	2.650	50
20	.3800	.9250	.4108	2.434	1.081	2.632	40
30	.3827	.9239	.4142	2.414	1.082	2.613	30
40	.3854	.9228	.4176	2.394	1.084	2.595	20
50	.3881	.9216	.4210	2.375	1.085	2.577	10
23°00′	.3907	.9205	.4245	2.356	1.086	2.559	**67°00′**
10	.3934	.9194	.4279	2.337	1.088	2.542	50
20	.3961	.9182	.4314	2.318	1.089	2.525	40
30	.3987	.9171	.4348	2.300	1.090	2.508	30
40	.4014	.9159	.4383	2.282	1.092	2.491	20
50	.4041	.9147	.4417	2.264	1.093	2.475	10
24°00′	.4067	.9135	.4452	2.246	1.095	2.459	**66°00′**
10	.4094	.9124	.4487	2.229	1.096	2.443	50
20	.4120	.9112	.4522	2.211	1.097	2.427	40
30	.4147	.9100	.4557	2.194	1.099	2.411	30
40	.4173	.9088	.4592	2.177	1.100	2.396	20
50	.4200	.9075	.4628	2.161	1.102	2.381	10
25°00′	.4226	.9063	.4663	2.145	1.103	2.366	**65°00′**
10	.4253	.9051	.4699	2.128	1.105	2.352	50
20	.4279	.9038	.4734	2.112	1.106	2.337	40
30	.4305	.9026	.4770	2.097	1.108	2.323	30
40	.4331	.9013	.4806	2.081	1.109	2.309	20
50	.4358	.9001	.4841	2.066	1.111	2.295	10
26°00′	.4384	.8988	.4877	2.050	1.113	2.281	**64°00′**
10	.4410	.8975	.4913	2.035	1.114	2.268	50
20	.4436	.8962	.4950	2.020	1.116	2.254	40
30	.4462	.8949	.4986	2.006	1.117	2.241	30
40	.4488	.8936	.5022	1.991	1.119	2.228	20
50	.4514	.8923	.5059	1.977	1.121	2.215	10
27°00′	.4540	.8910	.5095	1.963	1.122	2.203	**63°00′**
Coangle	Cos	Sin	Cot	Tan	Csc	Sec	Angle

Table II. VALUES OF TRIGONOMETRIC FUNCTIONS (CONT.)

Angle	Sin	Cos	Tan	Cot	Sec	Csc	Coangle
27°00′	.4540	.8910	.5095	1.963	1.122	2.203	**63°00′**
10	.4566	.8897	.5132	1.949	1.124	2.190	50
20	.4592	.8884	.5169	1.935	1.126	2.178	40
30	.4617	.8870	.5206	1.921	1.127	2.166	30
40	.4643	.8857	.5243	1.907	1.129	2.154	20
50	.4669	.8843	.5280	1.894	1.131	2.142	10
28°00′	.4695	.8829	5.317	1.881	1.133	2.130	**62°00′**
10	.4720	.8816	.5354	1.868	1.134	2.118	50
20	.4746	.8802	.5392	1.855	1.136	2.107	40
30	.4772	.8788	.5430	1.842	1.138	2.096	30
40	.4797	.8774	.5467	1.829	1.140	2.085	20
50	.4823	.8760	.5505	1.816	1.142	2.074	10
29°00′	.4848	.8746	.5543	1.804	1.143	2.063	**61°00′**
10	.4874	.8732	.5581	1.792	1.145	2.052	50
20	.4899	.8718	.5619	1.780	1.147	2.041	40
30	.4924	.8704	.5658	1.767	1.149	2.031	30
40	.4950	.8689	.5696	1.756	1.151	2.020	20
50	.4975	.8675	.5735	1.744	1.153	2.010	10
30°00′	.5000	.8660	.5774	1.732	1.155	2.000	**60°00′**
10	.5025	.8646	.5812	1.720	1.157	1.990	50
20	.5050	.8631	.5851	1.709	1.159	1.980	40
30	.5075	.8616	.5890	1.698	1.161	1.970	30
40	.5100	.8601	.5930	1.686	1.163	1.961	20
50	.5125	.8587	.5969	1.675	1.165	1.951	10
31°00′	.5150	.8572	.6009	1.664	1.167	1.942	**59°00′**
10	.5175	.8557	.6048	1.653	1.169	1.932	50
20	.5200	.8542	.6088	1.643	1.171	1.923	40
30	.5225	.8526	.6128	1.632	1.173	1.914	30
40	.5250	.8511	.6168	1.621	1.175	1.905	20
50	.5275	.8496	.6208	1.611	1.177	1.896	10
32°00′	.5299	.8480	.6249	1.600	1.179	1.887	**58°00′**
10	.5324	.8465	.6289	1.590	1.181	1.878	50
20	.5348	.8450	.6330	1.580	1.184	1.870	40
30	.5373	.8434	.6371	1.570	1.186	1.861	30
40	.5398	.8418	.6412	1.560	1.818	1.853	20
50	.5422	.8403	.6453	1.550	1.190	1.844	10
33°00′	.5446	.8387	.6494	1.540	1.192	1.836	**57°00′**
10	.5471	.8371	.6536	1.530	1.195	1.828	50
20	.5495	.8355	.6577	1.520	1.197	1.820	40
30	.5519	.8339	.6619	1.511	1.199	1.812	30
40	.5544	.8323	.6661	1.501	1.202	1.804	20
50	.5568	.8307	.6703	1.492	1.204	1.796	10
34°00′	.5592	.8290	.6745	1.483	1.206	1.788	**56°00′**
10	.5616	.8274	.6787	1.473	1.209	1.781	50
20	.5640	.8258	.6830	1.464	1.211	1.773	40
30	.5664	.8241	.6873	1.455	1.213	1.766	30
40	.5688	.8225	.6916	1.446	1.216	1.758	20
50	.5712	.8208	.6959	1.437	1.218	1.751	10
35°00′	.5736	.8192	.7002	1.428	1.221	1.743	**55°00′**
10	.5760	.8175	.7046	1.419	1.223	1.736	50
20	.5783	.8158	.7089	1.411	1.226	1.729	40
30	.5807	.8141	.7133	1.402	1.228	1.722	30
40	.5831	.8124	.7177	1.393	1.231	1.715	20
50	.5854	.8107	.7221	1.385	1.233	1.708	10
36°00′	.5878	.8090	.7265	1.376	1.236	1.701	**54°00′**
Coangle	Cos	Sin	Cot	Tan	Csc	Sec	Angle

Table II. Values of Trigonometric Functions (cont.)

Angle	Sin	Cos	Tan	Cot	Sec	Csc	Coangle
36°00′	.5878	.8090	.7265	1.376	1.236	1.701	**54°00′**
10	.5901	.8073	.7310	1.368	1.239	1.695	50
20	.5925	.8056	.7355	1.360	1.241	1.688	40
30	.5948	.8039	.7400	1.351	1.244	1.681	30
40	.5972	.8021	.7445	1.343	1.247	1.675	20
50	.5995	.8004	.7490	1.335	1.249	1.668	10
37°00′	.6018	.7986	.7536	1.327	1.252	1.662	**53°00′**
10	.6041	.7969	.7581	1.319	1.255	1.655	50
20	.6065	.7951	.7627	1.311	1.258	1.649	40
30	.6088	.7934	.7673	1.303	1.260	1.643	30
40	.6111	.7916	.7720	1.295	1.263	1.636	20
50	.6134	.7898	.7766	1.288	1.266	1.630	10
38°00′	.6157	.7880	.7813	1.280	1.269	1.624	**52°00′**
10	.6180	.7862	.7860	1.272	1.272	1.618	50
20	.6202	.7844	.7907	1.265	1.275	1.612	40
30	.6225	.7826	.7954	1.257	1.278	1.606	30
40	.6248	.7808	.8002	1.250	1.281	1.601	20
50	.6271	.7790	.8050	1.242	1.284	1.595	10
39°00′	.6293	.7771	.8098	1.235	1.287	1.589	**51°00′**
10	.6316	.7753	.8146	1.228	1.290	1.583	50
20	.6338	.7735	.8195	1.220	1.293	1.578	40
30	.6361	.7716	.8243	1.213	1.296	1.572	30
40	.6383	.7698	.8292	1.206	1.299	1.567	20
50	.6406	.7679	.8342	1.199	1.302	1.561	10
40°00′	.6428	.7660	.8391	1.192	1.305	1.556	**50°00′**
10	.6450	.7642	.8441	1.185	1.309	1.550	50
20	.6472	.7623	.8491	1.178	1.312	1.545	40
30	.6494	.7604	.8541	1.171	1.315	1.540	30
40	.6517	.7585	.8591	1.164	1.318	1.535	20
50	.6539	.7566	.8642	1.157	1.322	1.529	10
41°00′	.6561	.7547	.8693	1.150	1.325	1.524	**49°00′**
10	.6583	.7528	.8744	1.144	1.328	1.519	50
20	.6604	.7509	.8796	1.137	1.332	1.514	40
30	.6626	.7490	.8847	1.130	1.335	1.509	30
40	.6648	.7470	.8899	1.124	1.339	1.504	20
50	.6670	.7451	.8952	1.117	1.342	1.499	10
42°00′	.6691	.7431	.9004	1.111	1.346	1.494	**48°00′**
10	.6713	.7412	.9057	1.104	1.349	1.490	50
20	.6734	.7392	.9110	1.098	1.353	1.485	40
30	.6756	.7373	.9163	1.091	1.356	1.480	30
40	.6777	.7353	.9217	1.085	1.360	1.476	20
50	.6799	.7333	.9271	1.079	1.364	1.471	10
43°00′	.6820	.7314	.9325	1.072	1.367	1.466	**47°00′**
10	.6841	.7294	.9380	1.066	1.371	1.462	50
20	.6862	.7274	.9435	1.060	1.375	1.457	40
30	.6884	.7254	.9490	1.054	1.379	1.453	30
40	.6905	.7234	.9545	1.048	1.382	1.448	20
50	.6926	.7214	.9601	1.042	1.386	1.444	10
44°00′	.6947	.7193	.9657	1.036	1.390	1.440	**46°00′**
10	.6967	.7173	.9713	1.030	1.394	1.435	50
20	.6988	.7153	.9770	1.024	1.398	1.431	40
30	.7009	.7133	.9827	1.018	1.402	1.427	30
40	.7030	.7112	.9884	1.012	1.406	1.423	20
50	.7050	.7092	.9942	1.006	1.410	1.418	10
45°00′	.7071	.7071	1.000	1.000	1.414	1.414	**45°00′**
Coangle	Cos	Sin	Cot	Tan	Csc	Sec	Angle

Table III. LOGARITHMS OF TRIGONOMETRIC FUNCTIONS

Angle	$\log_{10}$ Sine	$\log_{10}$ Tangent	$\log_{10}$ Cotangent	$\log_{10}$ Cosine	Coangle
0°00′					**90°00′**
10′	.4637 − 3	.4637 − 3	2.5363	.0000	50′
20′	.7648 − 3	.7648 − 3	2.2352	.0000	40′
30′	.9408 − 3	.9409 − 3	2.0591	.0000	30′
40′	.0658 − 2	.0658 − 2	1.9342	.0000	20′
50′	.1627 − 2	.1627 − 2	1.8373	.0000	10′
1°00′	.2419 − 2	.2419 − 2	1.7581	.9999 − 1	**89°00′**
10′	.3088 − 2	.3089 − 2	1.6911	.9999 − 1	50′
20′	.3668 − 2	.3669 − 2	1.6331	.9999 − 1	40′
30′	.4179 − 2	.4181 − 2	1.5819	.9999 − 1	30′
40′	.4637 − 2	.4638 − 2	1.5362	.9998 − 1	20′
50′	.5050 − 2	.5053 − 2	1.4947	.9998 − 1	10′
2°00′	.5428 − 2	.5431 − 2	1.4569	.9997 − 1	**88°00′**
10′	.5776 − 2	.5779 − 2	1.4221	.9997 − 1	50′
20′	.6097 − 2	.6101 − 2	1.3899	.9996 − 1	40′
30′	.6397 − 2	.6401 − 2	1.3599	.9996 − 1	30′
40′	.6677 − 2	.6682 − 2	1.3318	.9995 − 1	20′
50′	.6940 − 2	.6945 − 2	1.3055	.9995 − 1	10′
3°00′	.7188 − 2	.7194 − 2	1.2806	.9994 − 1	**87°00′**
10′	.7423 − 2	.7429 − 2	1.2571	.9993 − 1	50′
20′	.7645 − 2	.7652 − 2	1.2348	.9993 − 1	40′
30′	.7857 − 2	.7865 − 2	1.2135	.9992 − 1	30′
40′	.8059 − 2	.8067 − 2	1.1933	.9991 − 1	20′
50′	.8251 − 2	.8261 − 2	1.1739	.9990 − 1	10′
4°00′	.8436 − 2	.8446 − 2	1.1554	.9989 − 1	**86°00′**
10′	.8613 − 2	.8624 − 2	1.1376	.9989 − 1	50′
20′	.8783 − 2	.8795 − 2	1.1205	.9988 − 1	40′
30′	.8946 − 2	.8960 − 2	1.1040	.9987 − 1	30′
40′	.9104 − 2	.9118 − 2	1.0882	.9986 − 1	20′
50′	.9256 − 2	.9272 − 2	1.0728	.9985 − 1	10′
5°00′	.9403 − 2	.9420 − 2	1.0580	.9983 − 1	**85°00′**
10′	.9545 − 2	.9563 − 2	1.0437	.9982 − 1	50′
20′	.9682 − 2	.9701 − 2	1.0299	.9981 − 1	40′
30′	.9816 − 2	.9836 − 2	1.0164	.9980 − 1	30′
40′	.9945 − 2	.9966 − 2	1.0034	.9979 − 1	20′
50′	.0070 − 1	.0093 − 1	.9907	.9977 − 1	10′
6°00′	.0192 − 1	.0216 − 1	.9784	.9976 − 1	**84°00′**
10′	.0311 − 1	.0336 − 1	.9664	.9975 − 1	50′
20′	.0426 − 1	.0453 − 1	.9547	.9973 − 1	40′
30′	.0539 − 1	.0567 − 1	.9433	.9972 − 1	30′
40′	.0648 − 1	.0678 − 1	.9322	.9971 − 1	20′
50′	.0755 − 1	.0786 − 1	.9214	.9969 − 1	10′
7°00′	.0859 − 1	.0891 − 1	.9109	.9968 − 1	**83°00′**
10′	.0961 − 1	.0995 − 1	.9005	.9966 − 1	50′
20′	.1060 − 1	.1096 − 1	.8904	.9964 − 1	40′
30′	.1157 − 1	.1194 − 1	.8806	.9963 − 1	30′
40′	.1252 − 1	.1291 − 1	.8709	.9961 − 1	20′
50′	.1345 − 1	.1385 − 1	.8615	.9959 − 1	10′
8°00′	.1436 − 1	.1478 − 1	.8522	.9958 − 1	**82°00′**
10′	.1525 − 1	.1569 − 1	.8431	.9956 − 1	50′
20′	.1612 − 1	.1658 − 1	.8342	.9954 − 1	40′
30′	.1697 − 1	.1745 − 1	.8255	.9952 − 1	30′
40′	.1781 − 1	.1831 − 1	.8169	.9950 − 1	20′
50′	.1863 − 1	.1915 − 1	.8085	.9948 − 1	10′
9°00′	.1943 − 1	.1997 − 1	.8003	.9946 − 1	**81°00′**
Coangle	$\log_{10}$ Cosine	$\log_{10}$ Cotangent	$\log_{10}$ Tangent	$\log_{10}$ Sine	Angle

Table III. LOGARITHMS OF TRIGONOMETRIC FUNCTIONS (CONT.)

Angle	Log_{10} Sine	Log_{10} Tangent	Log_{10} Cotangent	Log_{10} Cosine	Coangle
9°00′	.1943 − 1	.1997 − 1	.8003	.9946 − 1	**81**°00′
10′	.2022 − 1	.2078 − 1	.7922	.9944 − 1	50′
20′	.2100 − 1	.2158 − 1	.7842	.9942 − 1	40′
30′	.2176 − 1	.2236 − 1	.7764	.9940 − 1	30′
40′	.2251 − 1	.2313 − 1	.7687	.9938 − 1	20′
50′	.2324 − 1	.2389 − 1	.7611	.9936 − 1	10′
10°00′	.2397 − 1	.2463 − 1	.7537	.9934 − 1	**80**°00′
10′	.2468 − 1	.2536 − 1	.7464	.9931 − 1	50′
20′	.2538 − 1	.2609 − 1	.7391	.9929 − 1	40′
30′	.2606 − 1	.2680 − 1	.7320	.9927 − 1	30′
40′	.2674 − 1	.2750 − 1	.7250	.9924 − 1	20′
50′	.2740 − 1	.2819 − 1	.7181	.9922 − 1	10′
11°00′	.2806 − 1	.2887 − 1	.7113	.9919 − 1	**79**°00′
10′	.2870 − 1	.2953 − 1	.7047	.9917 − 1	50′
20′	.2934 − 1	.3020 − 1	.6980	.9914 − 1	40′
30′	.2997 − 1	.3085 − 1	.6915	.9912 − 1	30′
40′	.3058 − 1	.3149 − 1	.6851	.9909 − 1	20′
50′	.3119 − 1	.3212 − 1	.6788	.9907 − 1	10′
12°00′	.3179 − 1	.3275 − 1	.6725	.9904 − 1	**78**°00′
10′	.3238 − 1	.3336 − 1	.6664	.9901 − 1	50′
20′	.3296 − 1	.3397 − 1	.6603	.9899 − 1	40′
30′	.3353 − 1	.3458 − 1	.6542	.9896 − 1	30′
40′	.3410 − 1	.3517 − 1	.6483	.9893 − 1	20′
50′	.3466 − 1	.3576 − 1	.6424	.9890 − 1	10′
13°00′	.3521 − 1	.3634 − 1	.6366	.9887 − 1	**77**°00′
10′	.3575 − 1	.3691 − 1	.6309	.9884 − 1	50′
20′	.3629 − 1	.3748 − 1	.6252	.9881 − 1	40′
30′	.3682 − 1	.3804 − 1	.6196	.9878 − 1	30′
40′	.3734 − 1	.3859 − 1	.6141	.9875 − 1	20′
50′	.3786 − 1	.3914 − 1	.6086	.9872 − 1	10′
14°00′	.3837 − 1	.3968 − 1	.6032	.9869 − 1	**76**°00′
10′	.3887 − 1	.4021 − 1	.5979	.9866 − 1	50′
20′	.3937 − 1	.4074 − 1	.5926	.9863 − 1	40′
30′	.3986 − 1	.4127 − 1	.5873	.9859 − 1	30′
40′	.4035 − 1	.4178 − 1	.5822	.9856 − 1	20′
50′	.4083 − 1	.4230 − 1	.5770	.9853 − 1	10′
15°00′	.4130 − 1	.4281 − 1	.5719	.9849 − 1	**75**°00′
10′	.4177 − 1	.4331 − 1	.5669	.9846 − 1	50′
20′	.4223 − 1	.4381 − 1	.5619	.9843 − 1	40′
30′	.4269 − 1	.4430 − 1	.5570	.9839 − 1	30′
40′	.4314 − 1	.4479 − 1	.5521	.9836 − 1	20′
50′	.4359 − 1	.4527 − 1	.5473	.9832 − 1	10′
16°00′	.4403 − 1	.4575 − 1	.5425	.9828 − 1	**74**°00′
10′	.4447 − 1	.4622 − 1	.5378	.9825 − 1	50′
20′	.4491 − 1	.4669 − 1	.5331	.9821 − 1	40′
30′	.4533 − 1	.4716 − 1	.5284	.9817 − 1	30′
40′	.4576 − 1	.4762 − 1	.5238	.9814 − 1	20′
50′	.4618 − 1	.4808 − 1	.5192	.9810 − 1	10′
17°00′	.4659 − 1	.4853 − 1	.5147	.9806 − 1	**73**°00′
10′	.4700 − 1	.4898 − 1	.5102	.9802 − 1	50′
20′	.4741 − 1	.4943 − 1	.5057	.9798 − 1	40′
30′	.4781 − 1	.4987 − 1	.5013	.9794 − 1	30′
40′	.4821 − 1	.5031 − 1	.4969	.9790 − 1	20′
50′	.4861 − 1	.5075 − 1	.4925	.9786 − 1	10′
18°00′	.4900 − 1	.5118 − 1	.4882	.9782 − 1	**72**°00′
Coangle	Log_{10} Cosine	Log_{10} Cotangent	Log_{10} Tangent	Log_{10} Sine	Angle

Table III. LOGARITHMS OF TRIGONOMETRIC FUNCTIONS (CONT.)

Angle	Log_{10} Sine	Log_{10} Tangent	Log_{10} Cotangent	Log_{10} Cosine	Coangle
18°00′	.4900 − 1	.5118 − 1	.4882	.9782 − 1	**72°00′**
10′	.4939 − 1	.5161 − 1	.4839	.9778 − 1	50′
20′	.4977 − 1	.5203 − 1	.4797	.9774 − 1	40′
30′	.5015 − 1	.5245 − 1	.4755	.9770 − 1	30′
40′	.5052 − 1	.5287 − 1	.4713	.9765 − 1	20′
50′	.5090 − 1	.5329 − 1	.4671	.9761 − 1	10′
19°00′	.5126 − 1	.5370 − 1	.4630	.9757 − 1	**71°00′**
10′	.5163 − 1	.5411 − 1	.4589	.9752 − 1	50′
20′	.5199 − 1	.5451 − 1	.4549	.9748 − 1	40′
30′	.5235 − 1	.5491 − 1	.4509	.9743 − 1	30′
40′	.5270 − 1	.5531 − 1	.4469	.9739 − 1	20′
50′	.5306 − 1	.5571 − 1	.4429	.9734 − 1	10′
20°00′	.5341 − 1	.5611 − 1	.4389	.9730 − 1	**70°00′**
10′	.5375 − 1	.5650 − 1	.4350	.9725 − 1	50′
20′	.5409 − 1	.5689 − 1	.4311	.9721 − 1	40′
30′	.5443 − 1	.5727 − 1	.4273	.9716 − 1	30′
40′	.5477 − 1	.5766 − 1	.4234	.9711 − 1	20′
50′	.5510 − 1	.5804 − 1	.4196	.9706 − 1	10′
21°00′	.5543 − 1	.5842 − 1	.4158	.9702 − 1	**69°00′**
10′	.5576 − 1	.5879 − 1	.4121	.9697 − 1	50′
20′	.5609 − 1	.5917 − 1	.4083	.9692 − 1	40′
30′	.5641 − 1	.5954 − 1	.4046	.9687 − 1	30′
40′	.5673 − 1	.5991 − 1	.4009	.9682 − 1	20′
50′	.5704 − 1	.6028 − 1	.3972	.9677 − 1	10′
22°00′	.5736 − 1	.6064 − 1	.3936	.9672 − 1	**68°00′**
10′	.5767 − 1	.6100 − 1	.3900	.9667 − 1	50′
20′	.5798 − 1	.6136 − 1	.3864	.9661 − 1	40′
30′	.5828 − 1	.6172 − 1	.3828	.9656 − 1	30′
40′	.5859 − 1	.6208 − 1	.3792	.9651 − 1	20′
50′	.5889 − 1	.6243 − 1	.3757	.9646 − 1	10′
23°00′	.5919 − 1	.6279 − 1	.3721	.9640 − 1	**67°00′**
10′	.5948 − 1	.6314 − 1	.3686	.9635 − 1	50′
20′	.5978 − 1	.6348 − 1	.3652	.9629 − 1	40′
30′	.6007 − 1	.6383 − 1	.3617	.9624 − 1	30′
40′	.6036 − 1	.6417 − 1	.3583	.9618 − 1	20′
50′	.6065 − 1	.6452 − 1	.3548	.9613 − 1	10′
24°00′	.6093 − 1	.6486 − 1	.3514	.9607 − 1	**66°00′**
10′	.6121 − 1	.6520 − 1	.3480	.9602 − 1	50′
20′	.6149 − 1	.6553 − 1	.3447	.9596 − 1	40′
30′	.6177 − 1	.6587 − 1	.3413	.9590 − 1	30′
40′	.6205 − 1	.6620 − 1	.3380	.9584 − 1	20′
50′	.6232 − 1	.6654 − 1	.3346	.9579 − 1	10′
25°00′	.6259 − 1	.6687 − 1	.3313	.9573 − 1	**65°00′**
10′	.6286 − 1	.6720 − 1	.3280	.9567 − 1	50′
20′	.6313 − 1	.6752 − 1	.3248	.9561 − 1	40′
30′	.6340 − 1	.6785 − 1	.3215	.9555 − 1	30′
40′	.6366 − 1	.6817 − 1	.3183	.9549 − 1	20′
50′	.6392 − 1	.6850 − 1	.3150	.9543 − 1	10′
26°00′	.6418 − 1	.6882 − 1	.3118	.9537 − 1	**64°00′**
10′	.6444 − 1	.6914 − 1	.3086	.9530 − 1	50′
20′	.6470 − 1	.6946 − 1	.3054	.9524 − 1	40′
30′	.6495 − 1	.6977 − 1	.3023	.9518 − 1	30′
40′	.6521 − 1	.7009 − 1	.2991	.9512 − 1	20′
50′	.6546 − 1	.7040 − 1	.2960	.9505 − 1	10′
27°00′	.6570 − 1	.7072 − 1	.2928	.9499 − 1	**63°00′**
Coangle	Log_{10} Cosine	Log_{10} Cotangent	Log_{10} Tangent	Log_{10} Sine	Angle

Table III. LOGARITHMS OF TRIGONOMETRIC FUNCTIONS (CONT.)

Angle	Log_{10} Sine	Log_{10} Tangent	Log_{10} Cotangent	Log_{10} Cosine	Coangle
27°00′	.6570 − 1	.7072 − 1	.2928	.9499 − 1	**63°00′**
10′	.6595 − 1	.7103 − 1	.2897	.9492 − 1	50′
20′	.6620 − 1	.7134 − 1	.2866	.9486 − 1	40′
30′	.6644 − 1	.7165 − 1	.2835	.9479 − 1	30′
40′	.6668 − 1	.7196 − 1	.2804	.9473 − 1	20′
50′	.6692 − 1	.7226 − 1	.2774	.9466 − 1	10′
28°00′	.6716 − 1	.7257 − 1	.2743	.9459 − 1	**62°00′**
10′	.6740 − 1	.7287 − 1	.2713	.9453 − 1	50′
20′	.6763 − 1	.7317 − 1	.2683	.9446 − 1	40′
30′	.6787 − 1	.7348 − 1	.2652	.9439 − 1	30′
40′	.6810 − 1	.7378 − 1	.2622	.9432 − 1	20′
50′	.6833 − 1	.7408 − 1	.2592	.9425 − 1	10′
29°00′	.6856 − 1	.7438 − 1	.2562	.9418 − 1	**61°00′**
10′	.6878 − 1	.7467 − 1	.2533	.9411 − 1	50′
20′	.6901 − 1	.7497 − 1	.2503	.9404 − 1	40′
30′	.6923 − 1	.7526 − 1	.2474	.9397 − 1	30′
40′	.6946 − 1	.7556 − 1	.2444	.9390 − 1	20′
50′	.6968 − 1	.7585 − 1	.2415	.9383 − 1	10′
30°00′	.6990 − 1	.7614 − 1	.2386	.9375 − 1	**60°00′**
10′	.7012 − 1	.7644 − 1	.2356	.9368 − 1	50′
20′	.7033 − 1	.7673 − 1	.2327	.9361 − 1	40′
30′	.7055 − 1	.7701 − 1	.2299	.9353 − 1	30′
40′	.7076 − 1	.7730 − 1	.2270	.9346 − 1	20′
50′	.7097 − 1	.7759 − 1	.2241	.9338 − 1	10′
31°00′	.7118 − 1	.7788 − 1	.2212	.9331 − 1	**59°00′**
10′	.7139 − 1	.7816 − 1	.2184	.9323 − 1	50′
20′	.7160 − 1	.7845 − 1	.2155	.9315 − 1	40′
30′	.7181 − 1	.7873 − 1	.2127	.9308 − 1	30′
40′	.7201 − 1	.7902 − 1	.2098	.9300 − 1	20′
50′	.7222 − 1	.7930 − 1	.2070	.9292 − 1	10′
32°00′	.7242 − 1	.7958 − 1	.2042	.9284 − 1	**58°00′**
10′	.7262 − 1	.7986 − 1	.2014	.9276 − 1	50′
20′	.7282 − 1	.8014 − 1	.1986	.9268 − 1	40′
30′	.7302 − 1	.8042 − 1	.1958	.9260 − 1	30′
40′	.7322 − 1	.8070 − 1	.1930	.9252 − 1	20′
50′	.7342 − 1	.8097 − 1	.1903	.9244 − 1	10′
33°00′	.7361 − 1	.8125 − 1	.1875	.9236 − 1	**57°00′**
10′	.7380 − 1	.8153 − 1	.1847	.9228 − 1	50′
20′	.7400 − 1	.8180 − 1	.1820	.9219 − 1	40′
30′	.7419 − 1	.8208 − 1	.1792	.9211 − 1	30′
40′	.7438 − 1	.8235 − 1	.1765	.9203 − 1	20′
50′	.7457 − 1	.8263 − 1	.1737	.9194 − 1	10′
34°00′	.7476 − 1	.8290 − 1	.1710	.9186 − 1	**56°00′**
10′	.7494 − 1	.8317 − 1	.1683	.9177 − 1	50′
20′	.7513 − 1	.8344 − 1	.1656	.9169 − 1	40′
30′	.7531 − 1	.8371 − 1	.1629	.9160 − 1	30′
40′	.7550 − 1	.8398 − 1	.1602	.9151 − 1	20′
50′	.7568 − 1	.8425 − 1	.1575	.9142 − 1	10′
35°00′	.7586 − 1	.8452 − 1	.1548	.9134 − 1	**55°00′**
10′	.7604 − 1	.8479 − 1	.1521	.9125 − 1	50′
20′	.7622 − 1	.8506 − 1	.1494	.9116 − 1	40′
30′	.7640 − 1	.8533 − 1	.1467	.9107 − 1	30′
40′	.7657 − 1	.8559 − 1	.1441	.9098 − 1	20′
50′	.7675 − 1	.8586 − 1	.1414	.9089 − 1	10′
36°00′	.7692 − 1	.8613 − 1	.1387	.9080 − 1	**54°00′**
Coangle	Log_{10} Cosine	Log_{10} Cotangent	Log_{10} Tangent	Log_{10} Sine	Angle

Table III. LOGARITHMS OF TRIGONOMETRIC FUNCTIONS (CONT.)

Angle	$\log_{10}$ Sine	$\log_{10}$ Tangent	$\log_{10}$ Cotangent	$\log_{10}$ Cosine	Coangle
36°00′	.7692 − 1	.8613 − 1	.1387	.9080 − 1	**54°00′**
10′	.7710 − 1	.8639 − 1	.1361	.9070 − 1	50′
20′	.7727 − 1	.8666 − 1	.1334	.9061 − 1	40′
30′	.7744 − 1	.8692 − 1	.1308	.9052 − 1	30′
40′	.7761 − 1	.8718 − 1	.1282	.9042 − 1	20′
50′	.7778 − 1	.8745 − 1	.1255	.9033 − 1	10′
37°00′	.7795 − 1	.8771 − 1	.1229	.9023 − 1	**53°00′**
10′	.7811 − 1	.8797 − 1	.1203	.9014 − 1	50′
20′	.7828 − 1	.8824 − 1	.1176	.9004 − 1	40′
30′	.7844 − 1	.8850 − 1	.1150	.8995 − 1	30′
40′	.7861 − 1	.8876 − 1	.1124	.8985 − 1	20′
50′	.7877 − 1	.8902 − 1	.1098	.8975 − 1	10′
38°00′	.7893 − 1	.8928 − 1	.1072	.8965 − 1	**52°00′**
10′	.7910 − 1	.8954 − 1	.1046	.8955 − 1	50′
20′	.7926 − 1	.8980 − 1	.1020	.8945 − 1	40′
30′	.7941 − 1	.9006 − 1	.0994	.8935 − 1	30′
40′	.7957 − 1	.9032 − 1	.0968	.8925 − 1	20′
50′	.7973 − 1	.9058 − 1	.0942	.8915 − 1	10′
39°00′	.7989 − 1	.9084 − 1	.0916	.8905 − 1	**51°00′**
10′	.8004 − 1	.9110 − 1	.0890	.8895 − 1	50′
20′	.8020 − 1	.9135 − 1	.0865	.8884 − 1	40′
30′	.8035 − 1	.9161 − 1	.0839	.8874 − 1	30′
40′	.8050 − 1	.9187 − 1	.0813	.8864 − 1	20′
50′	.8066 − 1	.9212 − 1	.0788	.8853 − 1	10′
40°00′	.8081 − 1	.9238 − 1	.0762	.8843 − 1	**50°00′**
10′	.8096 − 1	.9264 − 1	.0736	.8832 − 1	50′
20′	.8111 − 1	.9289 − 1	.0711	.8821 − 1	40′
30′	.8125 − 1	.9315 − 1	.0685	.8810 − 1	30′
40′	.8140 − 1	.9341 − 1	.0659	.8800 − 1	20′
50′	.8155 − 1	.9366 − 1	.0634	.8789 − 1	10′
41°00′	.8169 − 1	.9392 − 1	.0608	.8778 − 1	**49°00′**
10′	.8184 − 1	.9417 − 1	.0583	.8767 − 1	50′
20′	.8198 − 1	.9443 − 1	.0557	.8756 − 1	40′
30′	.8213 − 1	.9468 − 1	.0532	.8745 − 1	30′
40′	.8227 − 1	.9494 − 1	.0506	.8733 − 1	20′
50′	.8241 − 1	.9519 − 1	.0481	.8722 − 1	10′
42°00′	.8255 − 1	.9544 − 1	.0456	.8711 − 1	**48°00′**
10′	.8269 − 1	.9570 − 1	.0430	.8699 − 1	50′
20′	.8283 − 1	.9595 − 1	.0405	.8688 − 1	40′
30′	.8297 − 1	.9621 − 1	.0379	.8676 − 1	30′
40′	.8311 − 1	.9646 − 1	.0354	.8665 − 1	20′
50′	.8324 − 1	.9671 − 1	.0329	.8653 − 1	10′
43°00′	.8338 − 1	.9697 − 1	.0303	.8641 − 1	**47°00′**
10′	.8351 − 1	.9722 − 1	.0278	.8629 − 1	50′
20′	.8365 − 1	.9747 − 1	.0253	.8618 − 1	40′
30′	.8378 − 1	.9772 − 1	.0228	.8606 − 1	30′
40′	.8391 − 1	.9798 − 1	.0202	.8594 − 1	20′
50′	.8405 − 1	.9823 − 1	.0177	.8582 − 1	10′
44°00′	.8418 − 1	.9848 − 1	.0152	.8569 − 1	**46°00′**
10′	.8431 − 1	.9874 − 1	.0126	.8557 − 1	50′
20′	.8444 − 1	.9899 − 1	.0101	.8545 − 1	40′
30′	.8457 − 1	.9924 − 1	.0076	.8532 − 1	30′
40′	.8469 − 1	.9949 − 1	.0051	.8520 − 1	20′
50′	.8482 − 1	.9975 − 1	.0025	.8507 − 1	10′
45°00′	.8495 − 1	.0000	.0000	.8495 − 1	**45°00′**
Coangle	$\log_{10}$ Cosine	$\log_{10}$ Cotangent	$\log_{10}$ Tangent	$\log_{10}$ Sine	Angle

Answers To Odd-Numbered Problems

Problems 1–3 (page 6)

1. The number is between 2.3156 and 2.3157.

3. y is bigger than x, since x is less than 0.7655 and y is at least 0.7655.

5. y is bigger than, or equal to, x, since y is at least 0.2720. (The representation of x might be 0.27199999 . . . .)

7. $(2.645) \cdot (2.645) = 6.996025$ which is less than 7, whereas $(2.646) \cdot (2.646) = 7.001316$ which is greater than 7. Thus $\sqrt{7}$ must lie between 2.645 and 2.646.

Problems 1–4 (page 8)

1. $-3, -\frac{5}{3}, -1.4, \frac{3}{5}, 1, 2, 2.7, \pi$.

3. $17, -17$.

5. This statement is not true in general. For instance, if $a = 5$, $b = 3$, and $x = -4$, it says (since $5 > 3$) that $5 - 4 > 3$, which is false.

7. $-3 -(-5) = -3 + 5 = 2$, which is positive.

Problems 1–5 (page 12)

1. 1.765, 2, 0, 1.77, 1.8.

3. 0.000, 0, 0, 0.000488, 0.00049.

5. 0.333, 0, 0, 0.333, 0.33.

7. 1.091, 1, 0, 1.09, 1.1.

9. 5.500, 6 (or 5), 10, 5.50, 5.5.

11. 316.590, 317, 320, 317, 320.

13. 24.737, 25, 20, 24.7, 25.

15. 1.732, 1.73, 1.7.

17. 26.6.

Problems 2–1 (page 15)

1. a) 45 b) 105 c) $2a^2 + 4ab + 2b^2 - a - b$

3. a) -1 b) $\dfrac{\pi + 1}{\pi - 1}$ c) $\dfrac{10}{9}$

5. a) $\dfrac{4\pi^4}{3}$ b) 36π c) $-\dfrac{32\pi}{81}$

7. a) 35 b) 0 c) 0

9. a) $\dfrac{1}{2}$ b) $\dfrac{7}{24}$ c) $\dfrac{2\sqrt{2}+1}{28}$

11. domain: all real numbers
image: the real numbers which are bigger than or equal to $-1/8$.

13. domain: all real numbers except 1
image: all real numbers except 1.

15. domain: all real numbers except 0 and 5.
image: all real numbers which are bigger than or equal to $-1/128$, except $9/200$.

17. a) -3 b) $8a - 5$ c) 5

19. a) $\sqrt{2x^2 - 5}$ b) $|8t + 5|$ c) $2(t - |t|) - 10$

Problems 2–2 (page 20)

1. $f(x) = x^2 + x^3$.

3. $G(n) = \dfrac{n(n+1)}{2}$.

5. $F(x) = \dfrac{x^2}{4}$.

7.

x	0	1	$1\frac{1}{2}$	$1\frac{3}{4}$	$2\frac{1}{4}$	$2\frac{1}{2}$	3
$G(x)$	$-\frac{1}{2}$	$-\frac{3}{2}$	$-\frac{7}{2}$	$7\frac{1}{2}$	$8\frac{1}{2}$	$4\frac{1}{2}$	$2\frac{1}{2}$

9.

x	-5	-3	0	3	5
$h(x)$	-125	-27	0	27	125

11. (a) domain: all real numbers
image: all real numbers which are bigger than or equal to 0.

(b) domain: all real numbers
image: all real numbers which are bigger than or equal to 0.

13. domain: all real numbers
image: all real numbers y which satisfy an inequality $2n-1<y\leq 2n$ for some integer n.

15. $F(x)=9x^2$.

17. $F(x)=\dfrac{18x^2-24x+5}{9x-5}$.

Problems 2–3 (page 24)

1.

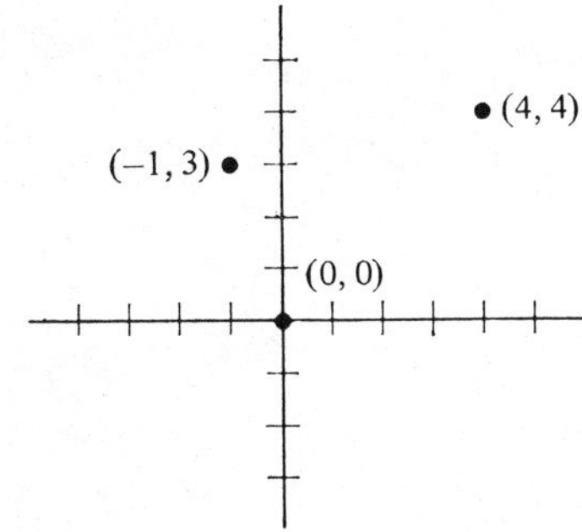

3.

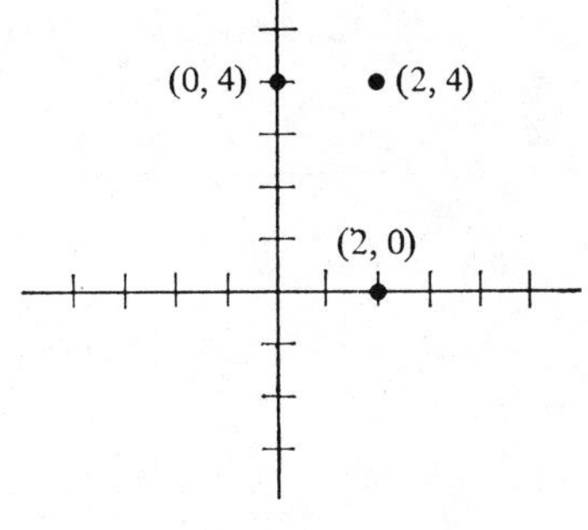

5.

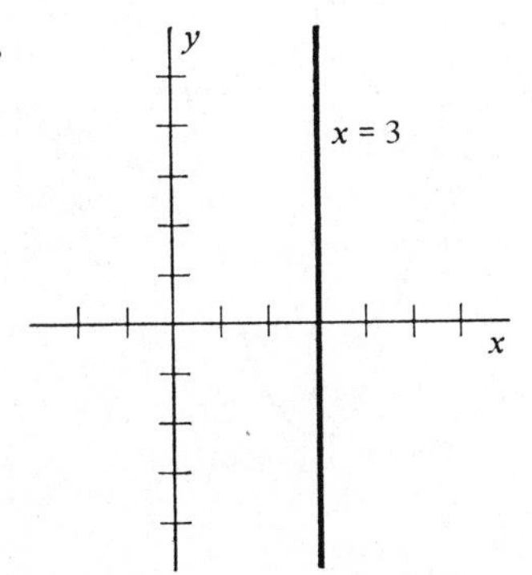

7.

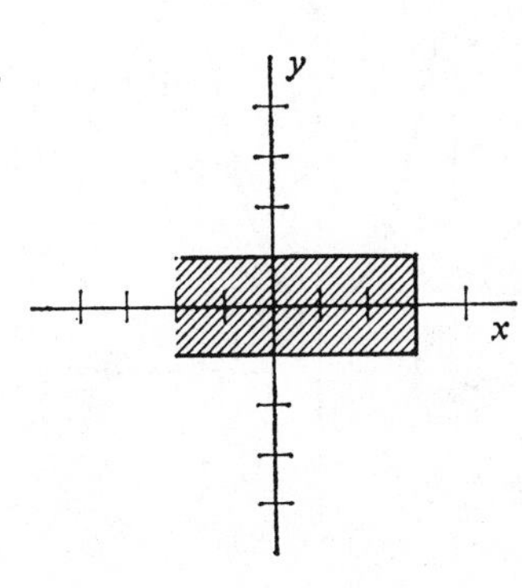

9. $\sqrt{87 - 12\sqrt{2}}$

11. $\sqrt{146}$

13.

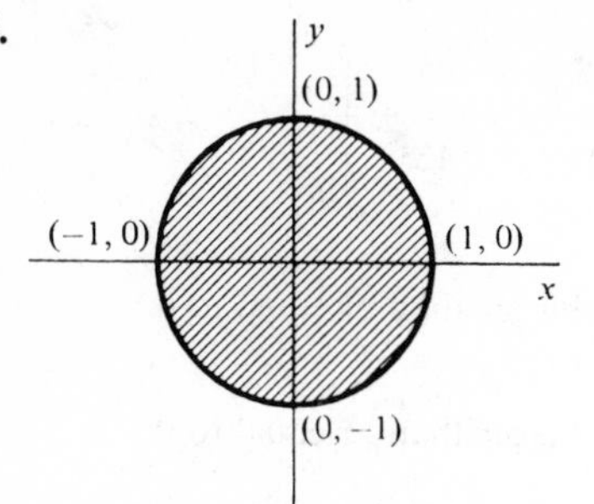

15.

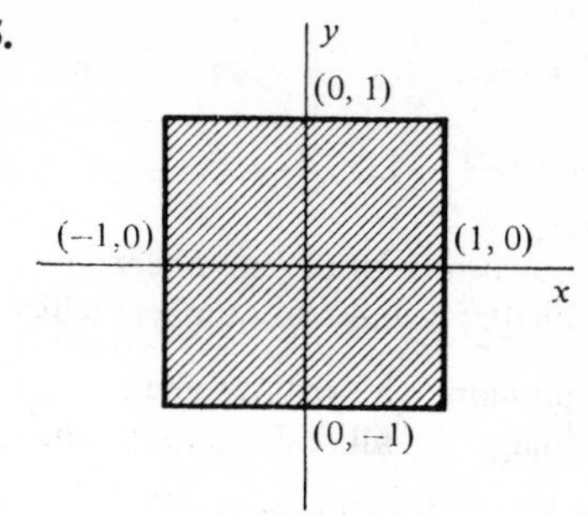

Problems 2–4 (page 30)

1.

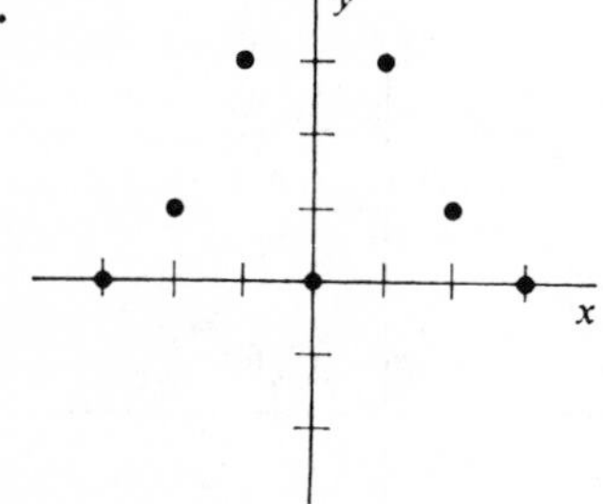

3. a)

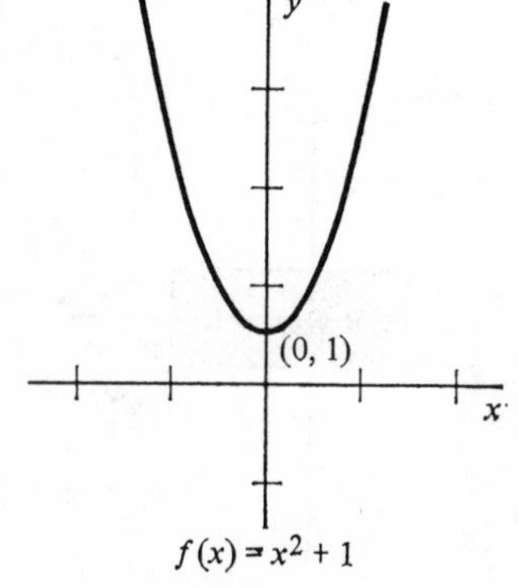

b)

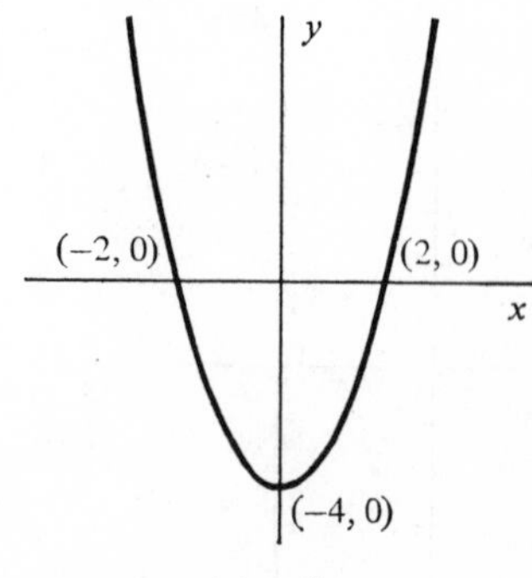

3. c)

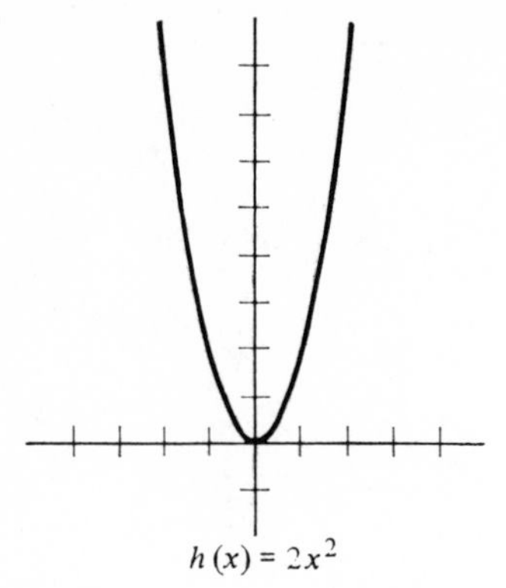

5. a)

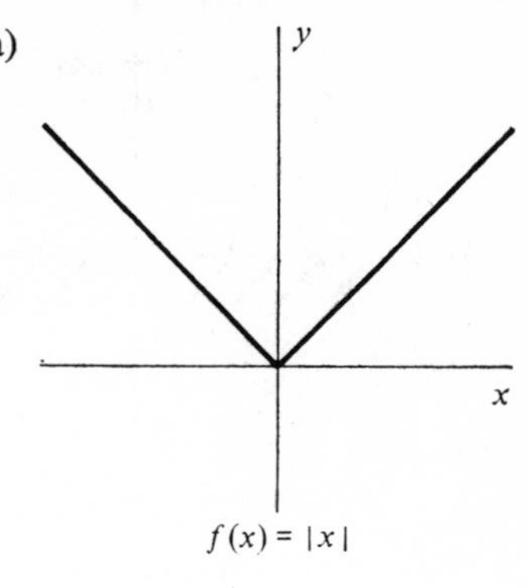

b)

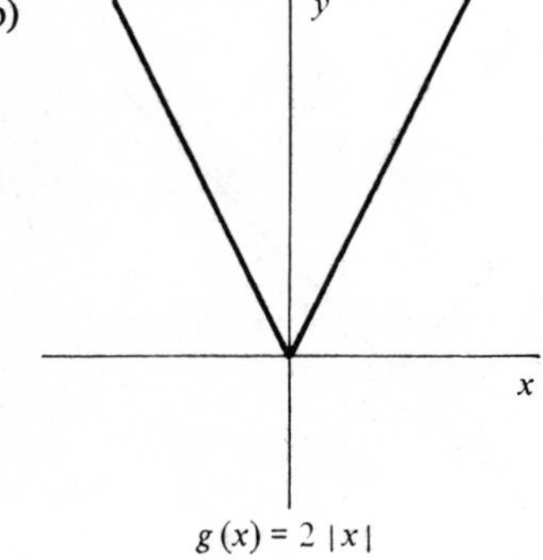

c)

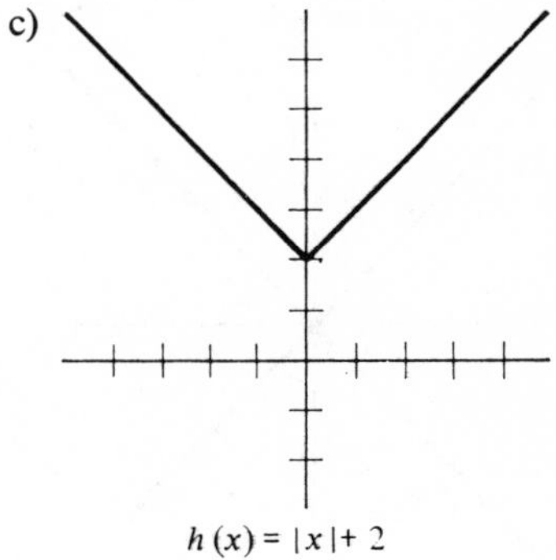

7. a)

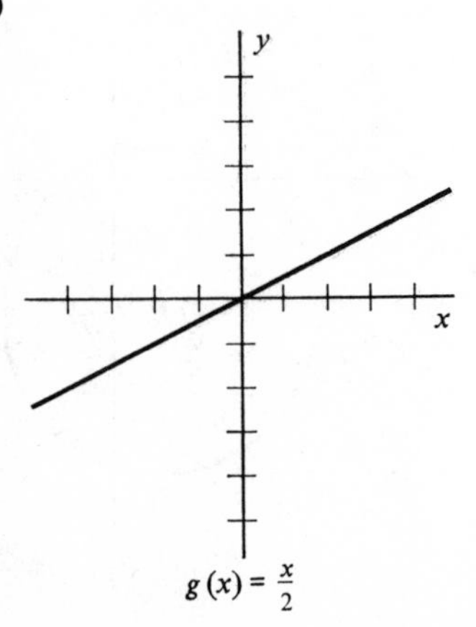

b)

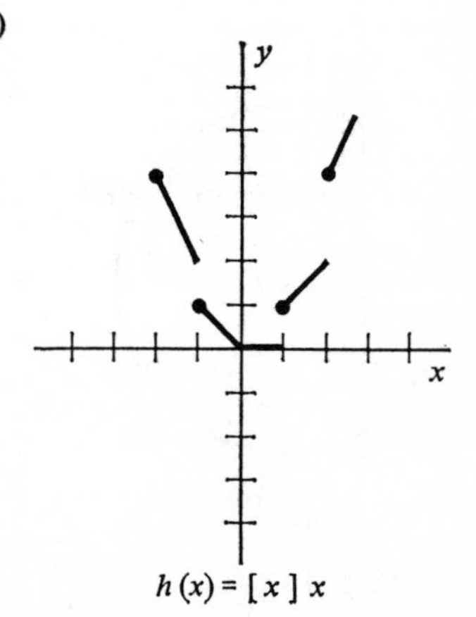

7. c)

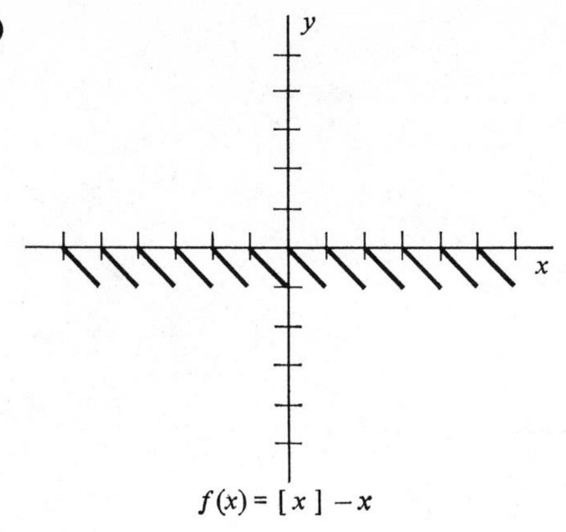

$f(x) = [x] - x$

9. a) 1.41 b) 1.77 c) 1.19
d) .707 e) 1.87

Problems 2–5 (page 34)

1.

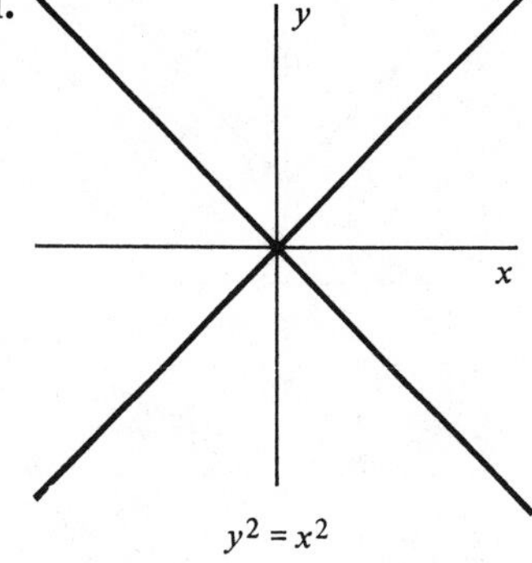

$y^2 = x^2$

3.

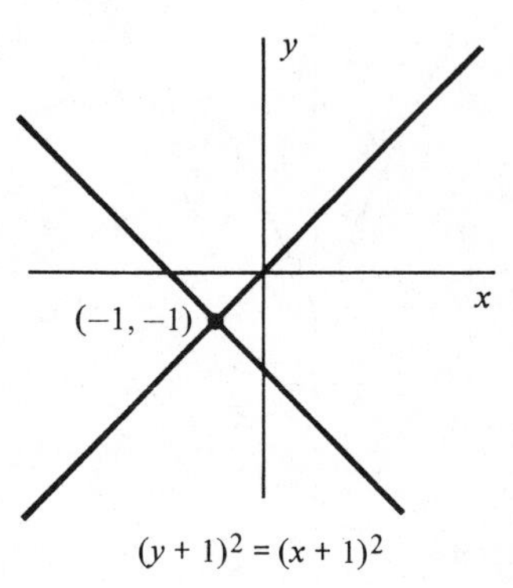

$(y + 1)^2 = (x + 1)^2$

5.

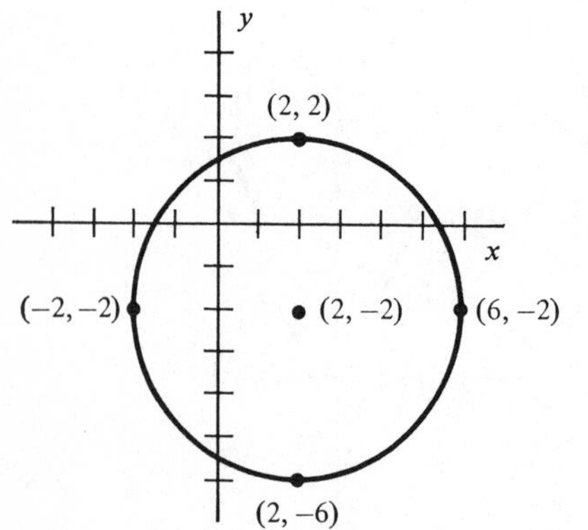

$(x - 2)^2 + (y + 2)^2 = 16$

7.

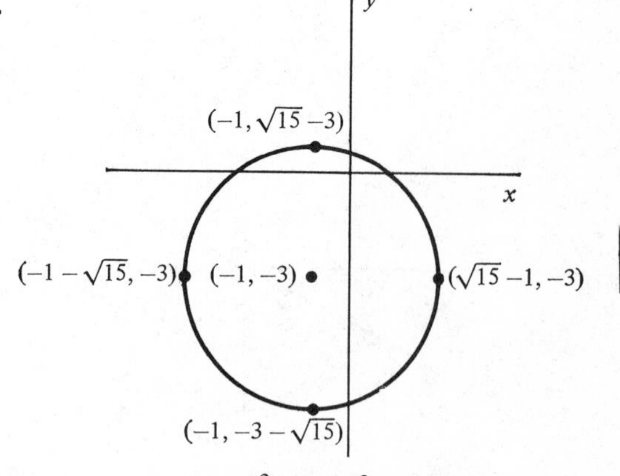

$x^2 + 2x + y^2 + 6y = 5$

9.

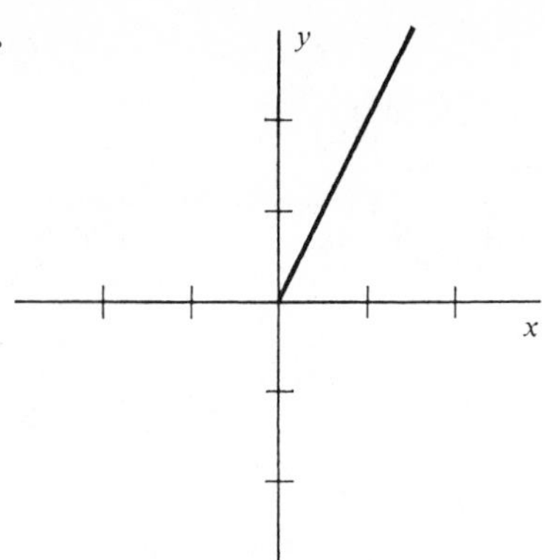

$y = |x| + x$

11.

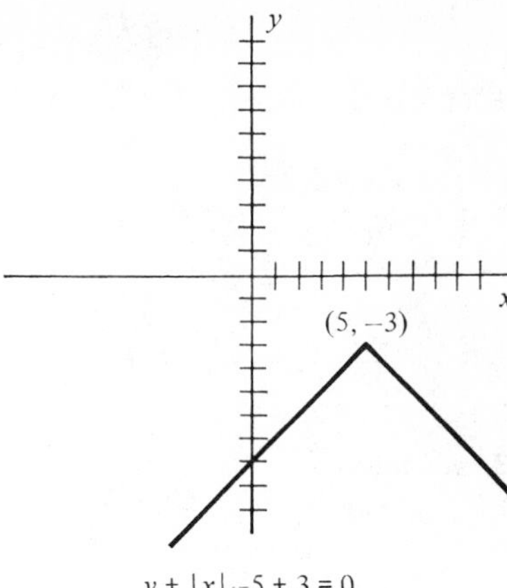

$y + |x| - 5 + 3 = 0$

13.

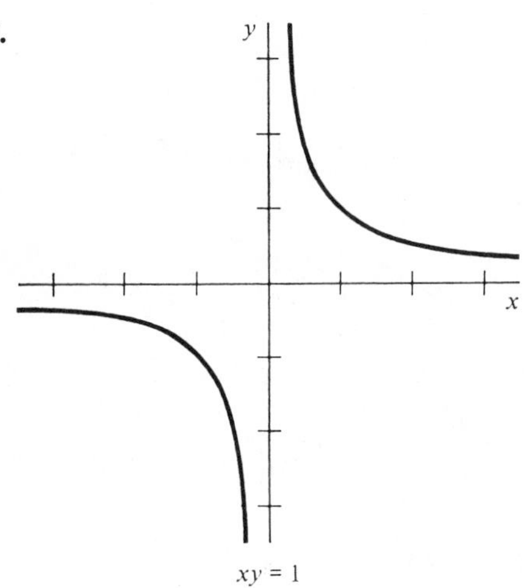

$xy = 1$

15.

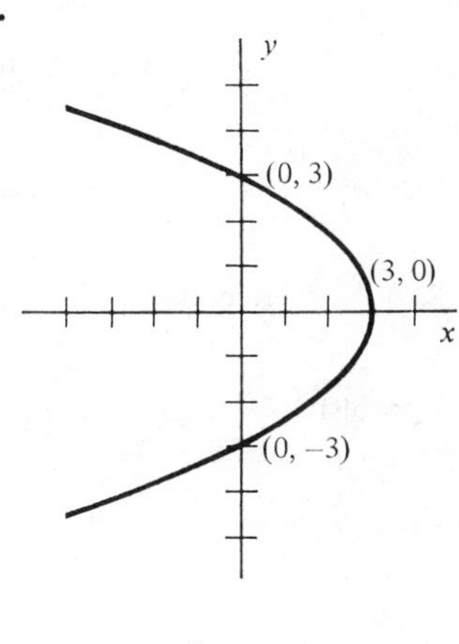

$y^2 + 3x = 9$

17.

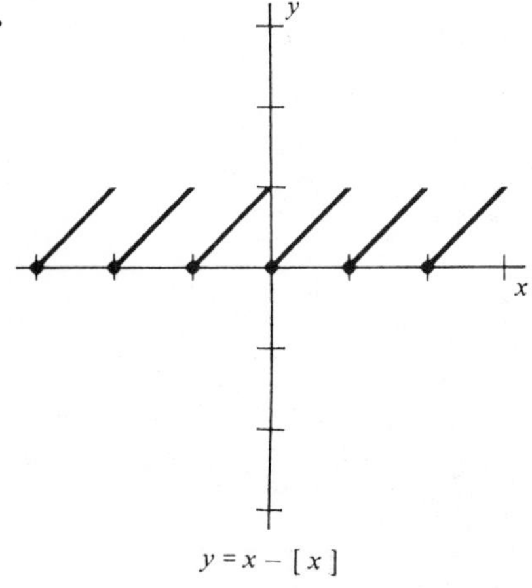

$y = x - [x]$

19.

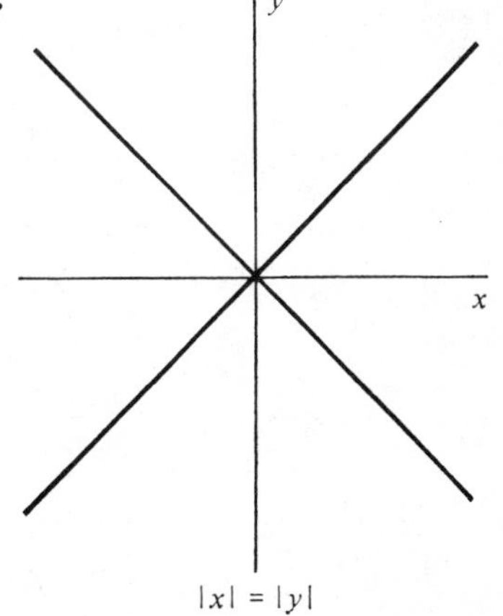

$|x| = |y|$

Problems 3–1 (page 41)

1. (1, 0) **3.** (−1, 0) **5.** (0, 1)

7. $\left(-\frac{\sqrt{2}}{2}, \frac{\sqrt{2}}{2}\right)$ **9.** $\left(-\frac{\sqrt{3}}{2}, \frac{1}{2}\right)$

11. $\left(\frac{\sqrt{2+\sqrt{2}}}{2}, \frac{\sqrt{2-\sqrt{2}}}{2}\right)$

13. second **15.** fourth **17.** third

Problems 3–2 (page 46)

1. 0, −1, 0, undefined, −1, undefined.

3. $-\frac{1}{2}, \frac{\sqrt{3}}{2}, -\frac{\sqrt{3}}{3}, -\sqrt{3}, \frac{2\sqrt{3}}{3}, -2.$

5. 0, 1, 0, undefined, 1, undefined.

In problems 7—23, $n = 0, \pm 1, \pm 2, \pm 3, \ldots$.

7. πn **9.** $\frac{\pi}{2} \pm \frac{\pi}{4} + 2\pi n$ **11.** $\frac{\pi}{2} + 2\pi n$

13. $\frac{3\pi}{2} + 2\pi n$ **15.** $\pm\frac{\pi}{3} + 2\pi n$ **17.** $\pm\frac{\pi}{6} + 2\pi n$

19. $\pi \pm \frac{\pi}{4} + 2\pi n$ **21.** $\pm\frac{\pi}{2} + 2\pi n$ **23.** $\pm\frac{\pi}{2} + 2\pi n$

25.
$$1 + \tan^2 t = 1 + \frac{\sin^2 t}{\cos^2 t} = \frac{\cos^2 t + \sin^2 t}{\cos^2 t} = \frac{1}{\cos^2 t} = \sec^2 t.$$

27.
$$\frac{\cos t + \sin^2 t \sec t}{\sec t} = \frac{\cos t + \sin^2 t\left(\frac{1}{\cos t}\right)}{\frac{1}{\cos t}} = \cos^2 t + \sin^2 t = 1.$$

29. $\tan(\pi - t) = \dfrac{\sin(\pi - t)}{\cos(\pi - t)} = \dfrac{-\sin(-t)}{-\cos(-t)} = \dfrac{\sin t}{-\cos t}$

$= -\tan t.$

31. $\dfrac{\cos t - \sin t}{\cos t} = 1 - \dfrac{\sin t}{\cos t} = 1 - \tan t.$

33. $\sec t - \cos t = \dfrac{1}{\cos t} - \cos t = \dfrac{1 - \cos^2 t}{\cos t}$

$= \dfrac{\sin^2 t}{\cos t} = \sin t \left(\dfrac{\sin t}{\cos t}\right)$

$= \sin t \tan t.$

35. $\dfrac{1}{\sec t - \tan t} = \dfrac{1}{\sec t - \tan t}\left(\dfrac{\sec t + \tan t}{\sec t + \tan t}\right)$

$= \dfrac{\sec t + \tan t}{\sec^2 t - \tan^2 t} = \dfrac{\sec t + \tan t}{1}$

$= \sec t + \tan t.$

Problems 3–3 (page 51)

1.

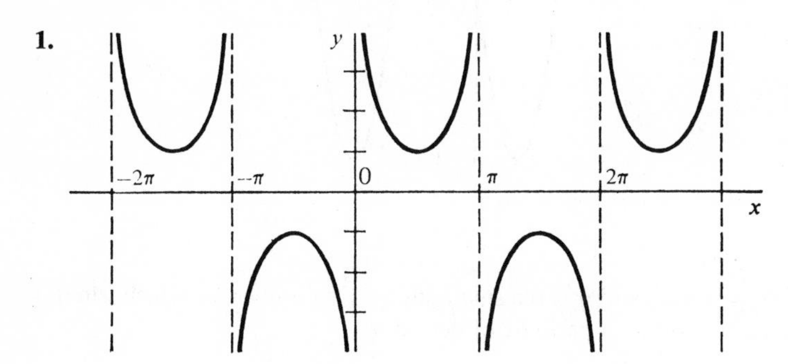

3. For $x > 0$, $\sin x < x$.

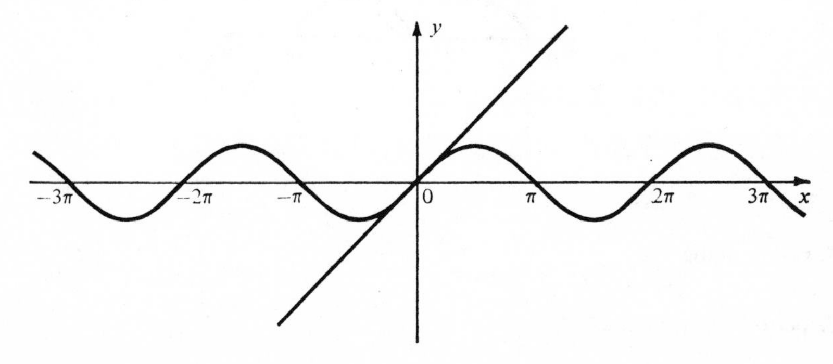

In problems 5, 7, and 9, $n = 0, \pm 1, \pm 2, \pm 3, \ldots$.

5. $2n\pi < x < (2n + 1)\pi$

7. $2n\pi < x < (2n + 1)\pi$

9. $(2n - 1)\pi < x < 2n\pi$

Problems 3–4 (page 58)

1. Since $\sin x$ is periodic of period 2π, $f(x) = \sin 2\pi x$ is periodic of period $\frac{2\pi}{|2\pi|} = 1$, by Theorem 2.

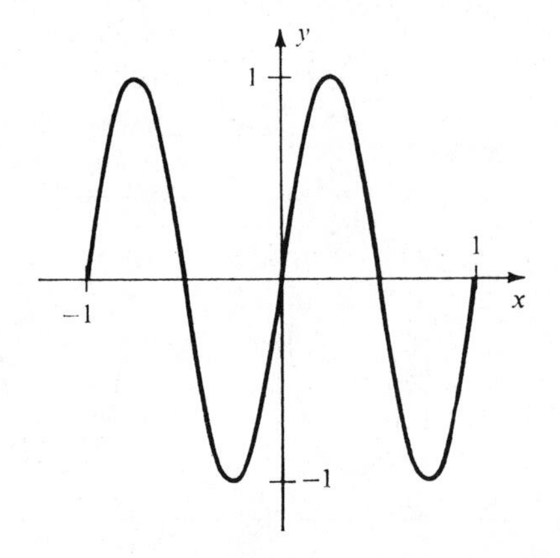

3. $|\sin (x + \pi)| = |\sin x|$, and π is the smallest positive number for which $|\sin 0| = |\sin \pi|$, so $f(x) = |\sin x|$ is periodic of period π.

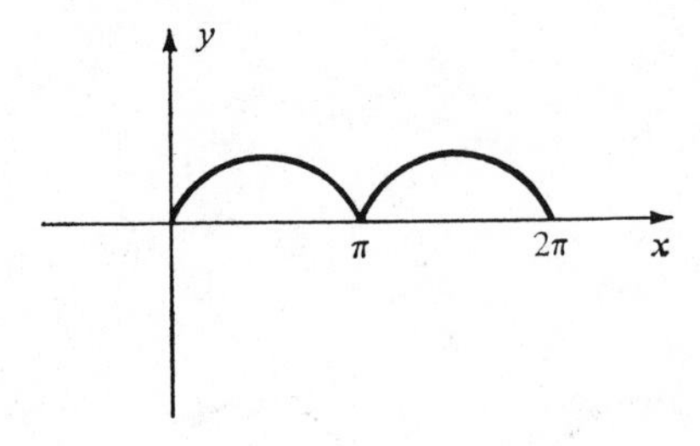

5. not periodic

7. periodic of period 2π

9.

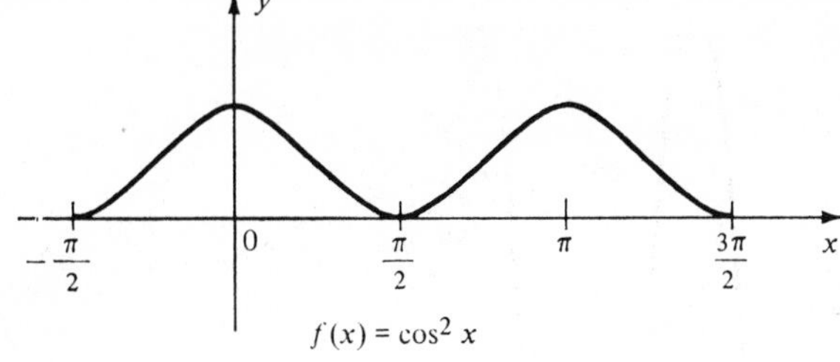

$f(x) = \cos^2 x$

11.

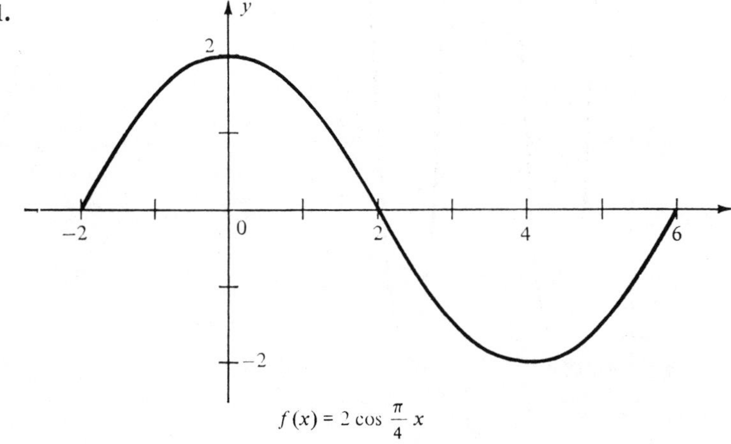

$f(x) = 2 \cos \frac{\pi}{4} x$

13.

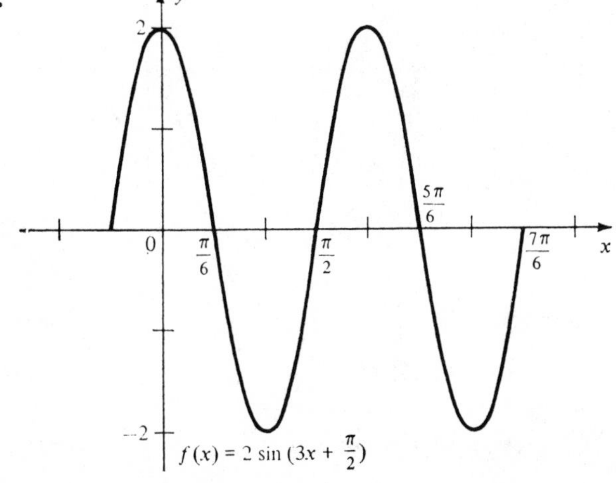

$f(x) = 2 \sin (3x + \frac{\pi}{2})$

15.

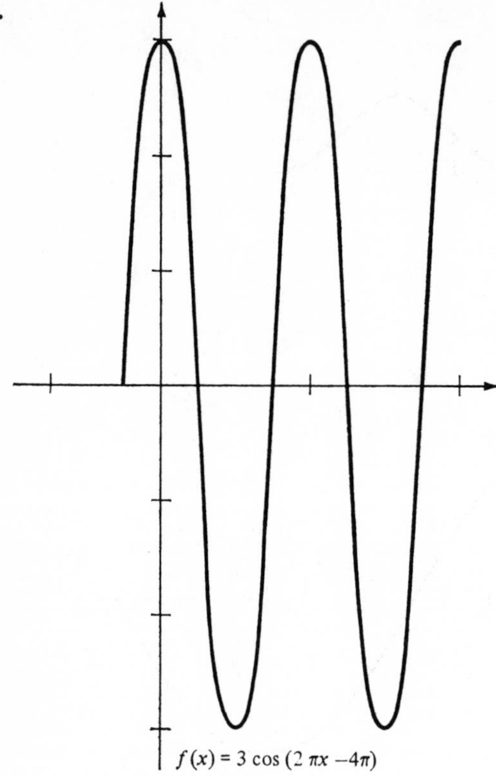

Problems 4–1 (page 63)

1.

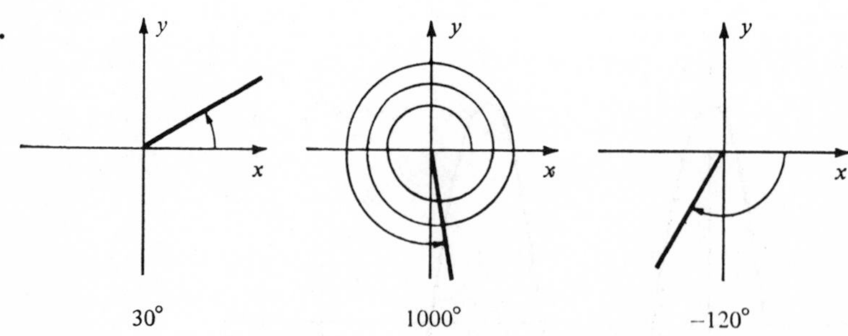

3. a) $\frac{5\pi}{18}$ b) $\frac{167\pi}{36}$ c) $\frac{13\pi}{900}$

5. a) 974.1° b) 57,264° c) −2880°

7. a) $\frac{\pi}{2}$ b) $17 - 4\pi$ c) $\frac{5\pi}{4}$

Problems 4–2 (page 65)

1. 109 feet

3. 8.7 feet

5. a) $\alpha = 30°$, $\beta = 60°$.

b) $\alpha = 45°$, $\beta = 45°$.

c) $\alpha = 60°$, $\beta = 30°$.

Problems 4–3 (page 70)

1. a) .4200 b) .1851 c) 1.111 d) 1.335

3. a) .8843 b) .1965 c) -17.17 d) .1883

5. a) $-.5324$ b) $-.1564$ c) -1.178 d) .0699

7. 170 feet

9. 60 feet

Problems 4–4 (page 73)

1. a) .5386 b) .7377 c) 7.381 d) .1181

3. a) .4884 b) .2837 c) 11.21 d) 2.031

5. a) $-.5334$ b) $-.1709$ c) .0907 d) -3.024

7. 2977 feet

Problems 4–5 (page 76)

1. a) $\beta = 68°$, $b = 34.65$, $c = 37.37$.

b) $\beta = 50°30'$, $b = 4.362$, $c = 5.653$.

c) $\beta = 73°50'$, $b = 1297$, $c = 1351$.

3. a) $\beta = 18°$, $a = 295.5$, $c = 310.7$.

b) $\beta = 52°25'$, $a = 10.70$, $c = 17.54$.

c) $\alpha = 40°47'$, $b = 500.8$, $c = 661.4$.

5. a) $\beta = 27°$, $a = 17.07$, $c = 19.17$.

b) $\beta = 76°37'$, $a = 3.147$, $c = 13.60$.

c) $\alpha = 32°3'$, $b = 9.151$, $c = 10.80$.

7. a) $\alpha = 68°12'$, $\beta = 21°48'$, $c = 5.385$.

b) $\alpha = 76°18'$, $\beta = 13°42'$, $c = 37.98$.

c) $\alpha = 70°41'$, $\beta = 19°19'$ $c = 807.4$.

9. a) $\alpha = 40°$, $\beta = 50°$, $b = 10.72$.

b) $\alpha = 47°46'$, $\beta = 42°14'$, $a = 22.58$.

c) $\alpha = 30°38'$, $\beta = 59°22'$, $b = 32.55$.

11. 36.06 feet

Problems 5–1 (page 81)

1. a) $\pm\frac{2\sqrt{6}}{5}$ and $\pm\frac{\sqrt{6}}{12}$

b) $\pm\frac{3\sqrt{7}}{8}$ and $\pm\frac{\sqrt{7}}{21}$

c) $\pm\frac{\sqrt{6}}{3}$ and $\pm\frac{\sqrt{2}}{2}$

3. a) $\pm\frac{\sqrt{33}}{7}$ and $\pm\frac{4\sqrt{33}}{33}$

b) $\pm\frac{5\sqrt{17}}{21}$ and $\pm\frac{4\sqrt{17}}{85}$

c) $\pm\frac{2\sqrt{2}}{3}$ and $\pm\frac{\sqrt{2}}{4}$

5. 1 **7.** 1 **9.** 0 **11.** 5

13. a) $\pm\frac{y\sqrt{y^2-1}}{y^2-1}$ b) $\pm\frac{\sqrt{y^2-1}}{y^2-1}$

15. a) $-\frac{\sqrt{3}}{2}$ b) $-\sqrt{3}$

Problems 5–2 (page 87)

1.
$$\begin{aligned}\cos(x-y) &= \cos(x+(-y))\\ &= \cos x\cos(-y) - \sin x\sin(-y)\\ &= \cos x\cos y + \sin x\sin y.\end{aligned}$$

3. $\sin(x+y+z) = \sin x\cos y\cos z - \sin x\sin y\sin z + \cos x\cos y\sin z + \cos x\sin y\cos z.$

5. $\frac{\sqrt{2}}{4}(\sqrt{3}+1)$

7. $-\frac{\sqrt{2}}{4}(\sqrt{3}+1)$

9. 3

11. 15

13. $6 \cos \theta \cos \phi$

Problems 5–3 (page 89)

1. $\frac{1}{2}\sqrt{2-\sqrt{2}}$

3. $\frac{1}{2}\sqrt{2-\sqrt{3}}$

5. $\tan 2\theta = \dfrac{2 \tan \theta}{1 - \tan^2\theta}$.

7. a) $\sqrt{2}-1$ b) $2-\sqrt{3}$ c) $-(\sqrt{2}+1)$

9. a) $\dfrac{9}{25}$ b) $\pm\dfrac{3}{5}$ c) $\pm\dfrac{24}{25}$

d) $\dfrac{2\sqrt{5}}{5}$ or $\dfrac{\sqrt{5}}{5}$ e) $-\dfrac{7}{25}$ f) $\dfrac{44}{125}$

11. $0, \dfrac{2\pi}{3}, \dfrac{4\pi}{3}$

13. $1 + \sin^2\theta$

15. $2 \cos \theta$, if $\cos \theta \neq 0$. (The expression is undefined when $\cos \theta = 0$.)

17. 1, if $\theta \neq n\pi$ and $\theta \neq (2n+1)\dfrac{\pi}{4}$ for any integer n. (The expression is undefined in these cases.)

19. $4 \cos^2\theta$, if $\theta \neq (2n+1)\dfrac{\pi}{2}$ for any integer n. (The expression is undefined in these cases.)

Problems 5–4 (page 92)

1.
$$\begin{aligned}\sin \phi - \sin \theta &= \sin \phi + \sin(-\theta)\\ &= 2 \sin \frac{\phi + (-\theta)}{2} \cos \frac{\phi - (-\theta)}{2}\\ &= 2 \sin \frac{\phi - \theta}{2} \cos \frac{\phi + \theta}{2}.\end{aligned}$$

3.
$$\begin{aligned}\sin 3\theta &= \sin (\theta + 2\theta) = \sin \theta \cos 2\theta + \cos \theta \sin 2\theta\\ &= \sin \theta\,(1 - 2 \sin^2\theta) + \cos \theta\,(2 \sin \theta \cos \theta)\\ &= \sin \theta - 2 \sin^3\theta + 2 \sin \theta\,(1 - \sin^2\theta)\\ &= 3 \sin \theta - 4 \sin^3\theta.\end{aligned}$$

5. $\frac{1}{2}(1 - \cos 2\theta) = \frac{1}{2}(1 - 2\cos^2\theta + 1)$
$= 1 - \cos^2\theta = \sin^2\theta.$

7. $\frac{1}{2}(1 + \cos 2\theta) = \frac{1}{2}(1 + 2\cos^2\theta - 1) = \cos^2\theta.$

9. $\frac{1}{2}\cos(\alpha - \beta) - \frac{1}{2}\cos(\alpha + \beta)$
$= \frac{1}{2}\cos\alpha\cos\beta + \frac{1}{2}\sin\alpha\sin\beta - \frac{1}{2}\cos\alpha\cos\beta + \frac{1}{2}\sin\alpha\sin\beta$
$= \sin\alpha\sin\beta.$

11. $\frac{1}{2}\sin(\alpha + \beta) + \frac{1}{2}\sin(\alpha - \beta)$
$= \frac{1}{2}\sin\alpha\cos\beta + \frac{1}{2}\sin\beta\cos\alpha + \frac{1}{2}\sin\alpha\cos\beta - \frac{1}{2}\sin\beta\cos\alpha$
$= \sin\alpha\cos\beta.$

Problems 6–1 (page 95)

1. 2 **3.** $1 - i$ **5.** $6 + 5i$

7. $3 - i$ **9.** $6 - 5i$ **11.** $6 - 4i$

13. $-1 + 5i$ **15.** 5 **17.** $26 - 22i$

19. $34 + 2i$ **21.** $-10i$ **23.** $-i$

25. $\frac{1}{2} - \frac{1}{2}i$ **27.** $\frac{14}{25} + \frac{2}{25}i$ **29.** $2i$

31. $\frac{31}{13} - \frac{12}{13}i$ **33.** i

35. $\frac{3}{10} + \frac{1}{10}i$ **37.** 0

Problems 6–2 (page 98)

1.

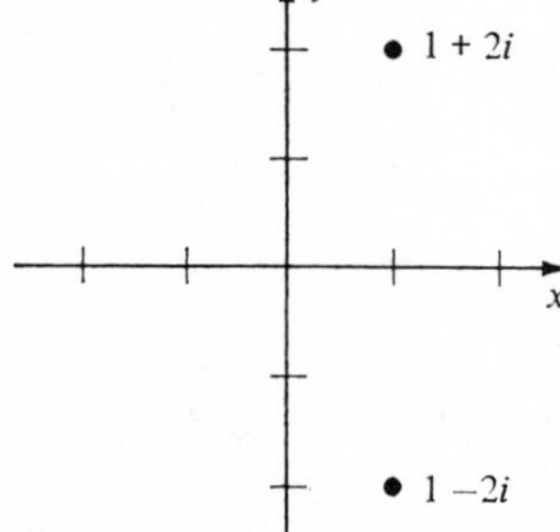

3.

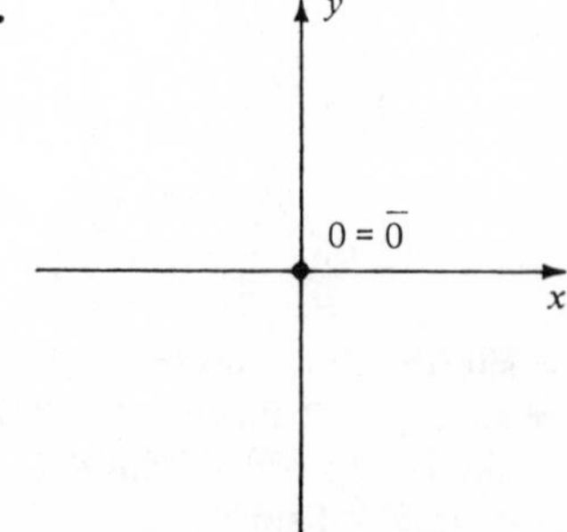

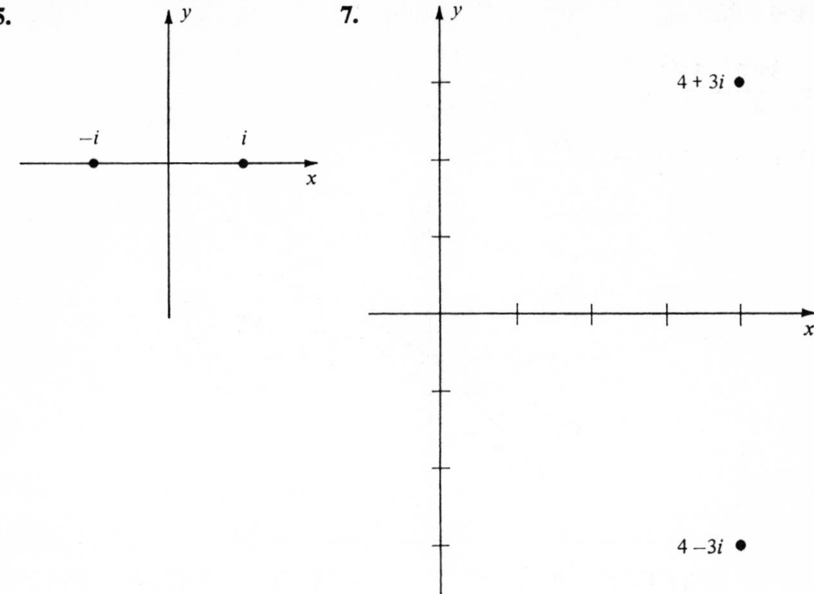

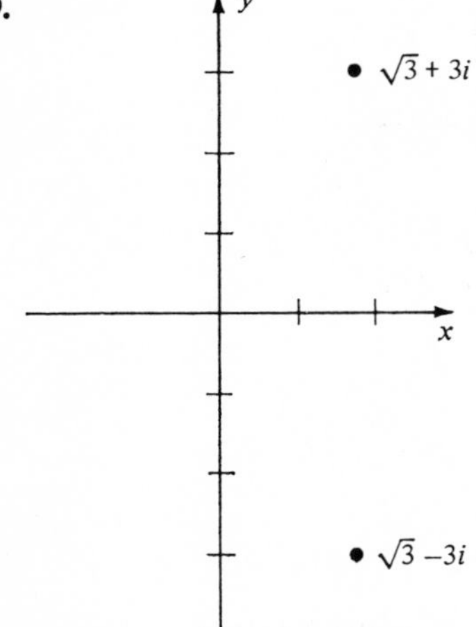

11. $\sqrt{2}(\cos 45° + i \sin 45°)$, $\sqrt{2}(\cos(-45)° + i \sin(-45)°)$.

13. $\cos 0° + i \sin 0°$, $\cos 0° + i \sin 0°$.

15. $2(\cos 120° + i \sin 120°)$, $2(\cos(-120)° + i \sin(-120)°)$.

17. $3(\cos(-60)° + i \sin(-60)°)$, $3(\cos 60° + i \sin 60°)$.

19. $3(\cos 221° + i \sin 221°)$, $3(\cos 139° + i \sin 139°)$.

21. $17 + 0i$.

23. $0 - 2i$.

25. $\frac{3\sqrt{2}}{2} - \frac{3\sqrt{2}}{2} i$.

27. $z + w = 5 + i$ and $z - w = -3 - 3i$.

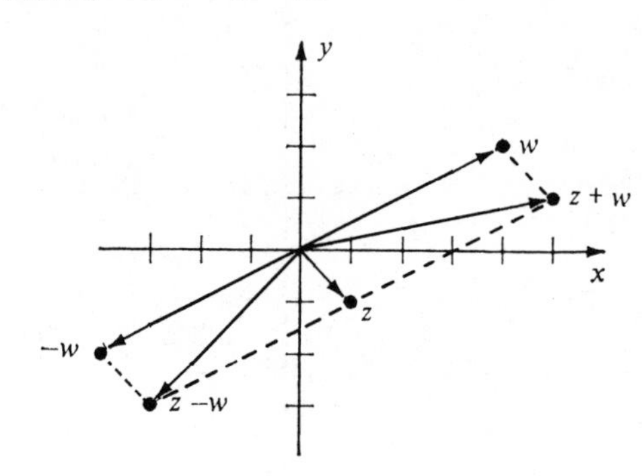

29. $z + w = \frac{3\sqrt{3} - 2}{2} + i\frac{2\sqrt{3} - 3}{2}$, $z - w = \frac{3\sqrt{3} + 2}{2} - i\frac{2\sqrt{3} + 3}{2}$.

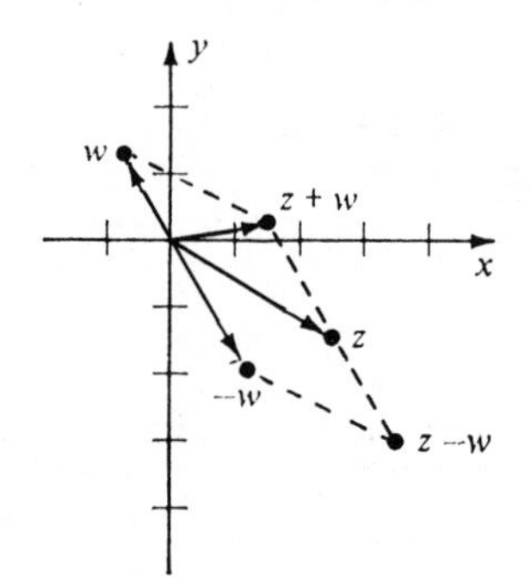

Problems 6–3 (page 101)

1. $\cos 11 + i \sin 11$.

3. $20\sqrt{2}(\cos 105 + i \sin 105)$.

5. $\frac{42\sqrt{3}}{5}(\cos 150° + i \sin 150°)$.

7. $\frac{\sqrt{2}}{4}(\cos 45° + i \sin 45°)$.

9. $\frac{1}{2}(\cos 329° + i \sin 329°)$.

11. i.

13. i.

15. 1.

17. $64i$.

19. $\frac{1}{2} + \frac{\sqrt{3}}{2} i$.

21. $5^{1/5}$
$5^{1/5}(\cos 72° + i \sin 72°)$
$5^{1/5}(\cos 144° + i \sin 144°)$
$5^{1/5}(\cos 216° + i \sin 216°)$
$5^{1/5}(\cos 288° + i \sin 288°)$.

23. $\cos 30° + i \sin 30° = \frac{\sqrt{3}}{2} + \frac{1}{2}i$

$\cos 150° + i \sin 150° = -\frac{\sqrt{3}}{2} + \frac{1}{2}i$

$\cos 270° + i \sin 270° = -i$.

25. $4(\cos 75° + i \sin 75°)$
$4(\cos 165° + i \sin 165°)$
$4(\cos 255° + i \sin 255°)$
$4(\cos 345° + i \sin 345°)$.

27. The four solutions for z are
$\cos (135/2)° + i \sin (135/2)°$
$\cos (315/2)° + i \sin (315/2)°$
$\cos (495/2)° + i \sin (495/2)°$
$\cos (675/2)° + i \sin (675/2)°$.

Problems 7–1 (page 108)

1.

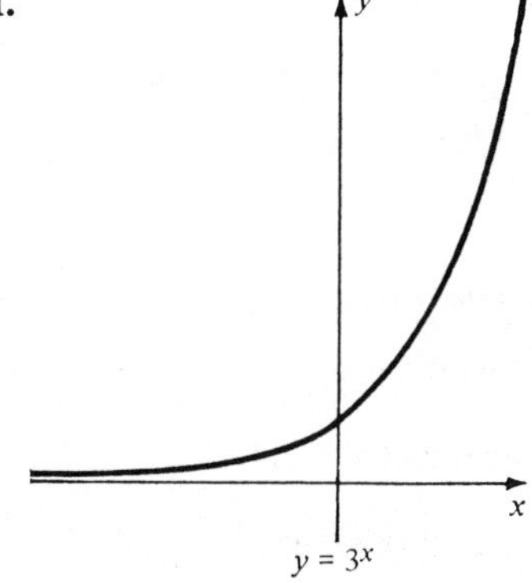

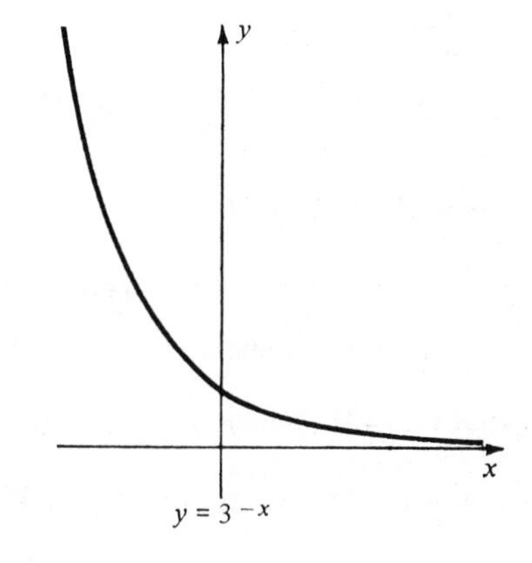

3. a) $1\frac{1}{4}$ b) $1\frac{3}{4}$ c) $\frac{3}{4}$ d) $1\frac{7}{8}$

5.

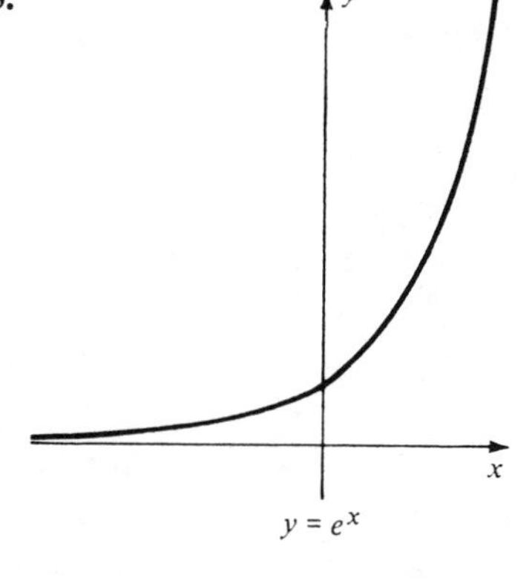

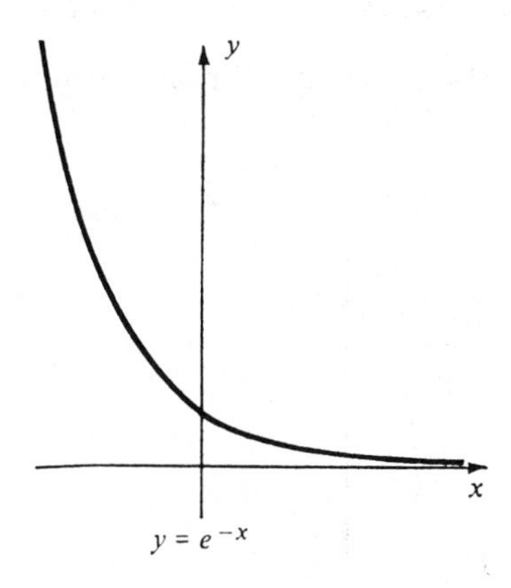

7. $f(x) = b^x$, so $f(x + y) = b^{x+y} = b^x b^y = f(x)f(y)$.

9. $f(x) = a^x$, $g(x) = b^x$, so $k(x) = f(x)g(x) = a^x b^x = (ab)^x$.

11. a) $f(x) = 2^x 3^x = (2 \cdot 3)^x = 6^x$, so f is exponential, $b = 6$.

b) $f(x) = 2^{3x} = (2^3)^x = 8^x$, so f is exponential, $b = 8$.

c) $f(x) = 1 = 1^x$, so $f(x)$ is exponential, $b = 1$.

d) $f(x) = 2$ is not exponential.

13. a) $f(x) = 2^x$ b) none c) all

15. a)

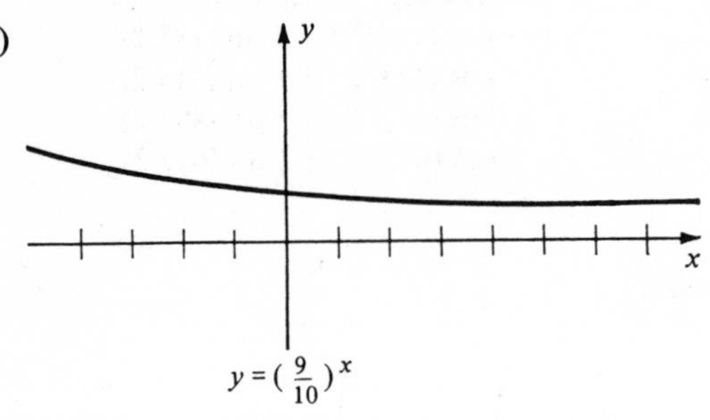

b) $6\frac{1}{2}$

Problems 7–2 (page 112)

1. $f^{-1}(x) = x + 7$; domain of f^{-1} is all the real numbers.

3. $f^{-1}(x) = (x + 1)/2$; domain of f^{-1} is all the real numbers.

5. $f^{-1}(x) = \sqrt{x - 3}$; domain of f^{-1} is those x such that $x \geq 3$.

7. $f^{-1}(x) = \sqrt{x} - 3$; domain of f^{-1} is those x such that $x \geq 0$.

9. $f^{-1}(x) = 1/x$; domain of f^{-1} is those x such that $x \neq 0$.

11. $f^{-1}(x) = (3/x) - 1$; domain is those x such that $x \neq 0$.

13. $f^{-1}(x) = (x - 5)/2x$; domain is those x such that $x \neq 0$.

15.

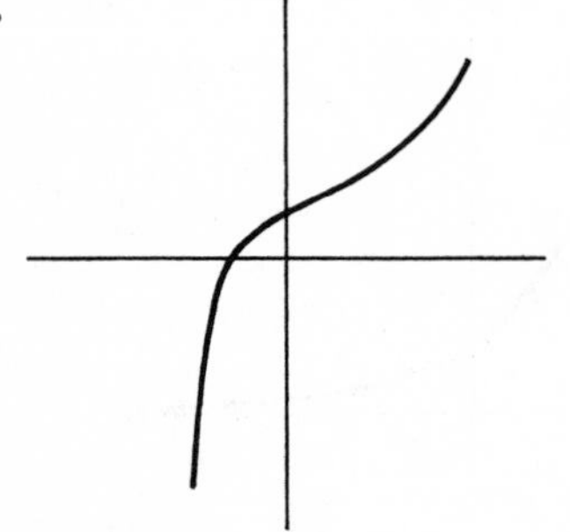

17. no inverse

19. no inverse

Problems 7–3 (page 116)

1. 1. **3.** 1/2. **5.** −1. **7.** 0.

9. $x = 1$. **11.** $x = 2$. **13.** $x = 3$. **15.** $x = 4$.

17. $\log_b(x^2 - 1) - \log_b(x - 1)^2 = \log_b \dfrac{(x^2 - 1)}{(x - 1)^2}$

$= \log_b \dfrac{(x + 1)}{(x - 1)}$, if $x > 1$.

19. $\log_b \sqrt{\dfrac{x + y}{x - y}} + \log_b \sqrt{x - y} = \log_b \sqrt{\dfrac{x + y}{x - y}}\sqrt{x - y}$

$= \log_b \sqrt{x + y} = \frac{1}{2} \log_b (x + y)$, for $x > |y|$.

21. $\log_b (x^3 + x^2 - 2x) - \log_b (x - 1) - \log_b (x + 2)$

$\log_b \dfrac{(x)(x + 2)(x - 1)}{(x - 1)(x + 2)} = \log_b x$, if $x > 1$.

23. $(\log_a b^2 - \log_a b) \log_b a = (2 \log_a b - \log_a b) \log_b a$

$= \log_a b \log_b a = 1$, since $(b^{\log_b a})^{\log_a b} = a^{\log_a b}$

$= b$.

25. $a^{(\log_b c)(\log_b a)} = a^{(\log_a c/\log_a b)(\log_b a)}$

$= c^{(\log_b a)/(\log_a b)} = c^{(\log_b a)(\log_b a)} = c^{(\log_b a)^2}$.

Problems 7–4 (page 120)

1. a) $(6.9)10^1$ b) $(6.96)10^2$ c) 10^{-3}

d) 10^3 e) $-(10^{-3})$

3. a) $.7168 + 1$ b) $.7168$

c) $.7168 - 1$ d) $.9090 - 6$

5. $(2.298) \cdot 10^3$ **7.** $(1.122) \cdot 10^{15}$

9. 4.726 **11.** 4.155

13. 12.198 **15.** 6.915

17. $x = .4667$ **19.** $x = 3.277$

21. $x = 1{,}000{,}001$

Problems 7–5 (page 123)

1. $0.7604 - 1 = -.2396$. **3.** $.2155$.

5. $0.9474 - 2 = -1.0526$. **7.** $0.8237 - 1 = -.1763$.

9. $-(0.4068-1)=.5932.$ **11.** $-(0.9717-1)=.0283.$

13. $58°10'$. **15.** $3°46'$.

17. $41°0'$. **19.** $46°15'$.

21. $B=53°50'$, $b=241$, $c=298$.

23. $A=61°57'$, $B=28°3'$, $c=35.52$.

25. $B=44°34'$, $a=1015$, $c=1426$.

27. $A=40°26'$, $B=49°34'$, $b=100.1$.

Problems 8–1 (page 128)

1. $\alpha=117°50'$, $B=2.082$, $C=1.657$.

3. $\beta=12°18'$, $A=2967$, $C=3489$.

5. $\beta=48°23'$, $\gamma=100°27'$, $C=118.8$, or
$\beta=131°37'$, $\gamma=17°13'$ $C=35,74$.

7. There is no such triangle, since log sin β would have to be log sin α $-$ log A + log $B=1.0729$, so sin β would be greater than 1.

9. $\alpha=40°12'$, $\beta=29°28'$, $B=19.35$.

11. $\alpha=95°23'$, $\gamma=47°57'$, $A=100.7$, or
$\alpha=11°17'$, $\gamma=123°3'$, $A=19.92$.

13. $\alpha=23°1'$, $\gamma=14°49'$, $C=9.874$.

15. $\gamma=37°42'$, $A=25.7$, $B=16.51$.

17. $\alpha=133°31'$, $B=9.232$, $C=12.87$.

Problems 8–2 (page 132)

1. $B=7.49$, $\alpha=35°35'$, $\gamma=19°25'$.

3. $A=61.57$, $\beta=52°3'$, $\gamma=56°7'$.

5. $A=7.47$, $\beta=44°4'$, $\gamma=6°16'$.

7. $\alpha=156°38'$, $\beta=20°57'$, $\gamma=2°25'$.

9. $\alpha=29°23'$, $\beta=46°30'$, $\gamma=104°6'$.

11. $\alpha=21°56'$, $\beta=30°22'$, $\gamma=127°42'$.

Problems 8–3 (page 133)

1. $\alpha=76°55'$, $\beta=100°50'$, $C=5.79$.

3. $\beta=35°37\frac{1}{2}'$, $\gamma=70°55\frac{1}{2}'$, $A=76.26$.

5. $\beta = 89°53'$, $\gamma = 47°49'$, $A = 48.56$.

7. $\alpha = 45°48'$, $\beta = 76°32'$, $C = 545.6$.

Problems 8–4 (page 136)

3. $\alpha = 97°2'$, $\beta = 7°14'$, $\gamma = 75°44'$.

5. 30.85.

Problems 9–1 (page 141)

1.

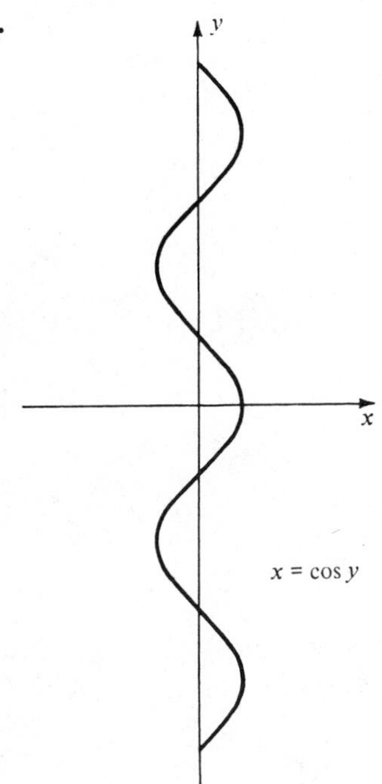

3. $\tan(\arccos t) = \dfrac{\sqrt{1-t^2}}{t}$, if $t \neq 0$.

5. $\sec(\arccos t) = \dfrac{1}{t}$, if $t \neq 0$.

7. 12°40′

9. −27°51′

11. 71°21′

13. 130°11′

Problems 9–2 (page 146)

1.

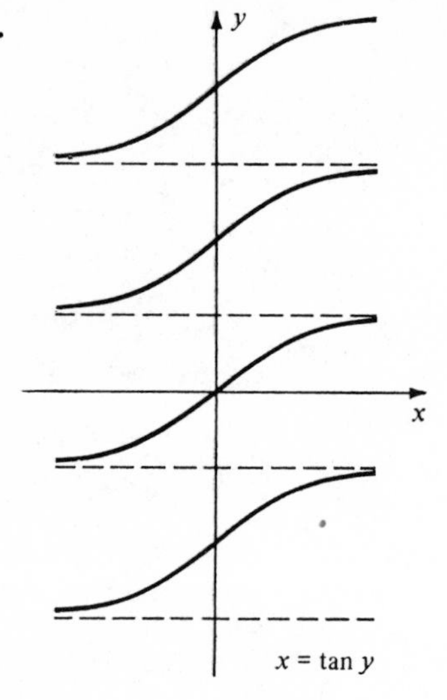

3.

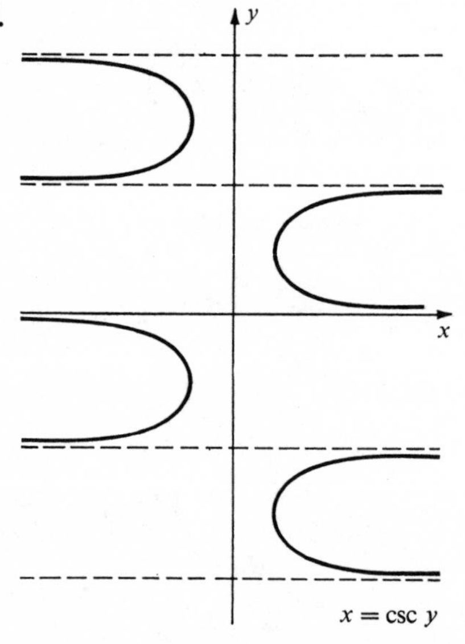

5. a) $\sin(\arctan t) = \dfrac{t}{\sqrt{1+t^2}}$

b) $\cos(\arctan t) = \dfrac{1}{\sqrt{1+t^2}}$

c) $\cot(\arctan t) = 1/t, \quad \text{if } t \neq 0$

d) $\sec(\arctan t) = \sqrt{1+t^2}$

e) $\csc(\arctan t) = \dfrac{\sqrt{1+t^2}}{t}$, if $t \neq 0$

7. a) $\sin(\operatorname{arcsec} t) = \dfrac{\sqrt{t^2-1}}{|t|}$, if $|t| \geq 1$

b) $\cos(\operatorname{arcsec} t) = 1/t$, if $|t| \geq 1$

c) $\tan(\operatorname{arcsec} t) = \dfrac{t\sqrt{t^2-1}}{|t|}$, if $|t| \geq 1$

d) $\cot(\operatorname{arcsec} t) = \dfrac{|t|}{t\sqrt{t^2-1}}$, if $|t| > 1$

e) $\csc(\operatorname{arcsec} t) = \dfrac{|t|}{\sqrt{t^2-1}}$, if $|t| > 1$

9. 82°52′ **11.** 87°24′ **13.** 62°48′

15. −84°2′ **17.** −72°25′ **19.** 93°54′

Prob lems 9–3 (page 150)

1. $t = \pm \arccos\left(\dfrac{\sqrt{5}-1}{2}\right) + n360° = \pm 51°50' + n360°.$

3. $\beta = n180°$, or
$\beta = \pm \arccos 1/2 + n360° = \pm 60° + n360°.$

5. $x = (-1)^n \operatorname{arccsc} y + n180°$ for $|y| \geq 1$. (There are no solutions for $|y| < 1$.)

7. $x = \arctan 2 + n180° = 63°26' + n180°.$

9. $t = (-1)^n \arcsin\left(\dfrac{\sqrt{22}-2}{3}\right) + n180°$
$= (-1)^n 63°45' + n180°.$

11. $\theta = (-1)^n \arcsin 1/5 + n180° = (-1)^n 11°32' + n180°.$

13. $x = (-1)^n \arcsin(\sqrt{6}-2) + n180°$
$= (-1)^n 26°43' + n180°.$

15. $y = (-1)^n \arcsin 1/8 + n180° = (-1)^n 7°11' + n180°.$

17. $x = n180°$, or
$x = \pm \arccos 5/8 + n360° = \pm 51°19' + n360°.$

19. $\theta = (-1)^n \arcsin\left(\dfrac{\sqrt{2} \pm \sqrt{42}}{20}\right) + n180°$, thus

$\theta = (-1)^n 23°15' + n180°$, or
$\theta = (-1)^n 345°20' + n180°.$

21. $t = \text{arccot}(2 \pm \sqrt{6}) + n180°$, thus

$t = 12°40' + n180°$, or

$t = 118°50'$.

23. $t = 1/5[\pm \arccos(\pm \sqrt{.795}) + n360°]$, thus
$t = 114°10' + n180°$
$t = \pm 5°23' + n36°$.

Problems 9–4 (page 154)

1. $C = 19.89$, $\theta = 4°59'$.

3. $C = 5.042$, $\theta = 1°3'$.

5. $C = 21.76$, $\theta = 256°30'$.

7. $y = 2\sin(8\pi t - \pi/2)$.

9. $y = 10\sin(t + \pi)$.

Index

1 2 3 4 5 6 7 8 9 10 11 12 13 14 15 16 17 18 19 20 21 22 23 24 25 78 77 76 75 74 73 72 71 70 69